The Physician Billing Process

12 Potholes to Avoid in the Road to Getting Paid

2nd Edition

Deborah Walker Keegan, PhD, FACMPE
Elizabeth W. Woodcock, MBA, FACMPE, CPC
Sara M. Larch, MSHA, FACMPE

D1597084

MGMA®
Defining Your Profession™

Production Credits
Publisher: Marilee E. Aust
Project manager: Erica Nikolaidis, MA
Composition and production: Virginia Howe
Cover design: Amy Kenreich, Studio Pattern
Copyeditor: Kelly Davis

Library of Congress Cataloging-in-Publication Data

Keegan, Deborah Walker.
 The physician billing process : 12 potholes to avoid in the road to getting paid /
Deborah Walker Keegan, Elizabeth W. Woodcock, Sara M. Larch. -- 2nd ed.
    p. ; cm.
 Includes bibliographical references and index.
 ISBN 978-1-56829-339-4
 1. Medicine--Practice--Finance--Handbooks, manuals, etc. 2. Medical offices--
Management--Handbooks, manuals, etc. 3. Health insurance claims--Handbooks,
manuals, etc. 4. Accounts receivable--Management--Handbooks, manuals, etc. 5.
Medical fees--Handbooks, manuals, etc. I. Woodcock, Elizabeth W. II. Larch, Sara M.
III. Medical Group Management Association. IV. Title.
 [DNLM: 1. Practice Management, Medical--economics. 2. Fees, Medical. 3.
Insurance, Health, Reimbursement. 4. Patient Credit and Collection--organization &
administration. 5. Reimbursement Mechanisms--organization & administration. W
80 K26p 2008]
 R728.K44 2008
 610.68'1--dc22
                            2008045627

Item 8079
ISBN: 978-1-56829-339-4

Printed in the United States of America
10 9 8 7 6 5 4 3 2 1

PRAISE FOR

The Physician Billing Process:
12 Potholes to Avoid in the Road to Getting Paid

2nd Edition

ॐ

Each information-packed chapter of this comprehensive and well-written book ... covers the entire gamut of topics that collectively can guarantee improved collections and fiscal success. Topics range from determining the credit worthiness of patients to providing enhanced patient education with regard to their billing responsibilities. Each chapter outlines explicitly the implementation steps required to improve each and every critical process associated with the revenue cycle ... The critical nature of this information is substantiated by our knowledge that when you are out of cash, you are out of options!

THOMAS C. ROYER, M.D.
President and CEO
CHRISTUS HEALTH

ॐ

This is an exceptionally valuable addition to the library of every practice executive. This IS the medical practice accounts receivable "PDR" — timely, informative, educational, and necessary for anyone working with a medical practice's patient accounts. Armed with this manual, physicians and practice executives can address every conceivable event they might encounter when dealing with medical practice charge protocols and the collection of those charges ... [The Physician Billing Process] is a valuable resource, filled with helpful tools that will improve collections and the entire billing experience, not only for the practice, but also for the patient.

MARSHALL M. BAKER, MS, FACMPE
President and CEO
PHYSICIAN ADVISORY SERVICES, INC.

ॐ

More praise ...

The Physician Billing Process *is without a doubt the most thorough guide I have ever read. Even in a complex, jargon-prone industry like ours, the information is presented well and easy to read. Individuals new to billing, as well as long-time practice management executives, will find value in the "12 potholes" chapters, numerous checklists, and sample policies and procedures. The section on benchmarking is a must-read for anyone involved in the physician revenue cycle. In addition to covering billing basics, the book thoroughly examines contemporary issues such as HIPAA requirements, electronic data exchange, pay-for-performance, and compliance risk.*

CLIFF SKINNER, MPA
Director, Medical Group Business Services
UNIVERSITY OF CALIFORNIA, SAN FRANCISCO

ॐ

Every practice knows that is it critical to maximize reimbursement and to effectively and efficiently collect for the professional services it provides. Most practices, however, do not know how to assess the job they are currently doing, or determine what to do if they find problems. This book tells you how to evaluate your current operations, set priorities, use technology, benchmark your staff and performance, increase collections productivity, and collect more cash. [The Physician Billing Process] *offers policies, checklists, audit tools, and comparative data that will enable your practice to collect money faster and more effectively.*

BETSY NICOLETTI, MS, CPC
Author, *The Field Guide to Physician Coding*

ॐ

A comprehensive guide to successful reimbursement, The Physician Billing Process *is a real-world compendium of helpful advice, tools, and resources to avoid becoming tangled in the web of health care reimbursement. The book presents proven, easy to understand and implement tools to help your medical practice avoid the pitfalls inherent in today's health care environment. This complete and proven system will assist you and your practice in today's consumer driven and heavily regulated health care world. Chock-full of "secrets" that even the most seasoned professional can benefit from in today's complex medical practice,* The Physician Billing Process *is a must-have resource for every practice manager.*

CHERIS L. CRAIG, MBA, CMPE
Practice Administrator
ATLANTA WOMEN'S OBSTETRICS & GYNECOLOGY, PC

About the Authors

Deborah Walker Keegan, PhD, FACMPE, is a nationally recognized consultant, keynote speaker, and author. As president of Medical Practice Dimensions, Inc., and principal with Woodcock & Walker Consulting, she helps medical practices improve productivity and efficiency. Her areas of expertise include physician-hospital integration, physician compensation, revenue cycle assessments, medical practice staffing and organization, and practice operations assessments. With more than 25 years of expertise in health care, Walker Keegan's breadth and scope of expertise has been embraced by clients to their benefit. She holds a PhD from The Peter F. Drucker Graduate School of Management, an MBA from UCLA's Anderson Graduate School of Management, and she is a fellow of the American College of Medical Practice Executives (AC-MPE). She is also the co-author of two other highly acclaimed books: *Physician Compensation Plans: State-of-the-Art Strategies* and *Rightsizing: Appropriate Staffing for Your Medical Practice.* (Contact information: deborahwalkerkeegan@msn.com; telephone: 828.651.9709.)

Elizabeth W. Woodcock, MBA, FACMPE, CPC, is a popular author, speaker, and consultant. Principal of Atlanta-based Woodcock & Associates and Woodcock & Walker Consulting, Woodcock has focused on medical practice operations and receivables management throughout her career. Combining innovation and analysis to teach practice operations and management, she has delivered presentations at regional and national conferences to thousands of physicians and managers, authored several practice management manuals and textbooks, and published numerous articles in national health care management journals. She is the author of the best-selling book, *Mastering Patient Flow,* and co-author of *Operating Policies and Procedures for Medical Practices.* A certified professional coder, Woodcock is a fellow of the American College of Medical Practice Executives (ACMPE). In addition to a bachelor of arts degree from Duke University, she holds a master's of business administration in health care management from the Wharton School of Business of the University of Pennsylvania. (Contact information: elizabeth@elizabethwoodcock.com; telephone: 404.373.6195.)

Sara M. Larch, MSHA, FACMPE, is vice president of Physician Services at the Inova Health System, a not-for-profit health care system of five hospitals, 16,000 employees, and nearly 3,000 physicians. She is the former COO of University Physicians, Inc. in Baltimore. Larch has more than 25 years of medical group experience in single- and multispecialty practices both small and large. She focuses on revenue cycle performance, ambulatory operations, key physician strategies, and leading organizational change. She has a master's degree in health sciences administration from Virginia Commonwealth University and is a fellow of the American College of Medical Practice Executives (ACMPE). Larch serves on the advisory board for the Women Business Leaders of the United States Health Care Industry Foundation. She is past board chair of the Medical Group Management Association (MGMA) and is past president of both the Academic Practice Assembly (APA) and the Association of Managers of Obstetrics and Gynecology (AMGO). Larch is a frequently invited professional speaker on topics such as billing and reimbursement, practice operations, and women leadership. (Contact information: sara.larch@inova.org; telephone: 703.205.2125.)

Dedication

This book is dedicated to our families. Thank you for your amazing support and unconditional love. Without you, this book would not have been possible.

We also want to extend our appreciation to the many physicians, hospital leaders, medical practice executives, and billing staff with whom we have worked on consulting projects and in day-to-day operations, and who have attended our seminars and conferences. We commend you for your commitment, dedication, and the exceptional efforts you make on behalf of your medical practices and the patients you serve.

Contents

List of Figures xiii
List of Tools xvii
List of Policies and Procedures xix
Foreword xxi
Introduction xxv

Chapter 1 ■ **The Changing Reimbursement Environment**............................ 1
Financing changes ■ Delivery system changes ■ Underlying themes

Chapter 2 ■ **The Revenue Cycle: An Overview**.. 9
Revenue cycle definitions ■ Front-end and back-end ■ Billing and collection billing and collection potholes ■ Staff workload ranges ■ Leading performance indicators ■ Cost to rework a claim ■ Recurring themes

Chapters 3 through 14 provide a step-by-step review of each of the billing potholes. Each chapter includes a description of a key billing function, advanced practices, figures, tools, performance indicators, staff workload ranges, and policies and procedures.

Chapter 3 ■ **POTHOLE 1: The Patient Financial Clearance Process** 19
Patient financial clearance functions ■ Pre-visit registration and insurance verification ■ Setting patients' expectations ■ Collecting payment prior to service ■ Determining credit worthiness ■ Patient financial policy ■ Referrals and authorizations ■ Real-time technologies ■ Price transparency

Chapter 4 ■ **POTHOLE 2: The Patient Check-in and Check-out Processes** 43
Role of patient check-in and check-out ■ Registration kiosks ■ Time-of-service collections ■ Automated receipt processes ■ Updates to patient information in real time ■ Waiver forms ■ Referral and pre-authorization confirmation ■ Performance feedback to front-end billing staff

Chapter 5 ■ **POTHOLE 3: The Charge Capture Process**.................................... 67

Charge capture responsibility ■ Charge capture tools and processes ■ Charge capture logs ■ Charge capture lag times ■ Charge capture audits ■ Service variance analyses ■ Charge tickets

Chapter 6 ■ **POTHOLE 4: The Coding Process**.. 85

Coding conventions ■ Coding responsibilities ■ Internal coding competency ■ Coding tools and technology ■ The link between coding and reimbursement ■ Regulatory compliance

Chapter 7 ■ **POTHOLE 5: The Charge Entry Process** 101

Charge entry responsibility ■ Timeliness of charge entry ■ Electronic charge entry ■ Pre-adjudication edits ■ Charge entry audits ■ Fee schedules

Chapter 8 ■ **POTHOLE 6: The Claims Management Process** 119

Claims clearinghouses ■ Electronic claims submission ■ Claim review and scrubbing ■ Tracking and resolving claim edits ■ Claim filing deadlines ■ Suspended claims ■ Secondary claims ■ Real-time claims adjudication ■ Payer Websites

Chapter 9 ■ **POTHOLE 7: The Patient Statement Process**............................. 139

Statement cycles ■ Patient-friendly statements ■ Online bill payment ■ Dunning cycles and statement messages ■ Returned mail

Chapter 10 ■ **POTHOLE 8: The Payment and Denial Posting Process** 149

Reading an explanation of benefits (EOB) ■ Payment posting methods ■ Denial posting methods ■ Electronic payment remittance (EPR) and electronic funds transfer (EFT) ■ Remote deposit and lockbox services ■ Account adjustments and their classifications ■ Credit balances and refunds ■ Prompt payment ■ Payment variance analysis

Chapter 11 ■ **POTHOLE 9: The Insurance Follow-up Process** 177

Open claims follow-up ■ Account follow-up structures ■ Account follow-up strategies ■ Insurance correspondence ■ Small balance adjustments

Chapter 12 ■ **POTHOLE 10: The Denial Management Process** 195

Reasons for denied claims ■ Denial management strategies ■ The appeals process ■ Payer report cards ■ Calculating the cost of rework

Chapter 13 ■ **POTHOLE 11: The Patient Collections Process** 225

Collections cycle ■ Patient account follow-up policies ■ Medical billing advocates ■ Patient correspondence ■ Non-sufficient funds ■ Payment plans ■ Collection agencies ■ Small claims court ■ Discounts and uninsured patients ■ Predictive dialers ■ Patient dismissal

Chapter 14 ▪ **POTHOLE 12: The Contract and Reimbursement Management Process** 257
Practice-payer relationships ▪ The credentialing process ▪ Contract negotiation tips ▪ Internal reimbursement expertise ▪ Payer reimbursement tactics

Chapter 15 ▪ **Staffing the Revenue Cycle** 273
Key staffing recommendations ▪ Staffing deployment models ▪ Organizational structures ▪ Staff training, competency, and accountability ▪ Incentive plans

Chapter 16 ▪ **Internal Controls for the Revenue Cycle**................................. 299
Segregation of duties ▪ Safeguarding cash ▪ Evaluating business risk ▪ Internal audits ▪ Physical security measures ▪ Red flags for fraud

Chapter 17 ▪ **The Debate: Centralize, Decentralize, or Outsource Billing?**............... 319
Decentralization ▪ Centralization ▪ Outsourcing ▪ Transition and change management

Chapter 18 ▪ **Leveraging Technology to Enhance the Revenue Cycle**.................... 333
Evaluating technology for your medical practice ▪ Technology to detect early warning signs ▪ Technologies to permit patient-focused billing ▪ Technologies that help your practice "do it right the first time" and minimize rework ▪ Technology to permit work to be conducted in real time ▪ Technology to ensure effective resource utilization

Chapter 19 ▪ **Measuring and Analyzing the Revenue Cycle** 353
Key impacts to revenue cycle performance ▪ Benchmarking revenue cycle performance ▪ Benchmarking the cost of your billing office ▪ Leading financial indicators ▪ Administrative dashboard ▪ Techniques for reimbursement management ▪ Keys to management reports ▪ Policies and procedures for the revenue cycle

Chapter 20 ▪ **Regulations Impacting the Revenue Cycle** 395
Compliance plans ▪ The Health Insurance Portability and Accountability Act (HIPAA)

Conclusion and Future Implications 407

Additional Billing and Collection Resources 411

Index 419

List of Figures

Introduction

Figure i How a Medical Service Becomes a Paid Bill xxvi

Figure ii Medical Practice Self-audit: Is Your Practice Leaving
Money Uncollected? xxvii

Chapter 1 ■ The Changing Reimbursement Environment

Figure 1.1 The Changing Reimbursement Environment 2

Chapter 2 ■ The Revenue Cycle: An Overview

Figure 2.1 Defining the Parties 9

Figure 2.2 The Revenue Cycle: Responsibility and
Functionality 11

Figure 2.3 The Revenue Cycle: Critical Billing and
Collection Tasks 12

Figure 2.4 Front-end and Back-end Billing Functions 13

Figure 2.5 Revenue Cycle Flowchart and Potholes 14

Figure 2.6 The Cost to Rework a Claim 17

Chapter 3 ■ Pothole 1: The Patient Financial Clearance Process

Figure 3.1 Patient Financial Clearance Functions 21

Chapter 5 ■ Pothole 3: The Charge Capture Process

Figure 5.1 Inpatient Charge Capture Log 72

Figure 5.2 Closed-loop Charge Capture Process 73

Figure 5.3 Track Charge Lags 74

Chapter 6 ■ Pothole 4: The Coding Process

Figure 6.1 Common Coding Terms in Physician Billing 86

Figure 6.2 Place-of-Service Codes for Professional Claims 94

Chapter 7 ■ Pothole 5: The Charge Entry Process

Figure 7.1 Sample Fee Schedule Determination 104

Figure 7.2 Pre-adjudication Tools 108

Chapter 8 ■ **Pothole 6: The Claims Management Process**

Figure 8.1 Payer Claims Adjudication Process 122

Figure 8.2 From Paper to E-claims 123

Figure 8.3 The Electronic Claim Journey....................... 126

Figure 8.4 Claims Edit Report Example........................ 129

Figure 8.5 Real-time Claims Adjudication (RTCA) 133

Chapter 10 ■ **Pothole 8: The Payment and Denial Posting Process**

Figure 10.1 Sample Explanation of Benefits.................... 151

Figure 10.2 Payment Posting: Three Scenarios 157

Figure 10.3 Payment Code Structure........................... 161

Chapter 11 ■ **Pothole 9: The Insurance Follow-up Process**

Figure 11.1 Open Claims Follow-up Script..................... 182

Chapter 12 ■ **Pothole 10: The Denial Management Process**

Figure 12.1 Reasons for Denied Claims........................ 196

Figure 12.2 Translating Payer Denials 197

Figure 12.3 Sample Definition of Medical Necessity 207

Figure 12.4 Cost of Rework 220

Chapter 13 ■ **Pothole 11: The Patient Collections Process**

Figure 13.1 Collection Code of Ethics 229

Chapter 14 ■ **Pothole 12: The Contract and Reimbursement Management Process**

Figure 14.1 Credentialing Requirements 261

Chapter 15 ■ **Staffing the Revenue Cycle**

Figure 15.1 Staff Time Devoted to Key Billing Functions 280

Figure 15.2 Staffing Levels Compared to Benchmarks 280

Figure 15.3 Staffing Levels by Function with Comparison to Benchmarks.................................... 281

Figure 15.4 Calculation of Total Difficulty Index (TDI).......... 282

Figure 15.5 Weighting Claims with the TDI 283

Figure 15.6 Staff Assignment Based on Work 283

Figure 15.7 Staff Workload Ranges by Activity................. 287

Figure 15.8 Revenue Cycle Organization—Small Medical Practice... 290

Figure 15.9 Revenue Cycle Organization—Medium-sized Medical Practice................................. 291

Figure 15.10 Revenue Cycle Organization—Large Medical Practice... 292

Chapter 16 ■ **Internal Controls for the Revenue Cycle**
Figure 16.1 Impact of Mishandled Payments 309
Figure 16.2 Impact of Incorrect Account Write-offs 310
Figure 16.3 Impact of Incorrect Refund Management 310

Chapter 17 ■ **The Debate: Centralize, Decentralize, or Outsource Billing?**
Figure 17.1 Code of Commitments for Physician Billing 325

Chapter 18 ■ **Leveraging Technology to Enhance the Revenue Cycle**
Figure 18.1 Technologies to Enhance Your Revenue Cycle 335
Figure 18.2 Rework Associated with Incomplete Process
Handoffs 344

Chapter 19 ■ **Measuring and Analyzing the Revenue Cycle**
Figure 19.1 Benchmarking Case Study 362
Figure 19.2 Reasons for Low Collections 365
Figure 19.3 Sample Liquidation Table 373
Figure 19.4 Sample Errors and Omissions in Medicare
Enrollment 374
Figure 19.5 Key Revenue Indices: Issues to Investigate 375
Figure 19.6 Snapshot of Leading Financial Indicators
and Targets 377
Figure 19.7 Front-end Billing Costs 378
Figure 19.8 Back-end Billing: Cost as a Percentage of Net
Collections 378
Figure 19.9 Back-end Billing: Cost per Claim 379
Figure 19.10 The Efficient Frontier 380

Chapter 20 ■ **Regulations Impacting the Revenue Cycle**
Figure 20.1 Common Types of Fraud and Abuse 397
Figure 20.2 HIPAA Transaction and Code Sets 400
Figure 20.3 Using HIPAA Transactions as Part of Your
Workflow 402

List of Tools

Chapter 3 ▪ **Pothole 1: The Patient Financial Clearance Process**
Tool 1 Insurance Verification and Benefits Eligibility Form 25
Tool 2 Sample Financial Policy 31
Tool 3 Patient Financial Clearance Checklist.................... 32
Tool 4 Payer Guide 33

Chapter 4 ▪ **Pothole 2: The Patient Check-in and Check-out Processes**
Tool 5 Financial Agreement for Surgeries and Procedures....... 46
Tool 6 "About Your Bill" Sample 47
Tool 7 Front-office Audit Tool 49
Tool 8 Front-office Monthly Denial Report 50
Tool 9 Sample Cash-at-Time-of-Service Scripts 51
Tool 10 Patient Financial Agreement.......................... 54

Chapter 7 ▪ **Pothole 5: The Charge Entry Process**
Tool 11 Fee Schedule Review 107
Tool 12 Competency Assessment: Charge Entry................ 111

Chapter 8 ▪ **Pothole 6: The Claims Management Process**
Tool 13 E-claims Checklist.................................... 124
Tool 14 Clean Claims Checklist 128

Chapter 9 ▪ **Pothole 7: The Patient Statement Process**
Tool 15 Sample Statement Notes............................. 143

Chapter 10 ▪ **Pothole 8: The Payment and Denial Posting Process**
Tool 16 Payment Posting Checklist............................ 164
Tool 17 Payment Posting Audit Tool........................... 165
Tool 18 Verify Reimbursement Level by Payer 168
Tool 19 Sample Refund Request Form......................... 170

Chapter 11 ■ **Pothole 9: The Insurance Follow-up Process**
Tool 20 Prioritizing Your Outstanding Accounts Receivable 179
Tool 21 Payer Collection Checklist 186

Chapter 12 ■ **Pothole 10: The Denial Management Process**
Tool 22 Claim Denial Log 200
Tool 23 Graph of Denial Trends 201
Tool 24 Interpreting EOB Remark Codes........................ 202
Tool 25 Determining if Denied Claims are Appealable 203
Tool 26 Working a Duplicate Denial Code 206
Tool 27 Use Denial Data to Compare Payers................... 212
Tool 28 Sample Appeal Letters................................ 215
Tool 29 Sample Payer Report Card 219

Chapter 13 ■ **Pothole 11: The Patient Collections Process**
Tool 30 Sample Collection Policies 227
Tool 31 Sample Collection Letter 228
Tool 32 Payment Plan Agreement.............................. 230
Tool 33 Payment Plan Structure 231
Tool 34 Physician Approval Form — Accounts to Collection
         Agency 239
Tool 35 Billing Inquiry Call Log.............................. 244
Tool 36 Percentage of Patient Financial Responsibility Collected
         by the Medical Practice for Key Payers.................. 245
Tool 37 Segment Patients Based on Credit Worthiness 247
Tool 38 Using Federal Poverty Levels to Determine Credit
         Worthiness 248

Chapter 15 ■ **Staffing the Revenue Cycle**
Tool 39 Determine the Number of Staff for Back-end Billing 279
Tool 40 Competency Assessment: Payer Knowledge............ 294

Chapter 16 ■ **Internal Controls for the Revenue Cycle**
Tool 41 Internal Controls Checklist 307

Chapter 19 ■ **Measuring and Analyzing the Revenue Cycle**
Tool 42 Sample Accounts Receivable Aging Report 386
Tool 43 Sample Billing Financial Report 387
Tool 44 Sample Charge Lag Report............................ 388
Tool 45 Sample Denial Graph................................. 389
Tool 46 Sample Abbreviated Dashboard 390
Tool 47 Sample Charges and Accounts Receivable Trends....... 390

Chapter 20 ■ **Regulations Impacting the Revenue Cycle**
Tool 48 Sample Privacy Audit................................. 404

List of Policies and Procedures

Chapter 3 ■ **Pothole 1: The Patient Financial Clearance Process**
Policy 1 Patient Registration.................................... 38
Policy 2 Patient Information Brochure 39
Policy 3 Insurance Verification................................ 40
Policy 4 Financial Policy 40

Chapter 4 ■ **Pothole 2: The Patient Check-in and Check-out Processes**
Policy 5 Time-of-Service Payment............................. 62
Policy 6 Medicare Non-covered Services — Advance Beneficiary
          Notice (ABN).. 63
Policy 7 Waiver of Patient Financial Responsibility.............. 64
Policy 8 Financial Agreement for Surgeries and Procedures 64

Chapter 5 ■ **Pothole 3: The Charge Capture Process**
Policy 9   Manual Charge Ticket................................ 79
Policy 10 Charge Ticket Accuracy and Completeness 81
Policy 11 Charge and Office Visit Reconciliation 82
Policy 12 Charge and Service Reconciliation
           (Non-office Services)................................. 82

Chapter 7 ■ **Pothole 5: The Charge Entry Process**
Policy 13 Fee Schedule 115
Policy 14 Outpatient Charge Entry............................. 116
Policy 15 Timeliness and Accuracy of Data Entry 116
Policy 16 Lag Time: Date of Service to Date of Bill Release 117
Policy 17 Charge Correction 118

Chapter 8 ■ **Pothole 6: The Claims Management Process**
Policy 18 Timely Submission of Claims......................... 137
Policy 19 Billing Primary and Secondary Insurance Claims 137

Chapter 10 ■ **Pothole 8: The Payment and Denial Posting Process**
Policy 20 Payment Posting 173
Policy 21 Interest Payments 174
Policy 22 Credits and Refunds 174
Policy 23 Account Write-offs and Adjustments................ 175

Chapter 11 ■ **Pothole 9: The Insurance Follow-up Process**
Policy 24 The Insurance Follow-up Process 192
Policy 25 Small Balance Adjustments 193

Chapter 12 ■ **Pothole 10: The Denial Management Process**
Policy 26 Claim Denials 223

Chapter 13 ■ **Pothole 11: The Patient Collections Process**
Policy 27 Patient Collections.................................. 252
Policy 28 Collection Agency 253
Policy 29 Financial Hardship................................... 254
Policy 30 Payment Plan 255

Chapter 16 ■ **Internal Controls for the Revenue Cycle**
Policy 31 Employee Background Check......................... 313
Policy 32 Time-of-Service Payment Controls.................... 314
Policy 33 Deposit of Patient Receipts 317
Policy 34 Bank Statement Reconciliation...................... 318

Chapter 19 ■ **Measuring and Analyzing the Revenue Cycle**
Policies and Procedures for the Revenue Cycle 391

Foreword

We are pleased to present the second edition of what is now affectionately referred to as the "potholes" book. The health care reimbursement environment has dramatically changed over the past five years. This new edition of the book will help you align your revenue cycle with these important changes and will give you the advanced tools and resources you need to navigate today's potholes in the road to getting paid in order to optimize reimbursement.

In this new edition, we proceed through each key step in the revenue cycle and present advanced practices, tools, checklists, and policies and procedures to optimize your professional fee billing cycle, including diagnostic tools to help you evaluate each key step in your billing and collection process.

We have devoted an entire chapter to the changing reimbursement climate, which has included the consolidation of health plans, price transparency, real-time claims adjudication, reimbursement "conditions" dictated by payers, consumer-directed health plans with high deductibles and health savings accounts, and lifestyle plans that provide patients with a range of deductibles and coverage choices. Beyond these changes, medical practices must contemplate their position vis-à-vis changes to the delivery system itself, including retail-based clinics, retainer-based practices, changing provider models, and medical tourism. These changes have a direct impact on your revenue cycle and your medical practice's bottom line.

Meeting the challenges associated with increased patient financial engagement (and increased out-of-pocket payments by patients), we have provided a new chapter dedicated to "patient financial clearance" so that your medical practice can take a proactive role to assess credit worthiness, prioritize patient collections, and shrink your patient collections cycle. We now have three types of "self-pay" patients: (1) the patient with no resources, (2) the patient with resources (who elects to pay out of pocket for his/her care, particularly for elective services), and (3) what some consider to be the fastest-growing payer in the United States — the patient with a high-deductible or lifestyle plan that combines insurance coverage with a larger patient out-of-pocket obligation.

Medical practices need to take additional steps to identify the patient's insurance product and coverage and the out-of-pocket payments required by patients for their care. As financial advocates, we must help patients understand what their health plan will pay and what their personal out-of-pocket payments for health care services will be so that patients, too, can have a comfort level in making important decisions about their health. And we must make difficult decisions regarding whether our medical practice can continue to be a "financial lender" to the patient with lengthy patient collections cycles, budget plan agreements, and bad debt account adjustments, or whether we need to proactively refer patients to other parties to obtain financing for their health care services so that our medical practices can remain in business to see tomorrow's patients.

With more money being accepted at the point of care, another new chapter is devoted to internal controls related to billing and collection, and we discuss the need for risk segmentation for determining patient collection strategies. The financial controls in place in many medical practices today have been adequate for collecting copayments, but they are insufficient to appropriately safeguard patient payments that now consume an even greater portion of the revenue stream for a medical practice.

Diagnosis coding has always been part and parcel with physician billing, but it now has heightened importance related to reimbursement. Payers have instituted pay-for-performance and other "at risk" reimbursement arrangements with medical practices that typically originate with the patient's diagnosis, which triggers an algorithm for payment. We have responded by adding an entire chapter devoted to coding to alert you of the added importance of documentation and coding, not only for quality and compliance purposes, but for appropriate opportunity to capture "at risk" revenue.

Throughout this edition, we note the efficiencies that medical practices have achieved by leveraging technology. From insurance and benefits eligibility verification to real-time claims adjudication, to smart phones and electronic hand-held devices, to automated charge entry, to patient portals, to online tools, medical practices have been able to reduce the resources devoted to the revenue cycle and have, at the same time, streamlined their billing and collection process and reduced the time to payment for their services.

Physician billing, also known as Part B or professional fee billing, encompasses the many steps needed to translate a health care service into a billing claim and to follow that claim until it is paid. Unlike purchasing a loaf of bread, reimbursement for physician services is not at all straightforward. Rarely is it a simple process of exchanging cash for services rendered. Instead, it involves multiple steps that must be performed in a well-informed, consistent, relentless, timely, and accurate fashion if a medical practice seeks to optimize its revenue performance. We help you transition from a "best guess" approach that you were paid the right amount from the payer, to the use of tools to ensure that you are paid consistent with your contract terms.

There are a number of publications that feature physician billing; however, most of these discuss one aspect or only a few steps in the billing process or present an overview perspective, absent significant detail. In physician billing, the details matter. In this book, we provide a step-by-step review of the entire billing and collection process, from patient registration to collections.

As we proceed on the journey to getting paid, we discuss "potholes" in the road and advanced practices adopted by better-performing medical practices — potholes and advanced practices we have learned during our careers as consultants and practice executives responsible for the revenue cycle of a medical practice.

Physicians, medical practice executives, billing managers, and billing staff can use this book to diagnose their revenue cycle and initiate change efforts to enhance performance. This book gives you tools and resources to translate a clinical service into an adjudicated claim and to help you avoid the potholes in the road to getting paid. We provide specific tools, resources, and policies and procedures for key steps in the revenue cycle to promote improvements in your medical practice. We highlight advanced practices and diagnostic tools to draw attention to processes adopted by better-performing practices. These practices and tools will help you identify ways you can enhance billing and collection performance in your own medical practice. Although we refer to "medical practice" throughout this book, the policies, procedures, and practices provided apply to all professional services, including those performed in physicians' offices as well as surgery, endoscopy, imaging, and infusion centers.

Five years ago, we said that we fully expect that in our lifetimes we will see an innovation that will solve all of our billing potholes — perhaps a smart card that permits instantaneous transmission of services performed and electronic transfer of payment for these services. We are now seeing some real-time claims adjudication — the data is entered and the payment is adjudicated by the payer within seconds, with the funds electronically transferred to the medical practice's bank account — so we are getting close. But even with that innovation, at the present time we still must submit claims, reconcile explanation of benefits, and be alert to retroactive "corrections" of the payment that has been made. And until a real-time claims adjudication process is perfected, streamlined, offered by all payers for all services, and seamlessly integrated into our management information systems, we need to work with due diligence to optimize the complex billing and collection processes required to ensure a financially healthy bottom line.

Introduction

A medical practice is one of today's most complex businesses, and it must generate revenue if it is to survive. Typically, the majority of revenue in a medical practice is derived from payments made for physician professional services by government payers, health plans, and patients. There are exceptions to this, for example, medical practices with high levels of ancillary services, but in general, today's medical practice must "live off of" the revenue generated by its physicians.

In order to receive payments for professional services, the revenue cycle for a medical practice involves a labyrinth of process steps, handoffs, decisions, and pathways that require medical practice staff to make daily decisions that impact the practice's bottom line. Such decisions include the following:

- Is this payment consistent with our contract or should we appeal it as an under-profile payment?
- Are these zero payments on the explanation of benefits (EOB) really denials, and if so, should they be appealed?
- Are we contracted with the payer who paid the claim and took a network discount or is this a silent preferred provider organization (PPO) that is trying to take advantage of us?
- Should this patient be granted a payment plan or should he/she be referred to a financial lending institution to obtain health care credit?
- Is this claim denied due to a preventable error we made as part of the billing process, and if so, what code should be used to adjust the account off of the accounts receivable?

Medical practice staff need the tools and resources to make these and other difficult decisions that impact the financial health of the practice.

Many of us remember from civics courses in grade school how a bill becomes a law. Figure i demonstrates the complexity of how a health care service becomes a paid bill. It is a convoluted web of steps that requires sophisticated knowledge, due diligence, attention to detail, and persistence.

FIGURE i ■ How a Medical Service Becomes a Paid Bill

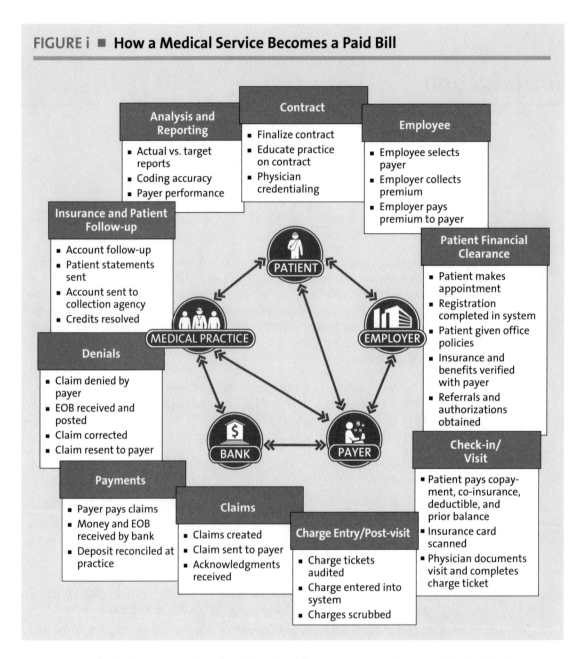

Reimbursement for physician health care services has steadily declined. Today, it is not unusual for a medical practice to report a gross collection rate of 60 percent or less. That means that for every $1.00 of health care services billed, the physician receives only 60 cents. Thus, it is important to bill for the service correctly the first time to avoid additional expenditures associated with billing rework.

Many of the medical practices with which we work review data relative to the billing and collection process on a monthly basis. Typically, they review gross charges, net collections, work relative value units, and patient and procedure volumes.

Unfortunately, these performance indices represent *lagging* indicators rather than *leading* indicators to affect change in the medical practice. By the time these data are available at month's end, it is often too late to affect change that is needed to bring about financial success. This book discusses leading performance indicators and advanced billing practices that permit early identification of revenue fluctuations so you can proactively manage billing and collection as an important asset. As reimbursement continues to decline from both government and non-government payers and as it gets more and more difficult to ensure a "clean" claim is submitted to payers, medical practices need to examine leading billing and collection indicators and ensure that they are using advanced billing practices to optimize reimbursement and profitability.

Before we begin the journey to getting paid, we suggest that you complete the following assessment to evaluate the billing and collection process in your medical practice and to determine how much you may be able to improve your revenue performance.

FIGURE ii ■ Medical Practice Self-audit: Is Your Practice Leaving Money Uncollected?

Answer each of the following questions by checking "YES," "NO," or "UNKNOWN."   YES   NO   UNKNOWN

1. Our practice has a financial policy in place and all patients have received a copy of that policy.   ___ ___   ___

2. Our practice's net collection rate is greater than 97 percent.   ___ ___   ___

3. Our practice verifies insurance and benefits eligibility prior to every office and outpatient service and prior to elective inpatient services.   ___ ___   ___

4. Our practice knows the type of plan each patient has and collects copayment, prior balance, deductible, and co-insurance at the point of care.   ___ ___   ___

5. Our practice collects the amount due from the patient prior to performing elective procedures.   ___ ___   ___

6. Our practice has management reports that enable us to review the quality of our staff's registration activity, and errors are communicated to the staff.   ___ ___   ___

7. Our practice's registration data are accurate and of high quality, with less than 2 percent errors.   ___ ___   ___

8. Our claims are denied by payers less than 7 percent of the time.   ___ ___   ___

9. Our practice offers online billing inquiries and online payment options to patients.   ___ ___   ___

10. Our practice physicians and staff know what contracts we have and what the critical elements of those contracts are to ensure compliance and appropriate reimbursement.   ___ ___   ___

11. Our patient statements are understandable and informative to our patients.   ___ ___   ___

12. Our practice provides detailed reporting of contractual and non-contractual adjustments and takes active steps to reduce non-contractual adjustments.   ___ ___   ___

13. Our practice has implemented effective internal controls to manage and monitor all money received in the medical practice.   ___ ___   ___

14. Our practice captures information needed to ensure prior authorization for all services.   ___ ___   ___

Total your responses: ___ ___   ___

YES   NO   UNKNOWN

Compare your total responses to the scores on the next page to assess your medical practice.

FIGURE ii ■ Medical Practice Self-audit: Is Your Practice Leaving Money Uncollected? (continued)

UNKNOWNs: If you recorded any "UNKNOWNs," we encourage you to focus on these particular sections of the book.

Number of NOs:

- 10–14 NOs: Dramatic improvement in revenue in your practice is possible.
- 4–9 NOs: Possibility of significant improvement.
- 1–3 NOs: Some improvement is possible.

Note: If you found yourself wanting to answer maybe or sometimes, count that as a No. If your practice's performance is inconsistent, then there is opportunity for improvement in your revenue.

© 2009 Walker, Woodcock, Larch. Reprinted with permission.

We are certain that some of you have performed extremely well on this assessment instrument. We congratulate you on your practice's adoption of advanced practices in its revenue cycle and your ability to make changes in your medical practice consistent with the current reimbursement environment. Regardless of how your medical practice performed on the self-audit, we hope this book expands the breadth and scope of your knowledge related to the detailed billing and collection steps required to maximize reimbursement and optimize profitability for your medical practice, particularly in today's reimbursement climate.

Oversight of the billing and collection process by state and federal agencies and other regulatory bodies has been heightened in recent years. It is important to remember that there is significant variation among states related to specific billing requirements. There is also variation among the hundreds of payers with which your practice contracts. Federal, state, and payer guidelines and requirements also frequently change, and the medical practice must consult and comply with all current rules in effect.

As a consequence, we remind you of the following:

None of the information or material presented is intended to encourage action on the part of the reader that would be in violation of federal or state law or violation of payer contract terms. When questions of a legal or regulatory nature arise, the reader is strongly encouraged to seek appropriate legal counsel.

Now let's proceed on the journey to getting paid!

CHAPTER 1

The Changing Reimbursement Environment

These are exciting times in health care — and we are inspired to meet today's challenges with advanced tools and techniques to optimize a medical practice's financial health. True, there are a number of potholes in the road to getting paid. At the same time, there are opportunities for medical practices to avoid the potholes and to optimize revenue cycle performance.

The drivers of change in the health care environment continue to be similar to the ones we have always faced — cost, quality, access, and service — yet the collective responses to these change drivers appear to be different than in years past and they are having a profound impact on the financial health of a medical practice.[1] In this book, we provide the advanced practices and tools you need to ensure that your revenue cycle performs optimally. Given the magnitude of the changes that are taking place today, these tools are vital if you are to be financially successful as a medical practice.

Though the drivers of change in health care today may be no different than in the past, what is different this time around is the magnitude of *responses* to the change and the impact this has on the professional fee billing cycle.[2] Adjustments to the reimbursement environment and modifications in the delivery system for health care services together have a major impact on a medical practice's financial performance. (See Figure 1.1.)

In this chapter, we cover:

- Financing changes
- Delivery system changes
- Underlying themes

---

[1] Walker Keegan, D., "Are you ready for the perfect storm: aligning your practice with the changing health care environment," *MGMA Connexion,* January 2008, pp. 30–33.

[2] Ibid.

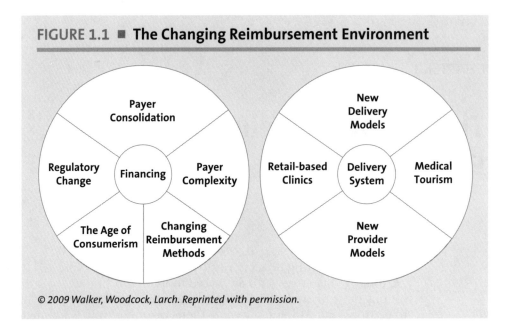

FIGURE 1.1 ■ The Changing Reimbursement Environment

© 2009 Walker, Woodcock, Larch. Reprinted with permission.

FINANCING CHANGES

There are a number of changes in the financing of health care that impact today's medical practice. These include payer consolidation and a growing government-sponsored plan base, payer-specific reimbursement requirements, new reimbursement methods (such as pay-for-performance), the rise of consumerism and regulatory changes that impact the type of revenue sources, and the distribution of revenue within a medical practice.

Payer Consolidation

The reimbursement environment that heretofore has typically been subject to incremental changes is now in flux. Not only do the uninsured and under-insured populations continue to increase, but also the percentage of patients covered by government plans is increasing.[3] It is no surprise that the non-governmental payers are actively consolidating. Based on size, the top five commercial payers represent 80 percent of the total.[4] In 95 percent of United States markets, a single insurer has a market share of 30 percent or greater; in 56 percent of the markets, a single insurer has a market share of 50 percent or greater.[5] This means that medical practices have less leverage than they have had in the past to negotiate favorable contracts, service carve-outs, and other terms that would permit a viable revenue stream for a practice.

---

[3] *Medical Cost Reference Guide,* Blue Cross Blue Shield Association, 2007. The percentage of patients covered by government plans is 46 percent as of this writing. Source: Centers for Medicare & Medicaid Services, 2006:9.

[4] Reuters.com. Insurance (Accident & Health): Company rankings, September 2007 as measured by market cap, www.investor.reuters.com/business/BusRankingsCompanies. aspx?sectorcode=FINANCE&industry=1NSACC&target=%2fbusiness%2fbussecindustry %2fbussecindfake%2fbusrankcomp (accessed September 17, 2007).

[5] *Competition in Health Insurance: A Comprehensive Study of U.S. Markets: 2007 Update by AMA,* http://www.ama-assn.org/ama1/pub/upload/mm/368/compstudy_52006.pdf (accessed February 14, 2008).

Payer Complexity

In addition to consolidation, payers continue to pose a tremendous administrative challenge to medical practices seeking payment for professional fee services. The type and frequency of services that are covered, the authorization requirements for services, and other related required hurdles create complications for many medical practices as they navigate the financial road of the revenue cycle. The complaints regarding the difficulty in working with particular payers have escalated to the point where some medical practices rank payers by degree of complexity and hassle factor. Many of the payers offshore portions of their adjudication processes, with medical practices and patients interacting with payer representatives who are across the globe.

Changing Reimbursement Methods

Adding to the financial changes are new reimbursement methods, including pay-for-performance (P4P) plans. These plans are linked to service, technology, patient access, and cost measures that require medical practices to manage data in a sophisticated manner in order to compete for these funds. While a number of medical practices have successfully secured additional reimbursement as part of their P4P strategies, others are faced with what looks similar to the payment withholds and risk pools of the past. Other changes in the reimbursement climate have also been introduced, including refusal to pay for medical errors, tiering, and other forms of physician ranking based on quality, with reimbursement tied to the rating, and other similar methods to ensure that the payer is reimbursing only "value-based" services.

The Age of Consumerism

Managed care failed to stem rising health care costs for employers. In response, employers began to shift financial responsibility to employees in an effort to reduce health care spending. The shift to employee financial responsibility has led health plans to alter their construct. No longer can a health plan be distinguished by a well-defined premium, copayment, co-insurance, and deductible. Instead, we have consumer-directed plans, with active engagement of patients in the finances associated with their health. High-deductible health plans, coupled with health savings accounts, were the first readily identifiable alterations of the more traditional health plan offering to patients and their families. These types of health plans are now transforming to recognize that patients do not want to accept a "one size fits all" plan but want to select a plan unique to their individual needs — a lifestyle plan that is unique to their health status, age, affordability, risk, and other related balancing factors. Though today, only 7 percent of adults ages 21 to 64 who have private insurance have enrolled in a consumer-directed health plan,[6] 24 percent of large employers are reported to offer some form of consumer-directed health plan, with 70 percent of the employers indicating that they plan to do so in the next five years.[7] Whether the high-deductible health

---

[6] Fronstin, P., and MacDonald, J., Employee Benefit Research Institute, "Consumer-Driven Health Plans: Are They Working?" *Wall Street Journal,* April 22, 2008, p. A17.

[7] Human Capital Practice of Deloitte Consulting LLP and the Deloitte Center for Health Care Solutions, *Reducing Corporate Health Care Costs 2006 Survey:* 2.www.deloitte.com/dtl/cda/doc/contents/us_chs_red_c or_hea_costs_0106.pdf (accessed September 16, 2007).

plan becomes prominent or whether other methods are used to reduce health care costs (such as employee or subscriber incentives to participate in various disease-management programs) is yet to be determined; however, the focus on consumerism and cost containment is certain to continue.

Regulatory Change

Finally, in the area of changes in financing, we have a regulatory environment that often requires physician and medical practice executives to analyze the fine detail associated with the Stark law, Medicare fee schedules (and the signaling effect Medicare has for other payers), Health Insurance Portability and Accountability Act (HIPAA), National Provider Identifier (NPI), and other similar regulatory changes. The implementation and execution of a number of these regulations has at times left many of us shaking our heads in wonder at displays that defy administrative logic. The administrative complexity of many of the regulatory changes represents a layering upon layering of business of medicine work, if not additional clinical work, for a practice and its physicians. A number of these regulatory changes have an impact on the structure of medical practices — at times, even "encouraging" medical practices to enter into physician-hospital integration arrangements and integrated delivery systems if they are to continue to survive.

DELIVERY SYSTEM CHANGES

Beyond the financing changes, we have significant changes to health care delivery systems. Patients seek greater access through a number of channels, not simply the traditional doctor-patient, face-to-face visit.

Medical Tourism

Consider medical tourism, with more than 300,000 Americans traveling to other countries to receive health care at reduced rates.[8] Rather than view these as temporary *shifts*, we watch with awe as major health care institutions now take the leadership in establishing these health care sites. If this offshoring of medical services grows, this will have a decided impact on the revenue and service mix of a practice.

Retail-based Clinics

The retail-based clinic has also managed to impact one of the staples of the primary care practice — the quick-check visit. Not only are these acute requests — as one family practitioner described them to us, his "quickie sickies" — the greatest volume of primary care, their impact on profitability is arguably the most significant to the bottom line of a primary care practice. With thousands of quick-access clinics projected to be in operation in the near future, forward-thinking primary care practices are developing competitive and collaborative

---

[8] "Traveling for Treatment," *AARP Bulletin,* September 2007: http://www.aarp.org/bulletin/yourhealth/traveling_for_treatment.html (accessed February 14, 2008).

strategies with retailers to mitigate the impact on these high-volume, high-margin services. A shift from the medical practice setting to the retail setting is sure to impact your revenue stream, yet experts predict the proliferation of quick access clinics largely as a result of projected physician shortages and increasing patient access demand.

New Delivery Models

Many other medical practices are working to define the "best" delivery system, yet how is "best" defined? Is it "best" if it meets the needs of the physicians? Is it "best" if it maintains health and wellness of the patient? Or is it "best" if it meets the needs of an entire community of patients? The medical home model, the retainer physician, the micropractice, and other similar models are working overtime to attempt to redefine the delivery system of tomorrow. One of the authors of this book is an acknowledged expert in the field of practice operations, and is furthering innovation by defining and promoting the patient-centered practice of the future™.[9] A combination of face-to-face visits, secured messaging, video visits, and telemedicine also have been introduced by medical practices with sophisticated electronic health records. Each of these new delivery models impacts provider productivity, charge capture, charge volume, and, of course, the bottom line.

New Provider Models

Of grave concern is the current and projected scarcity of physicians in many specialties and in many markets. With nearly half of United States physicians age 50 or older and with the growing baby boomer population and its accompanying chronic care conditions, there is a very real threat that patients and their families will not have access to needed services.[10] New provider models are appearing daily in an effort to "stretch" the physician's expertise and permit expanded patient access. For example, in a market with a shortage of medical oncologists, a physician may see the patient at the first visit, with the nurse practitioner seeing the patient the next three visits, followed by the physician again, and continuing on with this rotation. As another example, hospitals are employing more and more "hospitalist" services that are well beyond the traditional internal medicine hospitalist, to include obstetrics, neurology, trauma surgery, orthopedic trauma surgery, and many others, furthering a trend by many specialties to have a separation of office-based and hospital-based physicians. These changes will have a profound effect not only on patient access, but also on the revenue streams of today's medical practice.

The responses to these change drivers that have been outlined above — both financing and delivery system changes — challenge and inspire us to adopt new marketing, delivery system, and revenue cycle strategies so that we can continue to meet our strategic and tactical goals. In this book, we provide advanced practices, tools, resources, and action plans so that you can ensure

---

[9] Woodcock, E.W. *Mastering Patient Flow*, Chapter 14: The Patient-Centered Practice of the Future,™ MGMA, 2009.

[10] *Physician Compensation Report*, a HealthLeaders Media publication, December 2007, V. 8, No. 12. Page 7. Total pp. 1–8.

that your practice's revenue cycle is functioning on all cylinders and leave no stone unturned as you optimize revenue cycle performance.

Physicians and non-physician providers are working harder than ever. It is our job to ensure that the revenue for their hard work is received in a cost-effective and timely fashion — despite the fact that we are subject along the way to a complex and encumbered professional fee billing and collections process. But today we have at our disposal sophisticated tools and techniques to ensure that we can proactively manage the revenue cycle and encounter no surprises when it comes to your medical practice's financial health.

UNDERLYING THEMES

In this book, we share advanced practices for each of the key steps in the revenue cycle process — the process, people, technology, and quality — required to optimize billing and collection performance. The following beliefs shared by the authors underlie our recommendations:

1. A medical practice is not a financial lending institution; its margins simply will not support it to do such. As one colleague told us, "There is no 'bank' written on the outside of our building." We believe that other organizations and businesses are better suited to this role, including banks, lenders, and other financiers. We particularly believe that the new health plan products will require medical practices to dramatically shorten their patient collections cycle, given that more and more of the medical practice's revenue is dependent on patient payment (be it copayment, co-insurance, or deductibles). In addition, this trend will facilitate partnerships with organizations and businesses to assist in optimizing collections.

2. We advocate a patient-centric approach to the revenue cycle, while still running a viable business model. So, for example, we recommend that staff in the medical practice be designated as financial *advocates* to help the patient understand his/her health plan so that the patient has no surprises — and we encourage medical practices to obtain the patient's portion of payment for elective services in advance of the service. These are not mutually exclusive. Rather, we believe such policies are a win-win — for the patient who will not be faced with a surprising bill and for the medical practice that will not need to expend extended resources simply to collect money that it is owed. We recognize that a number of payers are trying to limit the ability of medical practices to collect from patients at the time of service, and we encourage medical practices to attempt to change contract language so that a cost-effective and efficient revenue cycle model can be adopted in the practice. We believe that a medical practice can be caring and at the same time approach the billing process with a business mindset so that it can continue to keep its doors open tomorrow for the next patient and the next.

3. The revenue cycle potholes to avoid are numerous (and at times deep), but we strongly believe that a revenue cycle involving well-defined processes,

staffing, technology, and quality is attainable. In today's environment we also recognize that a number of organizations can assist a medical practice in its revenue cycle performance — and have expertise in certain areas that the medical practice may not have developed. A hybrid organization involving medical practice staff and external vendors may be the best offense to capture every cent that is due the medical practice in a timely and cost-effective manner.

Innovation is on the horizon. We are beginning to see real-time claims adjudication *and* payment. Though the process is a bit cumbersome at present, this is a form of what we had envisioned in the previous edition of this book — a smart card that can be swiped, the service is entered, and money is electronically transferred to the practice's bank account.

Consumer-directed health care appears to be engaging patients in the finances of health care, and hopefully focusing patients more clearly on maintaining their own health, wellness, and active lifestyles.

Some of the regulatory changes appear to make good sense — and hopefully one day they will reduce administrative complexity as intended — HIPAA, NPI, and others. Although more effort certainly can be made to reduce the administrative burden of the billing and collections process, significant advances have been achieved.

Technology has streamlined a number of the revenue cycle processes that we have been forced to manually perform in the past, increasing the tools at our disposal to achieve successful revenue outcomes.

In each chapter of the book, we outline the steps you can take to ensure that your medical practice avoids (or minimizes) the potholes on the journey to getting paid. Whether you manage your own in-house professional fee billing operation, oversee others who manage it, or outsource your revenue cycle, this book gives you the tools and techniques you need to determine if you have optimized revenue performance. The advanced practices, tools, resources, checklists, action plans, and policies and procedures help you diagnose and treat your own revenue cycle.

Peter Drucker has said that patients truly seek one major overarching goal — peace of mind.[11] We know that your professional fee revenue cycle sometimes seems a bit crazy — after all, you provide a valuable (and at times life-saving) service to the patient but then have to wait three months to get paid, jump through a number of hoops along the way, and typically spend 6 to 10 percent of your revenue in billing-related expenses just to receive a payment that is deeply discounted from your stated charge. It is administrative complexity at its best. This book, however, helps you navigate this complexity and your revenue cycle with prowess and expertise — and we trust that it also gives you some peace of mind regarding your medical practice's financial health.

---

[11] Per classroom correspondence with Deborah Walker Keegan.

CHAPTER 2

The Revenue Cycle: An Overview

The revenue cycle begins at the time the contract is signed with an insurance company, or payer. In industry parlance, we often refer to the insurance company as the "third-party payer." This term originated from the fact that the payer is indeed the third party, as demonstrated in Figure 2.1.

There is also a contract between the first party — the patient — and the payer. The patient is considered a "subscriber" or "beneficiary" of the health plan offered by the payer. The subscriber may be financially responsible, or the subscriber may have a "guarantor" who is responsible for the account. The guarantor is often a spouse, parent, guardian, or the subscriber himself or herself. Depending on the structure of the health plan, the guarantor is typically financially responsible to pay a premium to his/her employer (or directly to the plan) for health insurance. Furthermore, when a patient accesses medical care, the guarantor is charged a copayment and/or co-insurance. Finally, the guarantor is responsible for paying out-of-pocket up to a deductible, which typically ranges from $500 to more than $5,000. After he/she meets the deductible, the payer

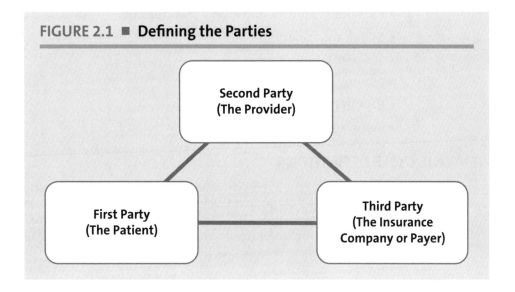

FIGURE 2.1 ■ Defining the Parties

Second Party
(The Provider)

First Party
(The Patient)

Third Party
(The Insurance
Company or Payer)

assumes responsibility. Of course, all of these factors depend on the health plan, and there are literally thousands available in the United States today.

The payer, in turn, has a contract with the provider. (If there is no contract, there are implications on the revenue cycle, which are discussed in Chapter 14: The Contract and Reimbursement Management Process.) The contract between the payer and the provider outlines the terms of claims processing and reimbursement.

The revenue cycle continues through patient scheduling, obtaining and verifying insurance and benefits information, and alerting patients to outstanding balances on their accounts. The process further rotates through claims submission, account follow-up, and payment posting. This requires a well-coordinated effort between the front office and billing office to ensure optimal billing and collection activities.

The entire process of billing and collection, what we term "the revenue cycle," must function in a streamlined fashion for it to be as effective as possible.

In this book, we address the revenue cycle for professional fee billing. Billing for facilities, equipment, pharmaceuticals, and other medical products and services is fundamentally different. Notably, there are physicians and non-physician providers who practice in a "provider-based" entity. A designation by the Centers for Medicare & Medicaid Services (CMS), "provider-based" entities must meet specific guidelines to be designated as such.[1] There are specific regulations regarding how claims should be submitted for provider-based clinics, so if your providers work in such a clinic, your billing office should be familiar with these requirements.

In this chapter, we cover:

- Revenue cycle definitions
- Front-end and back-end billing and collection
- Billing and collection potholes
- Staff workload ranges
- Leading performance indicators
- Cost to rework a claim
- Recurring themes

REVENUE CYCLE DEFINITIONS

The revenue cycle for a medical practice includes multiple functions that must be performed at optimal levels by all involved physicians, non-physician providers, managers, and staff. The revenue cycle is depicted in Figure 2.2. The long, horizontal arrow represents the entire revenue cycle, while the shorter arrow shows what has traditionally been considered the "billing office."

---

[1] For more information about provider-based billing, see CMS 42 CFR §413.65 at http://edocket.access.gpo.gov/cfr_2003/octqtr/pdf/42cfr413.65.pdf (accessed June 16, 2008).

FIGURE 2.2 ■ The Revenue Cycle: Responsibility and Functionality

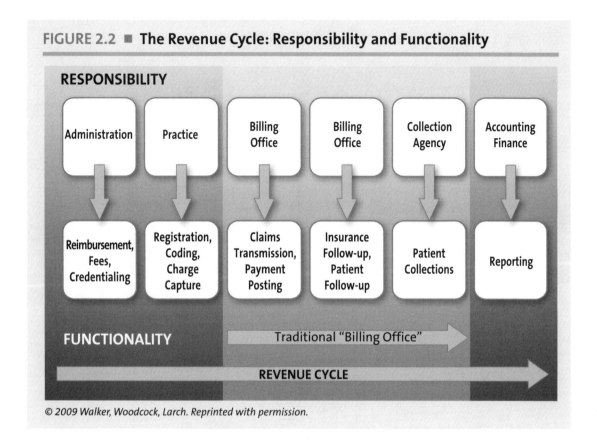

© 2009 Walker, Woodcock, Larch. Reprinted with permission.

Figure 2.3 is a more detailed depiction of the revenue cycle. This figure outlines critical tasks in the billing and collection process that must be performed. Note that what has historically been considered billing and collections is only a portion of the entire process. Payer contracts, patient financial clearance, front office functions, charge entry, account follow-up, payment posting, and reports and analysis are all steps that may include potholes that must be navigated in order for a practice to get paid.

As depicted in Figure 2.3, the billing process occurs at *every step* of the patient's interaction with the practice. Thus, it comes as no surprise that a medical practice should adopt a patient lens and ensure that its revenue cycle meets or exceeds patient service expectations. We have observed numerous instances in which patients have been pleased with the service provided by the physicians and office staff, only to become extremely agitated with the method and manner by which billing has been conducted.

Medical practices must also address compliance issues throughout the revenue cycle. Compliance with relevant laws, regulations, and established policies and procedures represents good business practices for a medical practice and reduces variation in the revenue cycle.

FIGURE 2.3 ■ The Revenue Cycle: Critical Billing and Collection Tasks

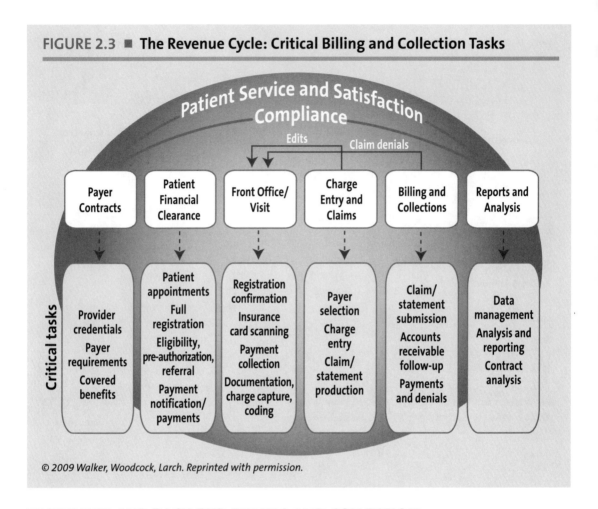

© 2009 Walker, Woodcock, Larch. Reprinted with permission.

FRONT-END AND BACK-END BILLING AND COLLECTION

The billing and collection process is often described as having both a "front end" and a "back end." In the past it was possible to consider billing and collection to be a back-end, localized function performed by staff assigned to "the billing office." As more payers instituted administrative hurdles to receive payment due, these requirements needed to be met. In order to reimburse physicians for their services, the end-to-end process evolved so that billing now starts when the patient calls to make an appointment.

Front-end billing and collection functions are typically performed at the practice site(s) where the patient is seen. Back-end billing and collection functions are typically performed in a billing office, which may or may not physically reside at the practice site.

The interface between both of these billing functions — front-end and back-end — must be transparent to ensure accountability and optimize revenue performance.

Figure 2.4 lists the front-end and back-end billing and collection functions. As one might expect, all of the functions — whether front-end or back-end — represent the practice's *reimbursement functions*. It is clear that billing and

FIGURE 2.4 ■ Front-end and Back-end Billing Functions

Front-end Functions
- Appointment scheduling
- Registration (demographic and insurance)
- Check-in process
- Check-out process
- Referrals and pre-authorizations
- Coding
- Charge capture and entry
- Financial counseling
- Cash at the time of service

Back-end Functions
- Billing edits
- Claims to payers
- Accounts receivable follow-up (by payer type)
- Statements to patients
- Payment posting
- Payment variance analysis
- Denial posting and resolution
- Reporting results and analysis

Training and performance management

Contracts, credentialing, and compliance

Information systems and technology support

© 2009 Walker, Woodcock, Larch. Reprinted with permission.

collection is no longer only a back-office responsibility. Billing and collection is now the responsibility of everyone, including physicians; non-physician providers; managers; and front-office, clinical, and billing-office staff. Physicians and non-physician providers are typically responsible for charge capture, documentation, and coding. Front-office staff are typically responsible for insurance data capture, insurance and eligibility verification, prior authorizations, and point-of-care collections. Clinical staff are involved in obtaining consents and waivers, and are often responsible for securing pre-authorization and pre-payment for elective procedures. Billing staff continue to hold the majority of the responsibility for the back-end billing functions.

BILLING AND COLLECTION POTHOLES

The revenue cycle flowchart in Figure 2.5 depicts the key billing and collection process steps. Now that we have outlined the responsibility and purpose of the revenue cycle and critical billing tasks, we view physician billing at the level of process steps. This figure outlines the 12 major potholes in the road to getting paid. The key potholes to navigate in the physician billing process include:

Pothole 1: Patient Financial Clearance

Pothole 2: Patient Check-in and Check-out

Pothole 3: Charge Capture

Pothole 4: Coding

Pothole 5: Charge Entry

Pothole 6: Claims Management

FIGURE 2.5 ■ Revenue Cycle Flowchart and Potholes

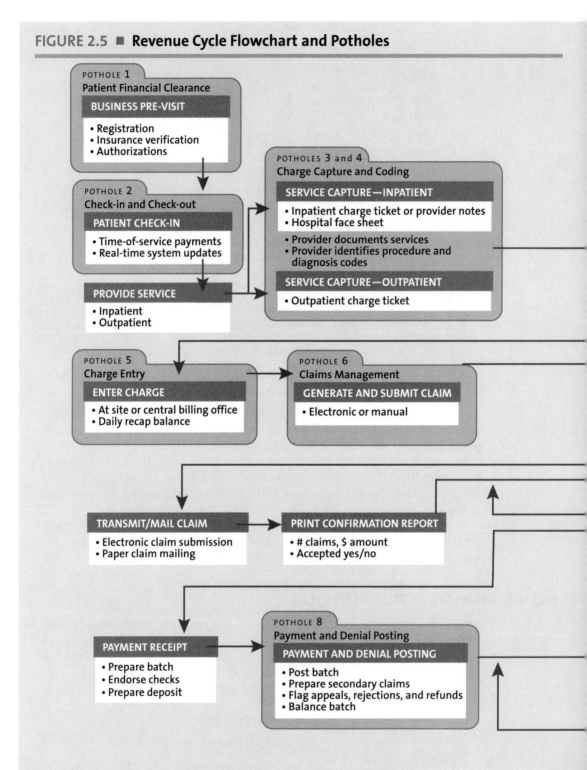

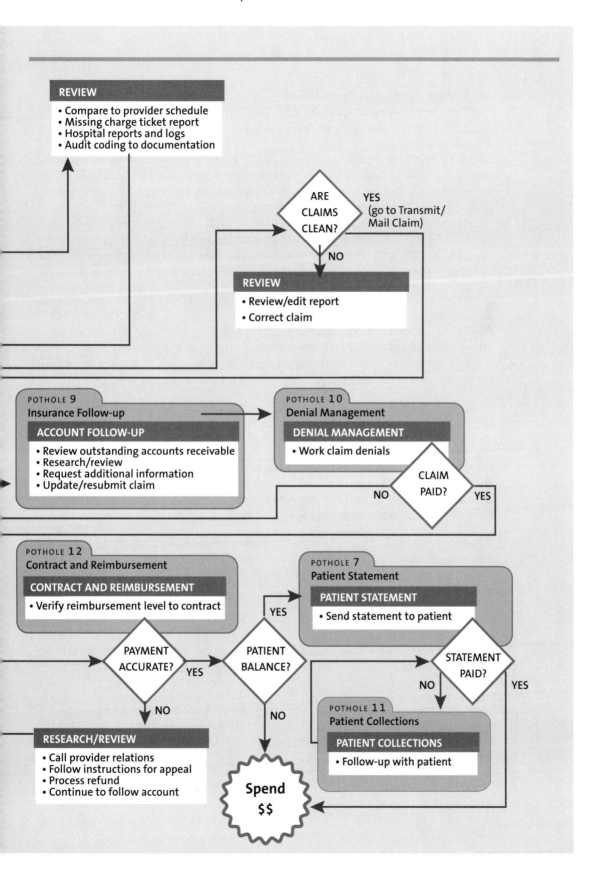

Pothole 7: Patient Statement

Pothole 8: Payment and Denial Posting

Pothole 9: Insurance Follow-up

Pothole 10: Denial Management

Pothole 11: Patient Collections

Pothole 12: Contract and Reimbursement Management

In the 12 "potholes" chapters in this book, we provide a step-by-step examination of the billing and collection processes for a medical practice. We describe expected performance outcomes and advanced practices that lead to optimal performance. The advanced practices that we provide throughout this book are steps you can take to optimize your revenue cycle. They represent billing and collection practices typically found in better-performing medical practices. We provide checklists so readers can diagnose their own revenue cycles and we provide relevant tools so readers can take steps to enhance revenue performance.

After the chapters devoted to each of the billing potholes, we present Chapter 15: Staffing the Revenue Cycle, which includes methods to determine if you have the right number of staff doing the right things in your revenue cycle. We provide sample organizational charts, competency assessments, and incentive compensation plans, and discuss methods to actively involve your staff in performance outcomes.

In Chapter 16, we discuss the need for internal controls, not only in the practice sites where more and more revenue is being collected from patients, but also related to payments that are received in the billing office.

Chapter 17 presents insights regarding a frequent debate: Whether to centralize, decentralize, or outsource your revenue cycle. We review the advantages and disadvantages of each of these strategies and provide a discourse about how to determine the best "fit" for your medical practice.

We discuss technology to leverage your revenue cycle in Chapter 18, including real-time claims adjudication, electronic charge entry, electronic funds transfer, document management, pre-adjudication edits, the use of smart phones, and many other technological tools.

In Chapter 19, we analyze the revenue cycle by benchmarking billing and collection performance and we investigate the reasons for low collections through the use of *leading* financial indicators. In this chapter, we also demonstrate how to evaluate the cost of your billing operation and present keys to management reporting.

We present approaches to assessing your compliance program and resourcing your compliance efforts in Chapter 20, where we also discuss the Health Insurance Portability and Accountability Act (HIPAA) and its impact on your revenue cycle.

The book concludes with additional resources regarding billing and collection that you may want to investigate as you continue to refine your journey on the road to getting paid.

STAFF WORKLOAD RANGES

Throughout this book, we provide expected staff performance workload ranges for various billing and collection functions. It should be noted that a number of practice-specific factors impact the ability of an employee to function at these levels. The medical practice's billing process, the technology, the facility, the patient population, the number of tasks assigned to staff, and many other factors impact the workload for a particular staff member. Thus, the workload ranges are offered as tools for determining whether there is a potential opportunity to *enhance efficiency.*

LEADING PERFORMANCE INDICATORS

It is important to remember that quality, particularly accuracy and timeliness, should always trump quantity as you work to optimize revenue cycle performance. In this new book edition, we highlight leading performance indicators for each key billing and collection process to help you assess opportunity to *optimize revenue cycle performance.*

COST TO REWORK A CLAIM

It is important for physicians and practice executives to recognize that there is a significant cost to the medical practice if the billing and collection process is not performed correctly the first time.

In addition to the cost to perform and bill for the service, there is a cost associated with reworking a claim that is denied. As demonstrated in Figure 2.6, we calculate the expense associated with the rework of a claim to be nearly $15.00. The cost of a denial includes receiving and researching the denial, corresponding with staff and/or physicians involved in the claim, requesting the medical record, reviewing the notes from the date of service, preparing an appeal, and

FIGURE 2.6 ■ The Cost to Rework a Claim

Staff time	$10.67
Supplies	$ 1.50
Interest	$ 1.75
Overhead	$ 1.00
TOTAL	$14.92

Assumptions:

"Staff time" includes 20 minutes of billing staff time at $22 per hour, plus 10 minutes of another staff member's time (for example, front office) valued at $20 per hour.

"Supplies" include telephone, paper, envelope, postage.

"Interest" calculated on $200, at 10 percent, compounded monthly, for 30 days.

"Overhead" includes management, equipment, space, and other fixed costs.

© 2009 Walker, Woodcock, Larch. Reprinted with permission.

submitting the appeal. A medical practice's profit margin is undoubtedly reduced if claims need to be reworked. The significant cost associated with managing denials demonstrates why we emphasize doing the work correctly the first time. If a medical practice seeks to optimize its revenue cycle and reduce its billing cost, it's critical to avoid the potholes in the road to being paid.

RECURRING THEMES

You will recognize a number of recurring themes in this book as you explore each of the billing potholes:

- Putting patients first and developing a patient-focused billing and collection process;
- Doing it right the first time, thereby minimizing rework and lost revenue opportunities and reducing billing costs;
- Performing work in real time, rather than batching work to be performed at a later date, thus enhancing efficiency;
- Emphasizing front-end billing, given the changes in the reimbursement environment and the increasing out-of-pocket payments by patients for their health care services;
- Leveraging technology to improve revenue cycle performance and resource utilization;
- Aligning your medical practice's policies and practices with the changing reimbursement environment;
- Measuring performance outcomes — both quantity and quality — to recognize early warning signs through leading performance indicators;
- Diagnosing each pothole in your revenue cycle to identify opportunities for improvement;
- Taking action to lead change in the medical practice involving billing and collection so that advanced billing practices can be adopted and implemented; and
- Using data to communicate the need for change and to measure and analyze change efforts.

These principles are important to ensure a successful revenue cycle. If you adhere to them, your journey on the road to getting paid should be smoother, resulting in improved revenue for your medical practice.

CHAPTER 3

Pothole 1
The Patient Financial Clearance Process

Patient financial clearance is the process of capturing patient demographic and insurance data before the visit and determining the patient's ability to pay for the service. While the patient financial clearance process is vital to ensuring accurate and timely receipt of information regarding the patient's ability to pay, many medical practices bypass this process. Those practices that disregard this process simply wait for the patient to present for a visit to begin capturing the important information needed to ensure they are paid. And that is where they get into financial trouble!

By starting the billing process *before* the patient sees the physician, you can avoid problems related to non-covered services, inaccurate insurance information, coverage ineligibility, and payment delays. In addition, the patient financial clearance process is a chance to establish an expectation regarding your patient's financial responsibility before the service is provided. Implementing a patient financial clearance process benefits both your medical practice and your patients, who appreciate — and increasingly demand — a greater understanding of their financial responsibility for the care they receive. Medical practices must be able to inform patients, before they receive a service, what their out-of-pocket costs will be.

In order for a patient to be "financially cleared" to receive a medical service, specific tasks must be completed prior to the service being provided. These include:

- Ensuring that all demographic and insurance information has been provided;
- Verifying active coverage and insurance benefits for an insured patient;
- Determining credit worthiness for patients without insurance;
- Ensuring that acceptable payments have been made;
- Ensuring that patients qualifying for Medicaid or other government programs have applied for these benefits;

- Ensuring that an application for financial hardship discounts has been completed; and

- Verifying that all documents, such as assignment of benefits and assumption of financial responsibility, have been signed by the patient or the patient's guarantor. (A guarantor is the person who is financially responsible for the patient's payment, for example, the subscriber of the health plan or the parent of an uninsured minor.)

How many times have you heard the front-office staff say, "I have too much to do"? And how many times have you cringed when you thought about the level of chaos that is almost constant at the front office? Remember that this is where your revenue cycle begins, and the chaos is a clear indication that many of the front-office billing steps should be moved upstream to an earlier point in your process. Investing in the patient financial clearance process ensures that billing is performed *right the first time*.

In this chapter, we cover the key elements of a successful patient financial clearance process:

- Patient financial clearance functions

- Pre-visit registration and insurance verification

- Setting patients' expectations

- Collecting payment prior to service

- Determining credit worthiness

- Patient financial policy

- Referrals and authorizations

- Real-time technologies

- Price transparency

Before the patient's visit, clinical staff perform many functions to prepare for the patient, including readying the exam or procedure room and previewing the patient's chart. Business functions should also be conducted *prior* to the patient visit because there is a greater need not only to enhance revenue performance for the medical practice, but also to ensure that patient-centric billing occurs during the process. Any paperwork, data capture, data updates, insurance verification, and other business functions that your medical practice handles prior to the visit will enhance the patient's experience during and after his/her encounter and ensure you have the data needed for a clean claim or accurate statement. Waiting until the patient arrives at the front office before collecting the information necessary to ensure a clean claim is not an efficient or effective way to start the revenue cycle.

To ensure a successful patient financial clearance process, we present proven strategies to enhance your revenue cycle.

ADVANCED PRACTICES: PATIENT FINANCIAL CLEARANCE

Conduct Pre-visit Financial Clearance

The pre-visit process involves capturing data prior to the patient visit. The information required in this front-end billing process includes registration, demographic and insurance updates, reviewing patient responsibility balances, verifying insurance and benefits eligibility, determining patient out-of-pocket payment levels, and obtaining prior authorization for services to be rendered. The front-office staff typically perform this data capture; however, responsibility may reside with the billing office as well. For example, a billing staff member might review the patient visit schedule two days prior to appointment and note the copayment or patient responsibility balance to be collected by front-office staff. Alternatively, this task may rest with the front-office staff as they prepare for the visit from a business perspective. Your practice management system can support this review by generating a report showing copayments due and prior balances.

Figure 3.1 outlines the business functions that must be performed as part of the patient financial clearance process.

Capture Patient Demographic and Insurance Information Prior to the Patient Visit

Regardless of who performs patient financial clearance, it is essential to obtain patient demographic and insurance information prior to the patient visit. One way to obtain this information is to capture it verbally when the patient calls to schedule an appointment. A high volume of patient scheduling calls, however, may preclude staff from obtaining the information during scheduling. Alternatively, a medical practice may transfer the patient to a registrar or collect registration information by calling the patient after the visit is scheduled. With

---

FIGURE 3.1 ■ Patient Financial Clearance Functions

- Determine prior account balance
- Verify insurance coverage and benefits eligibility
- Determine copayment level
- Determine co-insurance and deductible levels
- Learn pre-authorization requirements
- Make demographic and insurance updates
- Learn patient's no-show history
- Determine patient's credit worthiness

© 2009 Walker, Woodcock, Larch. Reprinted with permission.

this alternative, a member of the scheduling staff sets up a specified telephone meeting with the patient to obtain the information. Finally, the medical practice may establish a registration unit, with staff placing outbound calls to patients within the week prior to their appointments in order to perform the registration process.

Some medical practice executives might feel that they don't have enough staff resources to conduct a complete registration of the patient. If you can only obtain enough information about the patient's insurance so that you can verify active coverage with the payer, you'll likely need to contact the patient again. A better-performing practice uses the following script: "Ms. Jones, while I'm looking for an appointment time for you, would you be kind enough to get your insurance card out of your wallet?" This leaves ample time for the patient to locate the card, while not extending the call beyond a reasonable time.

Medical practices can also use several alternate means to capture registration information, as described below.

New patient registration packet

Some medical practices send a registration packet to new patients via mail. Patients are asked to complete the paperwork and return it to the practice, typically by bringing it to the first visit, unless time permits to mail or fax it to the practice. Alternatively, medical practices ask patients to download registration forms from their Websites. Others maintain a secure, encrypted Internet portal to permit patients to complete and transmit registration information directly to the medical practice. From there, the data may be received by the medical practice for manual keying or directly interfaced into the practice management system.

Appointment reminder process

For established patients, the patient financial clearance communication typically takes place during the appointment reminder process that is conducted 24 to 48 hours before the scheduled appointment. At that time, staff remind patients of any outstanding balances that are due; they can also obtain credit card payment over the telephone as well as any updates to demographic and insurance information. All of these responsibilities can be completed prior to the patient presenting for the visit.

Real-time patient financial clearance

Some medical practices have adopted advanced scheduling techniques that optimize a patient's ability to request and receive a same-day appointment. For these medical practices, insurance verification and benefits eligibility, authorization for services, and time-of-service payment responsibility levels are all determined in real time upon patient presentation to the medical practice or in the short time between the telephone call with the patient and the time of his/her same-day appointment. These medical practices have developed priority designations for this work based on payer, date of patient's prior visit to the practice, and other similar algorithms so that they can focus their resources accordingly. In many cases, work priorities are also developed to respond to claim denials so that these areas receive heighted focus at the time of financial clearance. These medical practices staff differently for these pre-visit functions that are performed essentially in real time.

If a medical practice cannot collect accurate and complete registration prior to the visit, then it is missing critical information necessary for the remaining steps of the revenue cycle. If the medical practice continues through the revenue cycle functions with incorrect information, it causes errors along the way, including:

- Incorrect amounts collected at the time of service;
- Denied claims; and
- Incorrect statements.

All of these can cause payment delays and increase collection costs. If all demographic and insurance information is collected accurately and in a timely manner, the medical practice's revenue cycle will commence with the complete and correct information essential to a clean claim.

Verify Insurance Coverage Prior to the Patient Visit

Once staff obtain the information from the patient, they need to verify the patient's insurance coverage with the payer. They can either call the payer or, ideally, query the information on the payer's Website. Finally, a medical practice can perform real-time eligibility if the payer offers access to its database of beneficiaries and the medical practice maintains the software to perform the eligibility check. While scheduling the appointment, the staff can obtain on-line confirmation of the patient's insurance coverage and benefits directly from a payer's database. If real-time eligibility is not available, medical practices can pursue batch electronic verification processes with their major payers to reduce the cost of insurance verification.

If resources permit, staff should verify insurance coverage for *all patients*. If there are limited resources, consider, for example, verifying Medicaid patients at each visit and Medicare patients only once a year, while verifying commercial coverage quarterly. Alternatively, you may wish to verify all patients who enter your medical practice through a certain place of service, such as an outpatient clinic serving primarily Medicaid patients that your physician staffs.

To decide on a specific strategy for verifying insurance coverage, hold a meeting with the billing office to review the claim denials for insurance eligibility during the past six months. Understanding what type and why your claims are being denied by your payers — whether for eligibility issues, incorrect payer, or other reasons — helps you effectively allocate your resources to patient financial clearance.

If your claim denial data indicates that a high percentage of claims are denied due to the patient not being eligible or due to incorrect payer, consider dedicating staff to the insurance verification function and increasing your investment in technology.

Verify Benefits Eligibility Prior to the Patient Visit

In addition to confirming active insurance coverage, better-performing medical practices verify information regarding benefits. Some medical practices verify benefits for all patients; others perform the check for patients scheduled for a specific service that is often not considered a benefit by payers or for those patients who indicate an insurance change or receipt of a new insurance card from their payers. Verify with the payer the scope of services covered. In particular, obtain information regarding the services that you may render to the patient. For example, an obstetrician would verify obstetrical benefits; a pediatrician would verify preventive services, in addition to coverage of acute illnesses, for a child. If the services are not covered, contact the patient prior to the visit. When a payer does not cover a child's immunizations, for example, explain this to the parents. This allows them to make a decision about whether to proceed with the service, and it allows you to confidently collect for the services from patients when they present for an appointment.

In addition to benefits, some medical practices query payers for their pre-authorization requirements for the services being rendered to the patient, as well as the patient's deductible, copayment, co-insurance, and any other pertinent information. (For more information about gathering information regarding patient financial responsibility before the visit, see Chapter 4: The Patient Check-in and Check-out Processes.)

Develop a customized verification and benefits eligibility form based on the needs of your specialty. (See Tool 1 for a sample form that can be customized for your medical practice.) Maintain the form electronically or as a part of the electronic record so that all staff can access it; at a minimum, place it in the patient's chart. This allows the medical practice to save precious time because nurses and referral staff have access to this information, which eliminates additional calls to the payer. To determine the content of your form and where to place your resources, use your denial data as your guide. You may choose to gather more or less information by payer, by service, or by site, depending on your history of claim denials.

The better informed your medical practice is before the visit, the more knowledge you can impart to your patients. An informed patient base is advantageous when it comes to maximizing your collections because patients will understand their financial responsibility for the service prior to it being rendered. Patients will be prepared to pay their portion of the bill, will know what services are covered, and won't be surprised regarding their insurance coverage and their personal out-of-pocket financial obligations.

Authenticate Address Prior to the Patient Visit

During the registration process, staff collect demographic information from patients, including current street address. The United States Postal Service (USPS) offers access to an address database. Available information includes confirmation of the address as valid, as well as verification of the current occupant.

TOOL 1	**Insurance Verification and Benefits Eligibility Form**

Patient name: _____   Date of verification: _____

Patient telephone number: _____   Date of birth: _____

Social Security number: _____   Physician the patient is seeing: _____

Appointment time and date: _____   Chief complaint: _____

Primary insurance company: _____   Network: _____

PCP (if in an HMO or POS plan): _____   Name of guarantor (insured person): _____

Relationship to patient: _____   Guarantor's date of birth: _____

Guarantor's Social Security number: _____   Employer: _____

Effective date: _____

Person contacted: _____   Telephone number/extension: _____

Who is covered under this plan? _____

Are there other insurance(s) listed? _____

Send claim to: _____   Group number: _____

Policy number: _____   Copayment: _____

Deductible: _____   Co-insurance: _____

   For family: _____

   For individual: _____

Policy coverage notes: _____   Lab and radiology: _____

Immunizations: _____   Well visits: _____

Referral required? _____   Other: _____

Staff name: _____

PCP: primary care physician
HMO: health maintenance organization
POS: point-of-service

© 2009 Walker, Woodcock, Larch. Reprinted with permission.

Technology vendors offer to link this USPS database to your practice management system. Ideally, the address verification process of matching the addresses your medical practice has on record in its practice management system to the USPS data should take place prior to the date of service. Furthermore, it should be electronically performed via batch mode, with only the exceptions (those that could not be verified) being reported and subject to manual processing. If an exception is reported — that is, a match does not exist — the patient can then be prompted to provide updated demographic information.

Ask Patients about Secondary Coverage

To avoid the common problems associated with coordination-of-benefits issues, ask patients for both primary and secondary insurance while you are scheduling their appointment. In addition, ask questions about the existence of secondary coverage when you verify insurance. Many payers, particularly Medicare, have additional coverage listed in their beneficiary databases.

Deploy a Patient Credit Segmentation Strategy

If there were a way to accurately predict, in advance, which patient would pay a high percentage of the time, would this be useful to you? From banks to automobile dealers, businesses of all types measure the probability that their customers will pay before extending credit. The health care industry has recently begun to embrace credit segmentation as a patient collections strategy.

Credit worthiness is determining the likelihood the patient will pay what he/she owes; credit segmentation is using that information to outline a strategy to collect what is due. Medical practices can utilize internal and external data about their patients to assist in determining the extent to which collections should be pursued prior to services being rendered, as well as whether patients may qualify for discounts, free services, or coverage from a state or federal payer (for example, Medicaid).

The following are examples of internal data about the patient — or the guarantor — that can be helpful on the account:

- Has the patient paid in the past?
- Is the patient employed?
- Is there a valid address and telephone number for this patient?

Utilizing new technology, you can also obtain external information about your patients. Software vendors specializing in credit worthiness offer customized screening tools that medical practices can use, at the time of service, to determine if a patient is eligible for Medicaid or a financial-hardship discount. If the patient qualifies, the software allows the user to download and print — or complete and submit online — applications. These tools can move a very labor- and paper-intensive process to a more efficient and streamlined process.

If the credit segmentation process determines that a patient is unlikely to pay, you can offer a financial hardship policy as part of the front-end billing process, which eliminates unnecessary collection efforts. If the process alerts you to available credit on a patient's credit card, then your medical practice can more comfortably collect at the time of service. With more information about the patient's current financial situation, you can better assist the patient in understanding his/her medical bills.

Medical practices can realize benefits from a credit segmentation strategy. Medical practices that invest in credit segmentation technology can ensure a more objective, equitable evaluation of patient financials and can transition from a manual process to a more automated process. These benefits include an increase in time-of-service collections and a potential reduction in time allocated for financial counseling. In addition, a credit segmentation strategy can reduce bad debt and resources allocated to post-service collections. For more information on credit worthiness, see Chapter 13: The Patient Collections Process.

Set Expectations Regarding Patient Financial Responsibility

The patient collections process can begin long before the patient arrives at your office. Communicate the importance of your patients' financial responsibility in your medical practice brochure and on your Website. During the appointment reminder call, remind patients of their time-of-service responsibility (for example, copayment), as well as a prior balance they may have on their account. Finally, a staff member should review the appointment schedule several days prior to the date of service, alert front-office staff to patients with problem accounts, and identify payments owed. Most practice management systems today offer some sort of flag or alert system so you can identify those patients needing financial counseling. A better-performing practice has access to and knowledge of the patient's account and access to scanned images or copies of the explanation of benefits (EOBs) in question at the front office so it can keep the patient fully informed and increase the likelihood of payment. These processes can enhance cash flow, improve patient service and education, and reduce the cost of attempting to collect from the patient after the visit.

Refer Patients to a Medical Lending Company

For years, lending companies have specialized in assisting patients to finance elective medical services; lenders typically exclusively financed expensive services. More recently, these financing companies have extended assistance to patients for all types of medical services at all levels of cost.

Medical practices can develop a relationship with one medical financing company or offer several options to patients to pursue on their own.

If your medical practice contracts with a lender, the lender reviews applications for patients referred for financing. If a patient's application is accepted, the medical practice will be paid the monies owed for the service, less an administrative fee. The patient is liable to the medical lending company, which charges the patient the balance due plus interest. In essence, a medical lending company allows the patient to take out a loan for his/her medical care.

Before establishing a relationship with a medical lending company, determine its experience in health care, analyze its application process to evaluate whether any of your patients will qualify, judge its customer service for your patients and for your medical practice, glean the amounts of administrative fees and interest rates, establish how and when your practice is paid, and, importantly, discover what happens if a patient defaults on the loan.

Embrace the Price Transparency Movement

As patients assume more financial responsibility for their medical care, they seek more information regarding the cost of care. Better-performing medical practices have the ability to provide patients with price estimates upon request. Offering knowledge regarding the cost of care results in a "transparent price" — and one that the patient can use in order to make a decision about whether to pursue elective care and/or where to receive it. This information is particularly valuable in pre-visit financial counseling and establishing payment at the time of service.

For example, a medical practice may create a central pricing office and assign staff to provide estimates to self-pay patients. As another example, the staff identify the likely procedure codes, consult payer contracts, verify patient's coverage, and determine what the patient will likely need to pay (copayments, co-insurance, and deductibles). As another example, the pricing notification can be provided by surgery and procedure schedulers who work with the patient to establish the date and time of surgery/procedure and the patient's financial responsibility prior to the service being performed. Once the patient portion of the payment is determined, it can then be collected prior to an elective visit or procedure, if that is consistent with your contract with the payer.

Develop a Written Financial Policy

A financial policy provides the details of your expectations — in writing. The following are examples of financial policies and the operational questions you should ask yourself (and answer!) as part of each policy:

Policy: Payers with which we participate require us to collect copayments at the time of service.

- Will we turn away a new patient who does not pay the copayment prior to the visit? Will we continue to schedule return visits if a patient owes copayment(s)? When will we collect the copayment (at check-in or check-out)? Will we contact the payer if the patient fails to pay his/her copayment? Will we charge the patient for failure to pay?

Policy: Referrals are required.

- How do we know what services require referrals? Will we obtain the referral before the patient schedules an appointment? Will we obtain the referral before the patient arrives for the appointment? Can we obtain the referral online? Can we store the information regarding the referral online? Will we reschedule a patient who does not provide a referral?

Policy: Prior balances must be paid in 30 days unless a signed payment plan has been executed.

- Who will identify prior balances and remind the patient? Will we schedule appointments for patients who owe prior balances or fail to pay pursuant to their agreed-upon payment plan? Will patients who fail to pay be dismissed from our practice? If so, when and how?

Policy: We will educate patients about their responsibility to pay.

- When will we educate patients about their responsibility to pay? On the telephone during appointment scheduling, at check-in, at check-out, or during the visit?
- Will we follow a different process for (1) new patients, (2) urgent same-day visits, and (3) elective services?

Other financial questions to resolve:

- If we are not participating with the patient's payer, will we see the patient? What financial arrangements must we follow?
- Will our medical practice adopt a financial hardship policy? How will we implement it?
- Will we give uninsured patients who are below a pre-determined income level a discount if they make payment at the time of service? Who will address their questions about payment if they ask at the front office? What language or scripting will we use to communicate this policy?
- What is our policy regarding patient payment plans?
- Will our medical practice charge additional fees, such as interest on past-due balances, a copayment rebilling fee, or pass-through the collection agency fee to the patient?
- If a patient has no insurance, will we collect payments at the time of service? Will we require a deposit paid at every visit and bill the remaining amount via a statement?
- If the patient has been sent to collections, but has not been discharged as a patient of the medical practice, will we schedule the patient for a future appointment?

As you can see from the examples above, your financial policy needs to include implementation guidelines so staff understand the action they should take, treat patients in an equitable fashion, and are aware of any exceptions that may be allowed.

Make sure you have only one financial policy for the medical practice, not separate financial policies for each physician in the practice. You cannot require copayments on Mondays but ignore time-of-service collections on Thursdays because different physicians work in the clinic on those days. Similarly, an individual physician should not be permitted to offer a discount to patients beyond any formal policy you have developed. In order to create a consistent financial policy, ask several physicians in your medical practice to participate in drafting your practice's financial policy. Once the policy is drafted, obtain approval through your normal governance channels and then communicate the policy to every physician and staff member. Put the policy in writing and share it with your patients. Review the policy at least once a year to determine if updates are needed. There should not only be specific policies, but also information on how to handle deviations from that policy.

Don't forget to include all financial expectations of patients in your policy. If you assess fees for any of the following, it should be mentioned in the financial policy that goes to the patients:

- Fees to complete disability or other forms
- No-show appointment fee
- Fee for failure to pay copayment at the time of service
- Collection agency fees
- Interest or finance charge on patient balances

Once you develop a clear financial policy, share it with patients. Depending on your medical practice's preference, you can communicate your financial policies to new patients by mailing a brochure prior to the first appointment. Alternatively, a staff member can meet with all new patients when they present for appointments to review the important elements. Most medical practices ask patients to sign a financial policy agreement. Remind established patients during scheduling calls or appointment reminder calls that appropriate payment is required at the time of service. Medical practices may find it necessary to audit their practice to ensure that the policy is being followed. For example, audit your medical practice twice a year to ensure that new patients are signing the financial policy. A sample financial policy is included in Tool 2.

Conduct Patient Financial Clearance for All Places of Service

This chapter has focused on patient financial clearance as it integrates with your office services. But it is just as critical that you perform financial clearance on inpatient and emergency services as well. To maximize your revenue performance, you need to financially clear all patients and understand what you expect to receive from both the payer and the patient. Prior to providing the service, patients need to be educated about what they will owe. Elective inpatient services should be cleared prior to admission; emergency services must be cleared the following business day. A sample Patient Financial Clearance Checklist is provided in Tool 3 that can be customized for your medical practice.

Process Referrals and Authorizations

Once you determine the patient's financial status and verify that he/she is insured for the service, review the appointment schedule to determine if the patient is scheduled for a service that requires a referral or authorization (or assess this requirement during the visit once the specific service type is determined). Process all referrals and authorizations in a timely manner. Most payers do not retroactively pay for services for which a required approval was not obtained, except in truly emergent situations. Use automated referral processing systems when payers make them available. Vigilance during your pre-visit process is critical to maximize your payments for these services.

| TOOL 2 | Sample Financial Policy |

It is the policy of _____ to have a financial policy that clearly outlines patient and practice financial responsibilities. We are committed to providing our patients with the best possible medical care and also minimizing administrative costs. This financial policy has been established with these objectives in mind and to avoid any misunderstanding or disagreement concerning payment for professional services.

- Our practice participates with numerous insurance companies. For patients who are beneficiaries of one of these insurance companies, our billing office will submit a claim for services rendered. All necessary insurance information, including special forms, must be completed by the patient prior to leaving the office.
- If a patient has insurance in which we do not participate, our office is happy to file the claim upon request; *however, payment in full is expected at the time of service.*
- It is the patient's responsibility to pay any deductible, copayment, or any portion of the charges as specified by the plan at the time of visit. Payments for medical services not covered by an individual's insurance plan are the patient's responsibility, and payment in full is due at the time of visit.
- Payment for professional services can be made with cash, check, or credit card.
- Financial assistance is available for qualified patients. If a patient feels that he or she may qualify for assistance, the practice receptionist should be notified for referral to the appropriate individual. Patients who do not have insurance are expected to pay for professional services at the time of service unless prior arrangements have been made with us.
- It is the patient's responsibility to ensure that any required referrals for treatment are provided to the practice *prior to the visit*. Visits may be rescheduled, or the patient may be financially responsible due to lack of the referral.
- It is the patient's responsibility to provide us with current insurance information and to bring his/her insurance card to each visit.
- Our staff is happy to help with insurance questions relating to how a claim was filed, or regarding any additional information the payer might need to process the claim. Specific coverage issues, however, can only be addressed by the insurance company member services department. (Telephone number is printed on the insurance card.)
- The adult accompanying a minor and the parents (or guardians of the minor) are responsible for payment at the time of service. For unaccompanied minors, non-emergent treatment will be denied unless charges have been pre-authorized or payment by credit card, cash, or check at the time of service has been verified.

Our practice firmly believes that a good physician-patient relationship is based upon understanding and good communications. Questions about financial arrangements should be directed to the medical practice. We are here to help you.

© 2009 Walker, Woodcock, Larch. Reprinted with permission.

TOOL 3	Patient Financial Clearance Checklist

This tool assists medical practices in conducting the patient financial clearance functions. It is intended to be a template only; we encourage medical practices to customize the form according to their specific needs.

Date of service _____

Patient's name _____

Account number _____

Staff member completing form/date of completion _____

(Check all that apply)

Signatures needed from patient

_____ New patient — all registration forms

_____ Change of insurance — all insurance forms

_____ Non-covered services waiver form

_____ Advance beneficiary notice (ABN) (Medicare only)

_____ Consent for treatment

_____ Medical history

_____ Financial policy

_____ Notice of privacy policy

_____ Other _____

Information required from patient

_____ Scan/copy insurance card

_____ Review driver's license/other identification

_____ Other _____

Insurance verification complete and documented?   Y/N   if N, please address: _____

Benefits eligibility complete and documented?   Y/N   if N, please address: _____

Referral(s) secured?   Y/N   if N, please address: _____

Should patient be requested to meet with the financial advocate?   Y/N

Collection of payments at the visit:

$ _____ Copayment

$ _____ Co-insurance

$ _____ Payment on deductible

$ _____ Payment plan

$ _____ Payment on account

$ _____ Other

Notes: _____

_____

Develop a Guide to Payers

Create a payer guide or insurance plan summary sheet and provide it to each of your practice sites, as well as to the billing staff. A typical guide includes an outline of the requirements for each of the major payer contracts, with specific items such as the need for pre-authorization, specified laboratory and radiology sites, copayment level, formulary, telephone number of provider relations department, and other pertinent referral-related information. Many medical practices have placed this information on a secure Website or local area network for access throughout all practice locations. Ideally, the link to the payer guide should be available via a link embedded in the registration screen in the practice management system to permit staff to review the payer guide during the registration process. A sample payer guide is provided in Tool 4.

Imagine if all the financial clearance steps were completed pre-visit. How different would the patient's experience be? The staff could focus on the patient's clinical experience because the financial matters have already been taken care of before the patient walked in the door. Check-in wait times would be shorter and physician schedules would be more apt to stay on time. The medical practice's financial risks would be eliminated or reduced. Establishing financial clearance functions, however, can be labor intensive and thus costly. Yet this cost must be weighed against the cost of not performing these functions at the pre-visit and instead performing them during back-end billing once a claim is denied or a payment requires follow-up with the patient. By prioritizing, investing in effective technology, and empowering your staff, you can reap the benefits of a successful financial clearance initiative.

TOOL 4	**Payer Guide**

We provide an example of a payer guide that can be constructed for each of your payers. This type of guide details the pertinent information required by all staff regarding payer-specific issues.

Payer's name _____   Financial class # _____

PAYER'S LOGO   *Payer's Website URL* _____

Date of update _____

PRODUCTS	REFERRAL/ AUTHORIZATION	REFERRAL LENGTH
Product A	Yes	▪ Up to 3 visits per referral
Product B	Yes	▪ Valid for 60 days from the date of issue
Product C Open Access	No	▪ Exceptions to 60-day window
Product D Opt-Out	No SEE BACK FOR MORE INFORMATION	(unless otherwise noted) • Allergists (1 year) • Hematologists (1 year) • Oncologists (1 year)

(continued on next page)

TOOL 4 *(continued)* Payer Guide

IMPORTANT TELEPHONE NUMBERS/WEBSITES
Eligibility 800-XXX-XXXX
Pre-certification/Admission 800-XXX-XXXX
Provider Relations 800-XXX-XXXX
Customer Service 800-XXX-XXXX
Case Management 888-XXX-XXXX
Care Management 866-XXX-XXXX
  (authorizations and others)
Claims 800-XXX-XXXX
Web Access www.XXXXXX

CONTRACTS/CONTRACT DATES
- Primary Care (6/01/09)
- Specialist/Tertiary Care (06/01/09)
- Hospital A (10/01/09)
- Hospital B (6/01/09)
- Hospital C (10/07/10)

LAB-OUTPATIENT SERVICES
Lab X: 800-XXX-XXXX
- Lab X requisition forms including the patient's ID# must be used when ordering lab tests or referring a member to a draw-station

RADIOLOGY-OUTPATIENT SERVICES
Imaging Center: XXX-XXX-XXXX
Any designated health care provider
- Patients referred to an approved radiology facility require a script from the referring physician

Certificate Numbers
Certificate number begins with XXX followed by numbers. Some ID cards may **not** have an alpha prefix. This indicates that the claims are handled outside the Payer X Program.

PCP name will be on the card.

Include image of insurance card FRONT

Include image of insurance card BACK

Claims address:
Street _____ City, State, Zip _____

Payer's name _____ **Financial class #** _____

GENERAL REFERRAL REQUIREMENTS (OFFICE)

All office visits to a participating specialist require a referral with the exception of:

- Routine and non-routine services provided by a participating OB/GYN for care performed in office setting
- Routine and non-routine services provided at a participating free-standing radiology facility listed in the payer's directory
- Routine vision exams by participating optometrists
- Mental health/substance abuse services, provided/coordinated by _____
- Services provided by a specialist to members with Payer's Opt-out Open Access
- Visits to a participating urgent care center
- Services provided by a participating provider while the member is inpatient

(continued on next page)

TOOL 4 *(continued)*	Payer Guide

Note: Additional authorization of ancillary services and a more limited 90-day authorization period may apply if services are performed in a hospital-based clinic. The rendering physician must identify the number of visits within the 90-day period to be utilized.

Long-standing referrals:
- Members are allowed up to one year of unlimited visits if all of the following criteria are met:
  - Member has life-threatening, degenerative, chronic, and/or disabling condition or disease requiring specialized medical care
  - Member's PCP determines in consultation with the specialist that the member needs continuing specialized care
  - The specialist has expertise in treating the patient's condition and is a participating provider

AUTHORIZATION REQUIREMENTS* (Admitting provider required to obtain authorization at least 5 days prior to admission/outpatient service)

- Any services provided in a setting other than a physician's office (regulated hospital-based clinics), except for lab and radiology facilities
- All hospital admissions or outpatient/ambulatory care procedures
- All diagnostic or pre-operative testing in a hospital setting
- Chemotherapy or intravenous therapy in a setting other than a practitioner's office and billed by a provider other than the practitioner
- Durable medical equipment for a diagnosis other than asthma, diabetes, and when provided by a contracted vendor
- Prosthetics and orthotics when provided by a contracted vendor
- Follow-up care provided by a non-participating practitioner following discharge from the hospital
- Radiation oncology, except when performed at a contracted freestanding center
- Hemodialysis
- Treatment of infertility
- Nutritional services
- Home health care
- Hospice care

SPECIAL INSTRUCTIONS:

Claims filing limits
- 6 months from the date of service

Claims appeals
- 6 months from the date of denial
  To: Street
      City, State, Zip

Emergency admissions
- Contact member's PCP or specialist. Hospital should contact _____.

Provider numbers
- Listed in dictionary #

Physical therapy
  PT practice: XXX-XXX-XXXX

Vision
  Mandated provider for routine vision:
      XXX-XXX-XXXX
  Mandated provider for non-routine services:
  - Any participating provider

Behavioral
  XXX-XXX-XXXX

Payer Guides are published by Mgt Team and can be obtained by calling XXX-XXX-XXXX

---

* The patient must meet the payer's eligibility requirements and services must be covered under the patient's health benefit plan for an authorization to be valid.

Source: University Physicians Inc, Practice Operations, 2009; Sample payer guide with specific payer blinded. Reprinted with permission.

STAFF WORKLOAD RANGES

The staff workload ranges for patient financial clearance that we typically expect are provided below. The ability to perform within these ranges may vary due to internal, practice-specific factors (such as facility layout, telephone system, and practice management system), as well as external factors, such as the speed of Web connectivity and the functionality of payers' Websites. Note that the workload ranges reflect *quantitative* performance levels. Note that *qualitative* performance — accuracy, completeness, appropriateness, and quality of these functions — should also be measured. When issues of quantity versus quality arise, we strongly recommend that quality be emphasized, even if the performance workload ranges for a particular function need to be relaxed from these levels.

Staff Function	Transaction Time
Insurance verification	
via Website	1 to 3 minutes
via telephone call	2 to 10 minutes
Benefits eligibility	
via Website	3 to 10 minutes
via telephone call	5 to 20 minutes

Note: Institute these workload ranges only if accuracy can be assured in this time frame. If not, you may need to increase the time to perform the function in order to avoid mistakes.

© 2009 Walker, Woodcock, Larch. Reprinted with permission.

LEADING PERFORMANCE INDICATORS

Use the following indicators to assess the performance of your patient financial clearance process. We refer to these measures as "leading" performance indicators. If your medical practice is successful in achieving these levels in the patient financial clearance process, you are on the correct path to optimizing your revenue cycle.

Claim edits and denials due to registration and referrals:	< 2 percent
Percentage of insurance verified:	98 percent
Number of patients cleared* prior to visit:	90 percent

* Cleared is defined as demographic and insurance data necessary for claims processing verified with the source of information (for example, payer for insurance information or USPS database for address information).

© 2009 Walker, Woodcock, Larch. Reprinted with permission.

THE PATIENT FINANCIAL CLEARANCE DIAGNOSTIC TOOL

The patient financial clearance diagnostic tool provided below helps ensure that the process, people, technology, and quality required for effective patient financial clearance are in place in your medical practice.

Process:

1. What are the key steps in your financial clearance process?
2. Do you collect all patient demographic and insurance information during the initial appointment telephone call?
3. Do you have a written financial policy approved by the physicians?
4. What is your financial clearance process for non-office services at all places of service?

People:

1. Have you trained staff in the best ways to obtain insurance information via telephone and payer Websites, and how to verify insurance and benefits?
2. Do the staff understand why it is important to do this work before the patient's visit?

Technology:

1. What technology do you utilize to track financial clearance? How do you know if a patient has been "cleared"?
2. Do you offer a Web portal to enable the patient to provide you with financial clearance information in a patient-friendly manner?
3. Have you evaluated real-time patient credit tools?

Quality:

1. What percentage of errors are found in the registrations audited?
2. What percentage of your patients are cleared prior to the visit?
3. How much information are check-in staff required to capture because it was not captured pre-visit?
4. How many patient complaints are received stating that the patient provided the insurance information to your staff but the patient got a statement in error because his/her account was never updated?

POLICIES AND PROCEDURES

At the end of each chapter, we provide policies and procedures to assist you in developing a policy and procedure manual for your medical practice. Below are four policies specific to the financial clearance process.

Policy 1: Patient Registration

Policy 2: Patient Information Brochure

Policy 3: Insurance Verification

Policy 4: Financial Policy

POLICY 1: PATIENT REGISTRATION

Policy:

Demographic and insurance information will be collected from all patients. This information will be verified prior to or at the time of the scheduled appointment.

Procedures:

1. Any patient being seen must be registered in our practice management system. This will ensure that pertinent patient demographic and insurance data are captured in the system for the purposes of billing, contracting, and data analysis.

2. A new patient may pre-register at the medical practice by telephoning the office or by presenting at the office to schedule an appointment. At this time, at least the following minimal demographic and insurance information will be collected by the practice staff:

   - Patient name (*);
   - Patient address (*);
   - Home, work, and cellular telephone number(s) (Home*);
   - Date of birth (*);
   - Social Security number (optional);
   - Primary insurance name (*);
   - Policy and group number(s);
   - Guarantor name; and
   - Guarantor address.

   * If time does not permit collecting all of this data, a telephone registration may be completed with this minimal information. Gathering this limited information is called a "mini-registration."

3. The scheduler/receptionist should ensure that all available information has been collected before the patient/guarantor ends the telephone conversation or leaves the office.

4. All new patients will be given, sent, or directed to the medical practice Website to download a new patient information packet, which includes:

   - Medical practice brochure;
   - No-show policy;
   - Financial policy; and
   - New patient registration form.

5. Three days prior to the appointment, all patient registration information will be reviewed. If there is information missing, the patient will be contacted regarding the missing information. The insurance will be verified *with the payer,* and based on a review of the nature of the appointment, benefits eligibility will be conducted. If coverage and/or benefits eligibility cannot be verified, the patient will be contacted by telephone 48 hours prior to the appointment. (Combine this call with the appointment reminder call.) The patient will be informed that coverage could not be verified and that the visit will be considered self-pay unless the patient chooses to present additional information regarding his/her coverage.

A new patient will be fully registered 24 hours prior to the visit. For patients who receive same-day appointments, the registration process will occur upon patient check-in and prior to the patient being seen.

POLICY 2: PATIENT INFORMATION BROCHURE

Policy:

All new patients will be presented with a patient information brochure that describes the medical practice's policies and procedures relevant to patients.

Procedures:

1. The patient information brochure includes the following information:
   - Medical practice's mission and vision statement;
   - Office hours;
   - Handling of emergencies;
   - Protocols, including telephone number, for appointment scheduling, test results, and prescription refills;
   - Specialty information;
   - Personal and professional information regarding physicians and other providers;
   - Directions to practice or map and information about parking;
   - Referral to specialty care (if applicable);
   - Financial policy, including the telephone number of the person to call regarding billing questions and what to bring to your first appointment (insurance card, copayment, and others);
   - Pertinent telephone numbers; and
   - Termination of services.

2. The patient information brochure will be posted on the medical practice's Website.

3. If a new patient appointment is made for more than one week in advance from the current date, patients will be referred to the Website and/or the brochure will be mailed to the patient. If the patient does not receive a brochure in the mail, patients will be referred to the Website and the brochure will be presented to the patient at the first appointment.

POLICY 3: INSURANCE VERIFICATION

Policy:

It is the policy of the medical practice that insurance coverage and benefits eligibility will be verified with the payer for all new patients, patients indicating changes in coverage, and patients receiving high-dollar procedures or services, including all inpatient services.

Procedures:

1. All new patient accounts and accounts with information changes noted will be pulled three days prior to the appointment date.

2. For each account, the payer will be contacted to verify coverage and benefits eligibility via Internet or telephone.

3. The insurance verification form will be completed for each account. (If possible, add a screen to the practice management system to allow for collection of information online.)

4. If insurance or benefits for the services scheduled to be rendered cannot be verified, the patient will be contacted immediately. The patient will be informed of the situation and asked to provide coverage information. If coverage is not available, the patient will be informed of his/her responsibility to pay for services rendered during the appointment. If the patient chooses (and the visit is non-urgent), the appointment may be rescheduled.

5. If time to appointment does not allow for this verification, staff will conduct insurance and benefits verification in real time upon patient presentation for (a) all new patients, (b) patients with a change to their insurance, and (c) patients who have not been seen in the past six months.

POLICY 4: FINANCIAL POLICY

Policy:

It is the policy of the medical practice to provide all patients with a copy of the medical practice's financial policy. The policy should include implementation guidelines so staff will understand the action they should take in different situations, so they will treat patients in an equitable fashion and are aware of any exceptions that may be allowed and by whom they must be authorized.

Procedures:

The financial policy will include information regarding the medical practice's policy as it relates to the following:

1. Insurance companies — participation and billing;

2. Time-of-service payment;

3. Patient's financial responsibility;

4. Referrals;

5. Workers' compensation;

6. Personal injury and automobile accidents;

7. Collections;

8. Contact information for the billing office; and

9. Fees for forms, collection accounts, no-show appointments, and others.

The financial policy will be posted on the medical practice's Website. The financial policy will be presented to patients upon their registration at the medical practice. Once patients read the financial policy, the patients will be asked if there are any questions. If yes, answers will be provided to clear up any misunderstandings. All patients will be asked to sign the policy to indicate that they have received and understand the financial policy.

CHAPTER 4

Pothole 2
The Patient Check-in
and Check-out Processes

The front-office staff control financial viability and access to the medical practice. We are well beyond just expecting these employees to smile and be nice. The front-office staff are the first opportunity for your medical practice to make a good impression. Their knowledge of the billing and collection process, their ability to clearly explain the financial policy to the patient and to define patient expectations, and their skill in accurately obtaining and recording data — and collecting money at the point of care — are critical to a streamlined billing and collection process.

The ability of your front-office staff to obtain and translate patient information accurately and efficiently is vital to ensuring that billing is conducted right the first time.

In this chapter, we cover:

- Role of patient check-in and check-out
- Registration kiosks
- Time-of-service collections
- Automated receipt processes
- Updates to patient information in real time
- Waiver forms
- Referral and pre-authorization confirmation
- Performance feedback to front-end billing staff

THE PRE-VISIT PROCESS

As discussed in Chapter 3: The Patient Financial Clearance Process, better-performing medical practices make efforts to perform the registration process, insurance and benefits verification, authorization verification, and time-of-service payment identification prior to the patient presenting for care. Pre-visit registration may include registration during the initial scheduling call, contacting patients a few days prior to their appointment to register them over the telephone, or providing instructions to patients to register online. By performing pre-visit registration, the medical practice can accomplish two goals: (1) patient identification, insurance verification, benefits eligibility, and payment expectations can be performed prior to the patient's arrival, thus facilitating the accuracy and timeliness required in a successful revenue cycle; and (2) the time that patients spend at the front office can be minimized.

In fact, a number of medical practices that have adopted pre-visit registration have eliminated the patient check-in step altogether.[1] Instead, the patient is greeted at the door and escorted to an exam room. Since registration, insurance verification, and authorization have already taken place, the only remaining steps are to confirm with the patient that there have been no changes subsequent to the pre-visit process, obtain necessary signatures, scan the insurance card (if needed), and collect time-of-service payments. This is done by the greeter or clinical staff while the patient is in the exam room.

Although there are obstacles to pre-visit registration, the benefits are significant. If a medical practice has the ability to pre-register even a portion of its patients, the pre-registration process is recommended. The pre-visit process initiates the patient to your medical practice.

Despite best efforts, some medical practices discover that they cannot perform pre-visit registration prior to patients' appointments. This may be a function of the specialty (for example, hospitalists, urgent care physicians, and pathologists), seeing patients on a same-day or walk-in basis, or having a patient population that is either reticent to provide information over the telephone or on a Website (for fear of identity theft, for example) or has no access to communication (no telephone, for example). Staffing for patient financial clearance can also prove to be a challenge.

If the pre-visit process is not conducted, these tasks must be performed at patient check-in. There are a number of steps to this process, so the medical practice should be staffed appropriately so that a bottleneck does not occur at patient check-in. In addition, much of the information obtained for registration is confidential, thus efforts to ensure patient confidentiality should be made, even in confined quarters.

THE PATIENT CHECK-IN PROCESS

When patients arrive for their visits, present them with all relevant paperwork. The paperwork should include forms to capture updates to the patient's demographic and insurance information, as well as notification of new or revised medical practice policies. Obtain the necessary signatures, copy or scan insurance and identification cards, and request payment. You may also direct

---

[1] For more information about eliminating check-in, read about the Patient-Centered Practice of the Future™ in *Mastering Patient Flow* by Elizabeth Woodcock, Medical Group Management Association, 2009.

patients to complete medical history forms. After the paperwork is completed and monies paid, notify the clinical staff manually or electronically that the patient is ready to be seen.

If your medical practice did not have the opportunity to conduct any pre-visit processes, verify insurance coverage and benefits eligibility in real time as the patient is completing the paperwork and reviewing the practice's financial policy. The insurance verification process, ideally, is performed electronically or by efficiently using the payer's Website. Obtain or confirm any necessary referrals and authorizations. After verifying eligibility and benefits, a waiver form may be needed so that patients understand their financial responsibility for non-covered services.

An alternative to onsite registration performed by a front-office staff member is the use of a registration kiosk. Better-performing practices locate their kiosks in the reception area, directing patients to use them for registration. Although most offer them as an alternative to registering with a staff member, patients are increasingly embracing kiosks as a convenient and fast way to register in a medical practice. Although the functionality of the kiosk depends on the device and the software, most can perform demographic and insurance data capture and verification, present patients with electronic registration forms to view and sign, scan insurance and identification cards, and request and accept payment.

If the patient is not physically present or subject to a formal registration process (for example, services are conducted by physicians without face-to-face visits, such as radiologists), obtain registration information from an alternate source such as the payer (if the patient's insurance information is known), referring physician, or hospital or other facility through which the patient was admitted. Conduct the rest of the registration process — including insurance verification and benefits eligibility directly with the payer — prior to charge entry.

THE PATIENT CHECK-OUT PROCESS

The patient check-out process is typically used to reschedule patients for their next appointments, schedule surgeries and other tests, secure external referrals and authorizations, collect residual time-of-service payments, offer discounts to patients consistent with your medical practice's policies and procedures, and enter charges. In medical practices with electronic health records, many have been able to eliminate the patient check-out station altogether by conducting these steps in the exam room with the clinical support staff.

The referral process itself is complex. Medical practice staff are often required to obtain pre-authorization for various diagnostic tests, procedures, and medications.

For patients who are scheduled for tests and procedures, the medical practice needs to determine if an authorization is required, the patient's status with his/her health plan (for example, how much of the deductible has been met, co-insurance required, and whether the physician is in- or out-of-network), and other similar details. Once this is learned, the medical practice can then populate a form to provide to the patient that reflects what the patient's insurance will pay and what will be required from the patient. The patient's portion of the payment, or, at minimum, a deposit is typically captured prior to the service being performed, unless the medical practice's contract with the payer prohibits pre-service collections. See Tool 5 for a sample financial agreement for surgeries and procedures.

TOOL 5	**Financial Agreement for Surgeries and Procedures**

Today's date: _____ Date of surgery/procedure: _____

Patient's name: _____ Patient's account number: _____

Description of surgery/procedures: _____

_____

Estimated total cost of surgery: _____

Amount patient's insurance is expected to pay: _____

Discounts (if applicable): _____

Total expected balance to patient: _____

Expected payment prior to surgery: _____

Remaining balance: _____

Patient cancellation (no-show) fee: _____

Payment plan?   Y / N   Terms: _____

Patient's/guarantor's signature: _____ Date: _____

Staff member's signature: _____ Date: _____

© 2009 Walker, Woodcock, Larch. Reprinted with permission.

The check-out process is an excellent time to provide the patient with information regarding billing. For example, a medical practice can present the patient with a handout that explains to the patient that he/she will receive two bills, one from the surgeon and one from the ambulatory surgery center. A sample "about your bill" handout is presented in Tool 6, which can be customized for your medical practice.

Staff who conduct patient check-out functions often perform charge entry for services provided in the office. Charge entry functions are discussed in detail in Chapter 7: The Charge Entry Process.

TIME-OF-SERVICE COLLECTIONS

A medical practice needs to determine the best time to collect time-of-service payments from patients. The majority of medical practices today attempt to collect copayments during the patient check-in process. In fact,

| TOOL 6 | "About Your Bill" Sample |

To our patients:

We are pleased that you have chosen our practice to provide your medical services. In our endeavor to provide quality care to our patients, we would like to make you aware of the following information regarding your bill.

Following your procedure, your insurance will be billed. You should expect to see the following separate bills related to your procedure:

1. **XYZ Medical Group** — This bill covers the physician's fee for performing your procedure. Once your insurance has paid if there is a balance to be paid by you, you will receive a statement. The billing office can be reached at XXX-YYYY.

2. **Surgery facility** — This is the fee for the operating room, nursing services, equipment, and supplies used during your procedure. You will receive a bill from one of the following:

   First Medical Center: XXX-YYYY

   Premier Surgical Center: XXX-YYYY

3. **Anesthesia** — This is the fee for the anesthesia services rendered during your procedure. You may call the anesthesiology billing department at XXX-YYYY to answer your questions regarding this bill.

4. **Laboratory** — If biopsies are taken during your procedure, you will receive a bill from the pathology department. Several labs are used, depending on your individual insurance coverage. You may contact their billing department at the telephone number that appears on the billing statement you receive from them.

We appreciate the opportunity to provide your medical care. Our staff is always available to answer your questions. You may reach us at any time by calling XXX-YYYY or e-mailing us at xyzmed@medicalpractice.com.

© 2009 Walker, Woodcock, Larch. Reprinted with permission.

those medical practices that collect payments prior to the physician-patient encounter have typically succeeded in increasing their collection efforts. Beyond copayments, patient-responsibility balances are also now routinely collected at patient check-in.

With the growing volume of health plans with higher patient financial responsibility (including co-insurance and deductibles), patients pay a higher portion of their health care bill out-of-pocket. Because co-insurance and deductibles cannot be calculated until the services are known, some medical practices have now shifted time-of-service collection activity to patient check-out. Migrating the process to check-out ensures that the medical practice knows what services have been provided and the total dollar amount owed.

Still other medical practices have elected to collect copayments and patient balances at check-in. Then, at check-out, they collect *again* for monies owed based on charges incurred for the visit.

The determination of where to collect payments from patients is medical practice-specific. Many factors dictate the decision, including payer mix, the rules and regulations of the payers with which your practice participates, the availability of charge information, and the physical layout of your practice site.

To ensure efficient and effective check-in and check-out processes, we present proven strategies to enhance your revenue cycle.

ADVANCED PRACTICES: THE PATIENT CHECK-IN AND CHECK-OUT PROCESSES

Create a Unified Team between the Front-office Staff and Billing Staff

Many better-performing medical practices create a formal reporting relationship between the front-office staff and the billing office. They recognize the importance of the check-in and check-out functions for reimbursement, and it is now common for these staff members to report to a manager who oversees all aspects of the revenue cycle. This tends to reduce the turf issues between front-end and back-end billing staff that some medical practices experience. If a medical practice does not institute this type of reporting relationship, it should develop clear performance expectations for the front-office staff regarding timeliness and accuracy of data to ensure attention to billing and collection functions. At minimum, the front-office staff and the billing staff need to realize that they are part of the same team. Written job descriptions, team goals and a code of commitment can help make that point. (For a sample code of commitment, see Figure 17.1 in Chapter 17: The Debate: Centralize, Decentralize, or Outsource Billing?)

Report Error Rates to the Front-office Staff

Report error rates involving inaccurate or incomplete demographic and insurance information to front-office staff on a regular basis. Capture and communicate claim edits and denials resulting from registration-related errors. For example, denials, as revealed on the explanation of benefits, include "subscriber not enrolled on the date of service" and "subscriber not identified." Many medical practices require front-office staff to correct the error as a learning opportunity; if no one tells the staff that errors are being made, they have no opportunity to improve their performance. However, the timeliness of this correction must be monitored. Communicating errors should be a training tool so that staff can recognize their errors and avoid repeating their mistakes. Tools 7 and 8 can help your medical practice audit your front-office performance and report errors to the staff so that they can improve front-end billing performance for the future.

TOOL 7   **Front-office Audit Tool**

This tool provides a systematic process for reviewing the work of the front-office staff involved in key front-end billing functions. We recommend that your medical practice conduct audits for both new and existing staff on a regular basis. Many medical practices elect to audit the front-office staff quarterly because of the need to keep current on changing payer rules, practice management systems, and other similar developments.

Level: 1 = Needs improvement; 2 = Meets expectations; 3 = Exceeds expectations

Pre-visit	Level
Does the medical practice prepare prior to a patient's visit and flag information to update forms as needed?	
Does the practice maintain a current list of insurance plans and critical plan elements to ensure compliance?	
Does the medical practice verify insurance and benefits eligibility for all patients?	
Does the medical practice communicate electronically with payers for eligibility and authorization? Does the practice verify eligibility prior to every visit/procedure?	
Does the medical practice obtain pre-authorization and referrals as needed for all services? Does the practice capture the referring physician for each service?	
Are updated procedure and diagnosis codes reflected on charge tickets, electronic charge capture devices, and/or the electronic health record?	

Patient check-in/reception	
Does the medical practice review all scheduled patient accounts for prior balances prior to appointments and issue reminders?	
Does the medical practice attempt to collect all prior balances at the time of service?	
Does the medical practice collect copayments required at the time of service?	
Does the medical practice have a policy regarding the steps to take if a patient fails to pay?	

Charge entry	
Is charge entry conducted within 24 hours of date of service?	
Does the medical practice have cash controls in place to ensure that all money is accounted for each day? Is charge entry reconciled to appropriate source documents?	
Does the medical practice complete requests for information to the billing office within 24 hours of request?	

TOOL 8	**Front-office Monthly Denial Report**

To track and report error rates incurred by front-office staff, create a spreadsheet delineating major error categories as demonstrated in the table below. You can obtain data for the spreadsheet by sampling the EOBs received by one payer during a one-week period. This tool is designed as an educational opportunity for front-office staff to ensure they enter billing data correctly the first time.

	Percentage of Denied Claims/Month		
Denial Reason	Main Office	Satellite Office	Total
Patient not eligible on date of service	5%	2%	4%
Claim filed in error to wrong payer	4%	1%	3%
No referral	1%	5%	2%
Services not covered	1%	1%	1%
Duplicate claim	2%	2%	2%
Claim returned—need additional information	1%	0%	1%
Total Denial Rate	14%	11%	13%

Interpret the data and take action — for example:

- Satellite office reduced its denials by improving its registration quality.

- Main office did not make progress in registration areas – more training will be held; individual registration audits will be completed this week.

- Referral management needs more attention at satellite office. Referral coordinator from main office will spend one day per week at satellite office.

© 2009 Walker, Woodcock, Larch. Reprinted with permission.

Systematically Collect at the Patient Visit

Many medical practices provide their staff with training on how to collect money at the time of service. This training includes role playing and brief scripts to use for different situations. Refer to Tool 9: Sample Cash-at-Time-of-Service Scripts for examples of scripts you can customize for your medical practice.

Institute a policy to collect all patient payments at the time of service — to include prior patient balance, deductibles, co-insurance, and fees for non-covered services — in addition to the copayment. As we shall see in a later chapter, the cost to produce a statement, mail the statement, and follow up with the patient is significant. Medical practices that have instituted systematic review of all patient financial responsibility amounts that are due are able to improve their payment cycle time and cash flow. Collecting patient outstanding payments at the time the patient is physically present in the office can substantially reduce billing expenditures. If the patient is unable to pay, give the patient a pre-addressed billing office envelope and establish a timeline as to when payment is expected.

TOOL 9	**Sample Cash-at-Time-of-Service Scripts**

Help your staff collect cash at the time of service by reviewing sample scripts so they know how you expect them to communicate with patients. This tool provides samples of phrases that they can use to overcome payment obstacles. Customize the tool based on your medical practice's preference regarding payment options and tolerance for payment delays.

ASKING FOR PAYMENT

"Your copayment for today's visit is $10.00 and you can pay that today by cash, check, credit, or debit card."

[This straightforward statement makes it difficult for the patient to respond any other way than how he/she will pay!]

"The fee for today's services is $200.00. As we explained, we do not participate with your insurance plan. You can handle payment by cash, check, credit, or debit card."

[State the full amount of the visit and acknowledge the fact that you know the patient was informed previously that his/her insurance was not accepted.]

PHRASES TO USE WHEN OVERCOMING OBSTACLES

Patient can't pay (for various reasons)

Don't say: "I want you to..."; "We require..."; "Our policy states..."

Do say: "Here is an envelope for you to mail your payment within three days."

"May I suggest payment by credit card, or do you have an ATM card?" "There is a convenient ATM machine around the corner."

"Okay, let's see, today is Tuesday. How much time will you need on the $200.00?"

Patient: Bill me

"I wish we could, but we need you to pay today."

"Your copayment is due at time of visit. This was explained in your insurance information, and your insurance requires us to collect the copay each time you see the doctor."

NOTE: If you're collecting payment **prior to the visit** and the patient refuses to pay, determine if your physicians want the patient to be rescheduled. This will obviously depend on the specialty of your practice and the reason for patient visit. If appropriate, state:

"You can pay today with check or credit/debit card, or we can reschedule your visit."

Patient: Bill my insurance company

"We will be happy to submit a claim to your insurance company for you. But the practice expects all patients to pay for services at the time they are provided if we do not participate in your insurance plan."

Patient: This policy doesn't make any sense

"I'm sorry you feel that way. The policy is to clear up any questions that may come up about what your financial responsibility is."

"I'll be happy to have my supervisor discuss it with you; however, I still need you to pay your copayment (or fee)."

Physicians or other professionals request a waiver or discount

"Our physicians adopted a policy that does not allow me to waive or discount your copayment. Here is a copy for you to review. How will you be paying today?" or "I am unable to waive or discount the payment; I'll be happy to refer you to my supervisor. Here is a copy of the policy adopted by our physicians."

© 2009 Walker, Woodcock, Larch. Reprinted with permission.

Don't Forget Prior Balances

Your financial policy should specifically discuss the collection of prior patient responsibility balances. Further, establish a policy regarding whether patients will be given return appointments when they have prior balances due, as discussed below.

Some prior balances are small amounts that can add up to big opportunities. Your patient statement process defines a minimum statement balance. For example, a patient statement will not be mailed unless the balance due is $10.00 or more. That means that all patient balances below that amount are waiting to be collected as prior balances. If your patients typically owe $5.00 and your medical practice saw 500 patients a week, you could collect $2,500 extra that week by paying attention to these small balances. That could translate to $10,000 more each month and $120,000 a year. Focusing on this sole issue, the medical practice can realize a great increase in cash at the time of service.

Develop Rescheduling Protocols

If a patient has a balance due on his/her account and/or does not have the funds to pay his/her copayment or other time-of-service amount, develop protocols that will be used related to the current visit. It is not appropriate to wait for the patient to present and then debate what you intend to do. If rescheduling is appropriate, a formal process and protocol is required to ensure that patients who indeed need to be seen are cared for at the medical practice. Some medical practices involve clinical staff in this decision-making; others use the scheduling type or date as a "cue" to the rescheduling need. For example, patients who are scheduled for a preventive visit qualify for rescheduling; those scheduled for an acute complaint are not automatically rescheduled. The point here is to develop your medical practice's protocol, that is clinically appropriate and consistent with your malpractice carrier's requirements, regarding seeing patients who have an outstanding balance or who present without funds.

In addition to patient rescheduling, determine what your medical practice's policy is regarding scheduling patients who are in bad-debt status or who have been sent to a collection agency. If these patients are to continue to be seen, determine if their new charge should be automatically transferred to the collection agency and reside with their prior balance or if the billing staff are expected to attempt collection of the new charges.

Remind Insured Patients of Their Payment Obligations

It is the patients' responsibility as beneficiaries of their insurance company to pay their portion of the contracted rate; your job is to facilitate the collection per the payer's rules and regulations. If patients have concerns about copayment amounts or deductible levels, direct them to their health plans.

Some medical practices also provide a letter to patients who fail to pay their copayment that indicates that they may be in violation of their contract with their payer. When patients do not regularly pay their copayment amounts, they should be reported to their payers' member services, as they are technically in violation of their contracts as subscribers.

To emphasize the patients' responsibility, some medical practices change the signs at the front office from "Payment is expected at the time of service" to "Your insurance company requires us to collect a copayment." The signage emphasizes the reason the patient is required to make a copayment.

Many medical practices have gone beyond this step, and have instituted a financial penalty if the patient fails to make the obligatory payment. The co-payment rebilling fee typically ranges from $10.00 to $25.00. If your medical practice plans to implement a penalty for failing to pay at the time of service, patients must be informed of the fee in writing. Most medical practices waive the fee if the patient brings in the payment by the end of the business day.

The policy is made clear during the registration process and via signage. For example, the practice announces, "Your insurance company requires us to collect a copayment. If you are unable to pay your copayment at the time of service, there will be an additional $25.00 fee."

Beyond copayment rebilling fees, some medical practices are successfully negotiating their contracts so that they can collect deductibles and co-insurance at the time of service. To further bring this point home, some medical practices have signage that reads, "Patient financial responsibility is collected at the time of service." This message extends the responsibility to make all payments, not exclusively copayments. In these instances, rebilling fees can also be applied as appropriate and/or elective procedures may be scheduled after the payment has been received in order to facilitate compliance. Medical practices that institute rebilling fees report that the additional fee has reduced non-payment levels.

Collect Payments for Procedures and Surgeries Prior to the Time of Service

Many medical practices collect payments for non-emergent procedures and surgeries prior to the time of service so they can capture patient payments and decrease billing costs. Patients respond well to this expectation if you present it as part of the financial policy. For example, when a medical procedure is determined to be necessary, develop a worksheet that records the payer's estimated payment for the service (and the practice's agreed-upon contractual write-off) in addition to the patient's responsibility. At that time, you can make payment arrangements or establish a payment plan with the patient. If you couch this as a service to your patients, this can be a win-win for the medical practice from the perspective of improving cash flow and saving billing costs, and for the patient, who is now informed. It is important for patients to not have any surprises related to their personal out-of-pocket payment obligation.

The following is a script used to communicate this message to the patient: "Let's determine what your insurance company will pay for this service so you will know the amount that you will need to pay prior to the procedure."

Tool 10 is a sample of a patient financial agreement for non-emergent services.

TOOL 10 | **Patient Financial Agreement**

Once you know the clinical service that is to be performed, contact the patient's payer to determine the patient's payment responsibilities. Collect the full amount, require a deposit, or establish a payment plan with the patient. Use this tool to record the information and to set up the payment plan in your practice management system.

Patient: _____

Guarantor/person responsible for payment: _____

Address: _____

City: _____ State: _____ Zip: _____

Home telephone: _____ Business telephone: _____ E-mail: _____

Service(s): $_____

Fee for services rendered $_____

Expected third-party reimbursement $_____

Estimated insurance benefits $_____

Estimated patient responsibility $_____

Payment plan options:

☐ I will pay 100 percent of the patient responsibility portion on the first appointment.

☐ I prefer to pay 50 percent of the patient responsibility portion on the first appointment. The remainder to be paid within 15 days after insurance has paid its portion.

In the event my account becomes delinquent for a period of thirty (30) days, I hereby acknowledge that I will be immediately responsible for the balance, interest, court costs, and/or attorney fees.

I hereby certify that I have read and received a copy of this statement.

This _____ day of _____, 2 _____

Signature: _____, Responsible Party

© 2009 Walker, Woodcock, Larch. Reprinted with permission.

Change Your Financial Counselor's Job Title

Although most medical practices refer to the front-office staff who are responsible for patient collections as "financial counselors" or "collectors," better-performing medical practices refer to the staff fulfilling this function as "financial advocates." This change in job title conveys to patients that the medical practice is their advocate with regard to their insurance companies.

Educate Patients to Ad Hoc Payments

Besides copayments, co-insurances, deductibles, and patient responsibility balances, a number of medical practices collect other fees at the point of care consistent with practice costs for these services, such as the following:

- Rebilling fee for failure to collect copayment at the point of care;
- No-show fee;

- Collection agency fee; and

- Forms completion fees (for example, physical forms, Family Medical Leave Act [FMLA] forms, disability forms, Department of Motor Vehicles [DMV] driving questionnaires, and sports physicals).

Make sure that patients understand these fees by including them in your financial policy. If applicable, indicate the turnaround time for forms completion.

Initiate an "If not, why not?" Program

Since time-of-service payments now extend beyond copayments and are integral to the revenue stream of a medical practice, consider initiating an "if not, why not" program with the staff. In this type of program, staff are required to document why they are not successful in collecting from the patient. Such a program can often serve as a useful tool to focus front-office staff on this responsibility.

In addition, keep track of the amount of money that is collected at the front office in comparison to the amount that was expected to be collected. In this fashion, staff can learn the results of their efforts and work to improve over time.

Remind your staff that monies collected at the time of service have reduced billing costs and zero days in accounts receivable. The more dollars collected by the front office, the better your overall revenue performance. Back-office billing staff no longer need to spend time collecting copayments and small balances and can focus on larger account balances.

Print the Explanation of Benefits (EOB) Form

For patients with a balance from a prior service due, copy or print the patient's relevant EOB(s). You can present the EOB(s) to the patient to substantiate your request for payment at the request of the payer and further your position as the patient's financial advocate.

Require a Deposit

For patients with no insurance coverage or insurance with which your medical practice does not participate, require a minimum deposit. The amount depends on your specialty, services offered, and patient mix. Examples include $50.00 for established patients and $100.00 for new patients. Although the deposit is "required," your medical practice needs to establish protocols to manage patients who present for care without any means of payment. Include your malpractice carrier in this discussion.

Determine Your Patient Discount Philosophy and Protocol

A number of medical practices have initiated a discount policy if the patient is uninsured and is paying out of pocket. We are often asked whether the discount should also be offered to patients with insurance plans with high deductibles. Each medical practice needs to determine its own philosophy; however, recognize that with patients with high-deductible health plans, the amount you collect from the patient is already "discounted" pursuant to your contract if your practice participates with that health plan. Between the payer and the patient, you can only collect the "allowable" that you are contracted to receive. By extending the self-pay discount to these patients, you further discount this level. Thus, the discount may be in violation of the contract you have with the payer.

See Chapter 13: The Patient Collections Process for further discussion of this topic.

Accept Credit and Debit Cards

Accept major credit and debit cards. Notably, patients may carry a health care-specific credit card, often referred to as an HSA card or benny card. Be sure patients know they can pay with credit or debit cards at the time of service and include this information on your patient statements. Offering credit and debit card options increases your patient collections. Some patients may not be able to pay more than their copayment amount in cash, but they typically have at least one credit card.

Credit cards reduce patient statements. Once the credit card has been accepted, the medical practice receives the entire dollar amount charged on the card. The credit card company takes over the responsibility (and the risk) for billing the patient.

Better-performing medical practices offer patients the option of giving the practice authorization to bill their credit card for balances not paid by insurance. These amounts usually include copayments, deductibles, and repeating amounts due for high-frequency services, such as physical therapy. Patients complete a form authorizing these charges, which is kept on file in the medical practice. To protect both parties, the authorization form should include the patient's signature and date of signing, as well as the period of time the patient is authorizing the credit card to be used. Every time the card is charged, the medical practice should send the patient a receipt of the transaction. Before implementing, research state laws related to credit card transactions to ensure your collections protocols comply with state law.

Credit card companies typically charge 2 to 7 percent for their services. Contact vendors to obtain the most favorable payment rates for your medical practice.

Refer Patients to a Financial Lender

As we discussed in Chapter 3: The Patient Financial Clearance Process, patients who cannot pay their personal obligation can be referred to a financial lending institution. Determine your medical practice's role with the lender, which may include an information card provided to the patient, application forms distributed to patients, assistance in completion of the loan applications, and other steps. Medical practices that encourage the use of a financial lender for patients typically include this information in their financial policy to educate patients about this option.

Use Waiver Forms

Insured patients may receive services that are not covered by their health plan. Some payers, such as Medicare, require that their beneficiaries be informed about the lack of coverage. The purpose of a waiver is to help patients make an informed choice about whether or not they want to receive these services, knowing that they may be financially responsible. The Centers for Medicare & Medicaid Services (CMS) requires the use of a particular form — the Advance Beneficiary Notification (ABN). Some payers may require specific forms, but most medical practices develop a generic form for use with all other patients. In addition to notifying patients about their financial responsibility for specific services, waivers can also be used when the medical practice cannot contact the payer and obtain verification or authorization regarding the patient's coverage for whatever reason.

Obtaining a waiver form, however, is only the first step. It does not guarantee payment. The waiver should be scanned into the patient's account and linked to the date of service in which the waiver was presented and signed. ABNs, for example, are only valid for services rendered on the date the waiver was presented and signed. If your medical practice does not employ scanning technology, the waiver form must be sent to the billing office or a note placed in the notes section on the patient's account in the practice management system. The existence of the waiver or the waiver itself needs to be transmitted to the billing office so they can ensure claims processing and patient payment consistent with the waiver, as appropriate. Finally, unless the payer disallows it, time-of-service collections should be attempted for all non-covered services when a waiver is signed.

Institute an Automated Receipt Process

In most medical practices, staff collect payments, they post them to the practice management system in real time, and the system generates an electronic receipt to give the patient at the time of service. This provides a higher level of internal controls than a discretionary receipt process and allows staff to balance cash receipts effectively. Note, however, that when staff post payments prior to charges being entered in the system, a reconciliation of the payment and charge is required. Typically, practice management systems can provide a report that identifies missing charges associated with a patient payment so that these can be easily resolved. Some practice management systems are even able to find the charge and payment match and auto-reconcile for you.

Conduct Real-time Patient Information Updates

Update the practice management system with changes in patient insurance and demographic information in real time. As patients provide new or updated information manually or electronically via a kiosk or Internet-based registration system, key it without delay into or electronically interface with your practice management system. Delays cause inaccurate claims and statements to be sent because the claim or the statement may be dropped before the new information is entered into the system. The more the information and paperwork is handed off to another staff member, the greater the opportunity for delays and errors.

Don't Ask Patients for the Same Information More Than Once

Patients should not be asked to repeat the information they already supplied during the pre-visit process. Only a brief verification is needed. Your staff can print out a "face sheet" that reports the patient's demographic and insurance information and ask the patient to review, verify, and sign the form. Or they can ask, "Ms. Smith, are you still living at XYZ address?" The verification can be performed electronically via a tablet PC or kiosk to which the patient is directed upon entering the medical practice. Missing data elements should be highlighted on the patient schedule, in the practice management system, or on the kiosk to ensure that patients are asked to provide this information at the time of the visit. (As discussed in Chapter 3: The Patient Financial Clearance Process, automatic address verification can be performed prior to the time of service, with only exceptions being reported for verification by the patient.)

Scan — Don't Copy — the Insurance Card

Using a small scanning terminal, record images of patients' insurance cards in a database. Or, if the scanning system is interfaced or integrated with your practice management system, the scanned copy is attached — in an electronic file — to the patient's account. Finally, the registration kiosk may offer scanning functionality as well. Regardless of the mechanism to capture the scanned copy of the card, the image allows all staff and physicians to have access to this critical information without having to spend time retrieving a paper copy of the card from manual files.

If scanning is not possible, copy the insurance card. Initial and date the copy, and file it in the patient's record.

Determine how frequently you want to scan or copy the card, for example, at each visit, at open enrollment periods, for patients who have not been seen for three months, or at other consistent intervals. Also, determine whether a copy of the card is really needed; if insurance verification has already been successfully performed, an actual copy or image of the card may not be necessary.

Be aware that copying or scanning patients' cards offers only a record of what patients presented as their insurance. It does not guarantee or imply coverage. You must also verify coverage and eligibility with the payer.

Verify the Patient's Identification

Unfortunately, there is a growing problem with patients "sharing" the same insurance card and insured patients "renting" their cards for others to use. Request to verify a patient's identification card with a photograph. The date of birth and the photograph helps ensure that the coverage is for the correct patient. New "Red Flag Alert" policies are available at MGMA.com.

Verify Insurance Eligibility and Benefits (if not conducted during the pre-visit process)

If you do not verify insurance before the patient presents at the office (this will happen with walk-in patients, patients who have scheduled same-day appointments for which there is no time to perform pre-visit verification, and patients who present with an insurance change that occurred after the pre-visit functions were performed), verify the patient's insurance at check-in by either placing a telephone call to the payer to confirm coverage and benefits eligibility or verifying this information online. Electronic access obviously streamlines this process if it is available with the payer and if your medical practice has the equipment. Increasingly, payers are offering insurance verification on their Websites or Web portals. If complete benefits eligibility is necessary, be sure you can perform it online; if not, resort to the telephone. The information is important to ensure payment, and it is worth dedicating staff resources to this function.

Develop Performance Expectations for External Staff Involved in Scheduling, Registration, and Check-in

Sometimes, employees of the hospital or other entity participate in your medical practice's scheduling, registration, and/or check-in processes, and these employees do not have a direct reporting relationship to your medical practice. If your medical practice relies on hospital staff or others outside of the practice to conduct the front-end billing process, establish performance expectations and communicate them to the employer of these individuals. Make sure the staff members are held accountable. Monitor error rates on a regular basis and agree on expectations for improvement. Regularly track and monitor time-of-service payment levels and give feedback to the supervisor of these staff. When you formally enter into a contract with an entity to provide these front-end billing services, include these types of performance expectations in the contract language and terms and review them annually. At a minimum, meet with the supervisors of these employees about the level of accuracy and timeliness that you are experiencing, as well as the impact of their staff's activities on your revenue cycle.

The check-in and check-out processes arguably define the patient's experience with your medical practice from a service and business perspective. Use the opportunity to capture accurate and timely information to commence the revenue cycle and, where possible, collect patient out-of-pocket payments at the point of care.

STAFF WORKLOAD RANGES

The staff workload ranges for patient check-in and check-out that we typically expect are provided below. The ability to perform within these ranges may vary due to internal practice-specific factors, as well as the scope of work delegated to the staff. The workload ranges are based on a staff member performing these functions approximately seven hours of productive time per day (allowing one hour for breaks, interruptions, and other down time). Note that the workload ranges reflect quantitative performance levels. Qualitative performance — accuracy, completeness, appropriateness, and quality of these functions — should also be measured. When issues of quantity versus quality arise, we strongly recommend that quality be emphasized, even if the performance workload ranges for a particular function need to be relaxed from these levels.

Staff Function	Patients per day	per hour
Pre- or site registration with insurance verification	60 to 80	9 to 11
Check-in with registration verification only	100 to 130	14 to 19
Check-in with registration verification and cashiering only	75 to 100	11 to 14
Appointment scheduling with no registration	75 to 125	11 to 18
Appointment scheduling with full registration	50 to 75	7 to 11
Referrals	10 to 13	10 to 13
Check-out with scheduling, cashiering	70 to 90	10 to 13
Check-out with scheduling, cashiering, charge entry	60 to 80	8 to 12

Note: Institute these workload ranges only if accuracy can be assured in this time frame. If not, you may need to increase the time to perform the functions to avoid mistakes.

© 2009 Walker, Woodcock, Larch. Reprinted with permission.

LEADING PERFORMANCE INDICATORS

Use the following indicators to assess the performance of your check-in and check-out processes. We refer to these measures as "leading" performance indicators. If your medical practice is successful in achieving these levels in the check-in and check-out processes, you are on the correct path to optimizing your revenue cycle.

Error rates due to front-end billing: < 2 percent

Time-of-service collections:

Copayments: 100 percent

All other time-of-service payments: 75 percent

© 2009 Walker, Woodcock, Larch. Reprinted with permission.

THE PATIENT CHECK-IN AND CHECK-OUT DIAGNOSTIC TOOL

The patient check-in and check-out diagnostic tool below helps ensure that the process, people, technology, and quality required for effective patient check-in and check-out are in place in your medical practice.

Process:

1. Are there more revenue cycle activities that can be performed on a pre-visit basis?
2. What information should be obtained at patient check-in?
3. What information should be obtained at patient check-out?
4. What is the time-of-service collection process?
5. What is the protocol for patient rescheduling due to lack of payment? Is it in writing and consistently applied?
6. When should insurance verification, benefits eligibility, type of plan, and authorization checks be performed?
7. Have attempts been made to collect patient responsibility balances prior to patient presentation, for example, via credit/debit card over the telephone?

People:

1. Who is responsible for performing insurance verification and benefits eligibility?
2. What tools have been provided to staff to alert them of time-of-service collections and alerts or notices on the accounts?
3. What training has the staff received regarding insurance products to identify the type of product and the impact that has on patient out-of-pocket responsibility?
4. Have scripts been written and provided to staff related to the communication with patients at check-in and check-out?

Technology:

1. Has technology been leveraged to assist in payer and benefits verification?
2. Has technology been leveraged to alert the front office to time-of-service collections and notices related to patients' accounts?

Quality:

1. What is our collection rate for time-of-service responsibility? Of the money we could collect, how much did we collect?
2. What is the error rate regarding claim edits and claim denials related to front-end registration information?
3. Are new staff audited to ensure they understand their role in front-end billing?
4. Are staff familiar with a CMS-1500 form? Do they know their role in obtaining the necessary information to populate the claim form?

POLICIES AND PROCEDURES

At the end of each chapter, we provide policies and procedures to assist you in developing a policy and procedure manual for your medical practice. Below are four policies specific to the patient check-in and check-out processes.

Policy 5: Time-of-Service Payment

Policy 6: Medicare Non-covered Services — Advance Beneficiary Notice (ABN)

Policy 7: Waiver of Patient Financial Responsibility

Policy 8: Financial Agreement for Surgeries and Procedures

POLICY 5: TIME-OF-SERVICE PAYMENT

Policy:

It is the policy of the medical practice to require payment at the time of service. Payment includes all monies for which the patient is financially responsible according to his/her insurance coverage.

Procedures:

Patients will be reminded of the expectation to make time-of-service payments via the medical practice's Website, written financial policy, appointment scheduling, and appointment reminders.

The amount due to the medical practice at the time of service will be determined prior to the patient's arrival based on an insurance verification and benefits eligibility check. The check may be performed manually or electronically.

The amount due may include one or more of the following:

- Balance;
- Deductible;
- Copayment;
- Co-insurance; and/or
- Pre-payment for procedure or surgery.

If the patient is self-insured or insured by a plan with which the medical practice does not participate, a minimum payment of $200.00 or the charge for the visit, whichever is less, will be collected.

If the patient is being seen for an employer-authorized work-related injury, the medical practice will bill workers' compensation directly. If the employer's verification of injury cannot be obtained, the patient will be told that he/she may be ultimately responsible for payment, and private patient billing information will be obtained.

If the patient is employed by a company that has established an account with the medical practice and the employer has authorized the visit, the medical practice will follow the billing arrangement established with the employer. Authorization can be recorded on the standard practice authorization form. Telephone or Website authorization must be documented in writing by the medical practice staff on the authorization form. The authorization form is placed in the back of the medical chart, with a copy sent to the billing office (or filed in the electronic health record).

Payments will be posted to the practice management system. A receipt will be automatically generated from the practice management system for any monies collected and it will be given to the patient.

The medical practice may grant a patient a discount based on two circumstances:

1. Uninsured patients or patients insured with a payer with which the practice does not participate may be granted a discount if payment is made at the time of service.

2. Patients who meet financial hardship criteria may receive a discount based on the level of hardship.

   See related policies and procedures regarding self-pay discounts and financial hardship.

The billing office will prepare a summary of the amount due. This will be attached to the daily schedule, to include any necessary specifics. An example follows:

> *Ms. Smith: $55.00 account balance from 1/1/10 visit (applied to her deductible); $20.00 co-insurance.*

In addition to a summary of time-of-service collections, the front-office staff will be trained and have access to scanned copies of explanation of benefits (EOBs) to utilize if patients have questions about past-due balances.

The billing office will be available to answer any questions that may arise from patients during time-of-service payment collection.

POLICY 6: MEDICARE NON-COVERED SERVICES — ADVANCE BENEFICIARY NOTICE (ABN)

Policy:

It is the policy of the medical practice to comply with communicating all non-covered services to Medicare beneficiaries. If the medical practice will perform a service that is non-covered, that fact will be communicated to the patient prior to treatment. Documentation of the patient's acceptance of financial responsibility will be obtained prior to providing the service.

Procedures:

1. At the time of appointment scheduling, if the service to be provided is recognized as one that is not covered by Medicare, the patient will be so informed.

2. When the medical practice determines to perform a service and identifies it as non-covered by Medicare, a completed ABN will be provided to the patient. The patient will be asked to sign the ABN as his/her acceptance of the financial responsibility for the service. ABN forms are available from CMS.[2]

3. ABN forms will be maintained in the examination room and in the electronic health record to facilitate the expedient completion of the form.

---

[2] ABN-forms are available at: http://www.cms.hhs.gov/bni/02_ABNGABNL.asp (accessed December 2, 2008).

POLICY 7: WAIVER OF PATIENT FINANCIAL RESPONSIBILITY

Policy:

It is the policy of the medical practice to treat all patients in an equitable fashion related to account balances. The medical practice will not routinely waive, fail to collect, or discount copayments, co-insurance, deductibles, or other patient financial responsibility in accordance with state and federal law, as well as participating agreements with payers.

Procedures:

1. A reasonable attempt must be made to collect the copayment, co-insurance, deductible, and any other financial responsibility assigned by the payer or that which is the responsibility of the patient with no insurance. The only exceptions to this procedure are outlined in this policy.

2. Full or partial financial responsibility may be waived only in the following situations:

   a. Financial hardship

   b. The entire fee is waived and no payer is billed any amount for the services rendered, upon approval of the practice executive or his/her designee.

   c. The patient is self-pay and maintains no health benefits (to the best of the medical practice's knowledge) or the patient maintains health benefits with a payer with which the practice is not contracted. The discount policy applies.

   d. Reasonable efforts have been made to collect on the account. Once the patient has proceeded through the medical practice's normal collections cycle and the amounts are deemed "uncollectible," the amounts can be sent to a collection agency (or adjusted as a small balance adjustment, if applicable).

   e. In situations in which the medical practice will realize administrative cost savings as a result of full payment, without having to pursue payment through the medical practice's normal billing and collections cycle. This includes time-of-service payments. The maximum discount is a level to be established by the practice executive; however, the discount will not be added to the discount to self-pay patients outlined above.

POLICY 8: FINANCIAL AGREEMENT FOR SURGERIES AND PROCEDURES

Policy:

It is the policy of the medical practice that patients who will be responsible for some portion of their bill will receive financial information regarding all non-emergent surgeries prior to the surgery being performed. This policy is established to (1) keep our patients informed to the best of our ability and (2) expedite the payment of the patient's portion of his/her bill for services rendered.

Procedures:

When a surgery is scheduled, the medical practice will complete all information regarding the surgery or procedure (to include the date of service) on the financial agreement form. The medical practice staff assigned to assist the patient will look up the patient's account and record the account number and payer on the form. The practice staff will contact the payer and/or query the payer's Website to inquire about authorization(s), the amount that the insurance company is expected to pay, and the expected patient portion of payment. The completed form will be reviewed with the patient.

The medical practice expects patients to pay a minimum of 50 percent of the expected patient responsibility prior to service.

If the patient is uninsured, the financial agreement will be based upon the medical practice's charge, and the patient will be granted a discount consistent with the patient discount policy if full payment is made prior to service.

Payment plans may be executed at the time of the agreement.

If the medical practice's participation agreement with the patient's payer prevents the medical practice from collecting prior to the service, these patients will be exempt from this requirement.

CHAPTER 5

Pothole 3
The Charge Capture Process

The charge capture process would seem to be relatively straightforward: render the service and capture the fact that it was performed. Unfortunately, this process is highly error-prone in many medical practices. Missing charges are one of the chief concerns of physicians and, unfortunately, as we have observed, can occur at a high rate if appropriate mechanisms are not in place to ensure a "closed-loop" charge capture process involving verifying charges with appropriate source documents.

In this chapter, we discuss:

- Charge capture responsibility
- Charge capture tools and processes
- Charge capture logs
- Charge capture lag times
- Charge capture audits
- Service variance analyses
- Charge tickets

Historically, medical practices have relied on the physician to capture charges, regardless of type or site of service. Today, medical practices can use "intelligent" tools built into electronic health records to ensure charge capture.

By far, the most challenging issue related to charge capture centers on services rendered outside of the office setting. Because the office is where the staff reside who typically assist with charge capture, it is relatively easier to be timely and accurate in charge capture. When the physician rounds at the local hospital, travels to a hospital-based outpatient clinic once a month, or performs procedures at an ambulatory surgery center across town, charge capture requires a "capture and carry" methodology. Better-performing medical practices move beyond the little white cards that physicians carry around and episodically provide to the billing office in favor of more technologically driven charge capture methods. The key to successfully capturing charges outside of the office is to create a systematic approach that is integrated in the workflow of the physicians and one that is used by all physicians, rather than have a physician-variable process.

Many medical practices neglect the important step of ensuring a "closed-loop" charge capture process involving comparison of the charges with source documents — either manually or electronically — to ensure a high probability for which each physician-provided service is accounted.

To ensure efficient and effective charge capture processes, we present proven strategies to enhance your revenue cycle.

ADVANCED PRACTICES: THE CHARGE CAPTURE PROCESS

Formally Designate Who Should Capture Charges by Charge Type

Each medical practice should clearly delineate the responsible party(ies) for charge capture for each specific type of charge (for example, office, durable medical equipment, drug, surgery, or procedure) and place of service (for example, office, outpatient, inpatient, nursing home, or surgery center). This should be detailed in a formal policy and procedure so that each party understands his/her role in this effort.

For medical practices with electronic health records and integrated charge capture processes, this step in the revenue cycle is streamlined. In effect, when the physician documents the service, the physician is prompted to select a code for the service and it remains in a "pended" state. The charge is then electronically entered into the practice management system (often after review by coder or billing office staff), and a claim is submitted to the payer or a statement is sent to the patient.

Physicians are responsible for documenting and coding their patient encounters. This documentation, electronic or paper, should serve as the source document for the charge entry process.

This does not mean, however, that the physician should not receive assistance in this effort. For example, in a number of specialties, such as dermatology and ophthalmology, a clinical staff member is in the exam room with the physician documenting the physician's exam. This "scribe" role enables these types of physicians to work smoothly through the patient exam as opposed to a more interrupted approach. Charge capture assistance may also be provided by a certified coder who provides education and audits charges and/or an automated coding support system. (The coding process is discussed in detail in Chapter 6: The Coding Process.)

Office and outpatient charges

Charge capture in the office or outpatient setting is typically assigned to the person who provides the service. This can be the physician, non-physician provider, nurse, or other clinical staff, such as a physical therapist or nuclear technologist. In this fashion, the person who performs the service is delegated the responsibility of capturing that fact for billing purposes.

Inpatient charges

There is no one "right" person to capture inpatient charges. Physicians, non-physician providers, clinical staff, and billing staff may be involved in the process. For example, a physician may initiate all of the charges on a smart phone or personal digital assistant that combines his/her schedule with charge capture, a nurse may be responsible for rounding with the physician and capturing the charges on a device that he/she carries, or a biller may be responsible for reviewing documentation and translating the services documented into charge documents. Other options include a non-physician provider, nurse, or certified coder who rounds with the physician to capture inpatient charges. Inpatient charges can also be captured by a certified coder who is assigned formal chart abstraction that involves reading and reviewing the chart and abstracting the services that were performed.

Surgery and procedure charges

Surgery and procedure charge capture is typically assigned to a certified coder. The coder either resides near the site of the service (for example, an operating room) with immediate discussions about the procedure between the surgeon and the coder, or the certified coder resides elsewhere and uses the written report that was dictated by the physician to capture the fact that a surgery or procedure was performed. Both approaches involve the dictated and transcribed report initiated by the physician. The advantage of a certified coder discussing the procedure with the physician is that the coder can be better informed rather than relying on the operative report alone. The source document for charge capture for these services is the formal operative or procedure report; however, the complexities of the procedure as described by the physician may alert the coder to enhanced documentation of the procedure that was performed and/or to recognize coding nuances that may not be readily apparent.

Standardize Charge Capture Tools

Regardless of the charge type, the tools used to capture charges should be standardized.

Office and outpatient charges

For medical practices without an electronic health record or electronic charge capture system, construct an office/outpatient charge ticket in a way that assists the physician in capturing the appropriate procedure and diagnosis codes, such as a checklist. Where appropriate, clinical support staff should assist in ensuring all charges are captured, to include supplies, electrocardiograms (EKGs), and other services provided by clinical staff.

Inpatient charges

While the charge ticket or electronic health record serves as the office or out-patient charge-capture tool, there are many methods by which medical practices capture inpatient charges. We recommend standardizing the inpatient charge capture process among all physicians in the medical practice. The variability of different approaches by physician can lead to billing inefficiencies and missed charges. Systems that can be used to capture inpatient charges include the following:

- The electronic health record to document the visit and respond to the charge prompt;
- Mobile devices such as smart phones, personal digital assistants (PDAs), pocket personal computers (PCs), and tablet PCs;
- A spreadsheet or rounding ticket provided to physicians with a record of the patients who are in the hospital, prompting them to see the patient and submit charges;
- Nurses, non-physician providers, or consult secretaries deployed to the hospital with the physicians to ensure that physicians document all services performed and to capture this documentation;
- Formal logs and tools to capture specific charges, particularly if this is a routine activity, such as reading echocardiograms, nuclear scans, and sleep tests;
- For services that require patients to reside in a facility for long periods of time, for example, hematology/oncology or pulmonology, a charge ticket is often included in the hospital's medical record, completed at the time the patient is seen, and collected by the billing staff on a weekly basis.

Charges for non-operating-hours activity

For a consult or admission conducted in the middle of the night by physicians who do not have electronic health records, many medical practices institute a telephone message line that allows physicians to simply call the line and provide the patient's name, identification (for example, date of birth), and the nature of the services rendered. When the staff member arrives in the morning, the calls are transcribed and the appropriate research is conducted, including querying the hospital's information system. Other medical practices require the physician to record the information on a designated form, which is submitted to the billing office the next morning. Alternatively, the medical practice may have an employee travel to the hospital to review the charts of patients seen by the medical practice's physicians. Or, as noted above, the physician records the charges on his/her mobile device or other automated charge capture system.

All other charges

Physicians practice in multiple locations such as ambulatory surgery centers, nursing homes, patients' homes, and so forth. Whether your medical practice develops a manual form or deploys mobile devices with appropriate software, the key is to have a process that allows physicians to record charges without undue effort, ensures capture for all services, and provides for accurate and timely submission of charges to the billing office. Some medical practices also schedule these types of services into their practice management system so that a missing charge reconciliation report is created to ensure these charges are captured for billing. The reconciliation report verifies that charges have been entered into the practice management system for each patient encounter that is performed.

Ensure That All Charges are Captured

Office and outpatient charges

Your medical practice should schedule all encounters, including nurse visits, walk-ins, e-mail consultations, activity at satellite clinics, and other services, in its practice management system to ensure the capture of all outpatient services. Conduct daily reconciliation of any missing charge tickets. You can achieve this by using an automated reconciliation report in your practice management system, by manually comparing charge tickets to an appointment schedule and/or sign-in sheet, or by using pre-numbered charge tickets. Ideally, this matching of charges to the appointment schedule is fully automated; the process can be integrated in your practice management system or electronic health record, with the outstanding charges remaining in a work file until they are completed.

Inpatient charges

Medical practices that provide services at the hospital should request electronic access to the hospital's registration and clinical systems. Access to demographic information, as well as clinical information, such as operative reports and discharge summaries, enables the medical practice to quickly verify data and capture missing data.

Verify charge capture with other source documents such as:

- Hospital discharge and transfer reports;
- Consultation requests;
- Operative reports;
- Discharge summaries;
- Clinical databases; and
- Logs, for example, labor and delivery log, catheterization laboratory log, sleep study log.

If your medical practice has the ability to upload documents that have been dictated by your physicians into a database, your coders can use this database to verify they have a charge for every dictated service.

Figure 5.1 shows a sample inpatient capture log. This log permits the billing office to verify that charges were indeed captured for a particular patient for each

FIGURE 5.1 ■ Inpatient Charge Capture Log

Period: January 1 thru 15

Last Name	First Name	Medical Record #	1	2	3	4	5	6	7	8	9	10	11	12	13	14	15
Smith	Mary	12345		A	X	X	X	X	X	D							
Jones	Thomas	13579					A	X	X	X	X	X	X	D			
Johnson	Bruce	24680									C						
Green	Marissa	15397										A	X	X	X	X	D

A = Admission date   D = Discharge date

C = Consult date   X = Inpatient visit

Note: Sample data.
© 2009 Walker, Woodcock, Larch. Reprinted with permission.

day of his/her hospital stay. If there are missing charges, the staff can then initiate discussions with the physician.

A verification process can help the practice avoid significant lost revenue opportunities.

Figure 5.2 outlines the formal responsibilities for each charge type to ensure that a "closed-loop" charge capture process has been created. Medical practices are encouraged to develop a similar table for their practices to document responsibility and accountability. Technology may replace some, if not all, of these manual processes. However, we still recommend designating the process for each type of service your practice renders. Even though some charges may be fully automated because of the breadth and depth of services being rendered, it's common for some services to fall outside of the automated process. Regardless of the process, categorize your charges by type and site of service, then record the steps for ensuring the closed-loop process.

For each category of charges in Figure 5.2, conduct a seven-point audit of the charge ticket, including:

1. Demographics;
2. Payer;
3. Provider;
4. Place of service;
5. Date of service;
6. Procedure code(s); and
7. Diagnosis code(s).

Supplement this audit with criteria specific to your medical practice and the services you perform.

FIGURE 5.2 ■ Closed-loop Charge Capture Process

Category	Closed-loop Process
Office and outpatient charges	The service is scheduled in the practice management system. Upon arrival to the practice, the patient is "arrived" in the practice management system. When performed, the service provided should be recorded on a charge ticket or in the charge capture module of the electronic health record. Check-out staff verify the patient arrived report with the charge tickets to ensure that all charges are captured and/or they utilize a missing charge ticket report to ensure all kept appointments have a charge entered to the system.
In-office tests	The test is scheduled in the practice management system. When performed, the test should be recorded on the charge ticket or charge capture module in the electronic health record by the nurse or technician. If applicable, a log is maintained for each service and provided to the billing office to verify charge capture or a nurse or technician is assigned to verify charge entry. If professional services are billed, in addition to the test being administered ("technical" component), the process accounts for the test being interpreted by the physician ("professional" component). Upon interpreting the test, the physician, transcriptionist, or coder/biller denotes the manual or electronic log as "read" or "dictated," finalizes the code(s) (which may be dependent on the finding of the test), and releases the charge for billing.
Inpatient charges	All procedures and surgeries are scheduled in the practice management system, including emergent services added retrospectively. When performed, the service is documented and coded (by the physician or by a certified coder). The codes are submitted manually or electronically to the billing office. The charges are verified via a missing charge ticket report. As services are performed, each physician completes an inpatient record (for example, card or electronic record) daily when on attending service. In the billing office, the inpatient charges are transferred to a spreadsheet that is maintained for each patient's stay, recorded in the patient's account, or downloaded directly into the practice management system. The billing office staff review the hospital registration information by printing the face sheet or downloading the information via an interface between the hospital and the practice's information system to ensure all patient demographic and insurance fields are completed and correct on the practice's billing system. Billing office staff also research discrepancies in the data, for example, missing referring physician, discrepancy in discharge date with visits noted on charge ticket, and number of days the physician saw the patient in-house compared to discharge date.
Injections	The billing staff receive the charge via a charge ticket. Nursing staff maintain a manual list or electronic log of injections performed that is then manually or automatically reconciled to the practice management system.
Supplies	The determination of supplies to be billed originates with clinical staff. The charge tickets are audited by the nursing and practice site staff.

Track Charge Lag Times

Comparing the lag time between the date of service and the date the claim or statement is submitted to the party who is financially responsible is an important measure of the timeliness of the billing process. The lag may actually represent one or more processes, as demonstrated in Figure 5.3.

FIGURE 5.3 ■ Track Charge Lags

- Date of service to date of documentation

- Date of documentation to date of coding

- Date of coding to date of charge entry

- Date of charge entry to date of bill release

© 2009 Walker, Woodcock, Larch. Reprinted with permission.

In order to improve the timeliness of the charge capture process, measure each lag. The process steps may vary by place of service, coder, charge entry staff, and/or physician. As you measure performance, identify outliers in each step. Work toward a goal of timely charge entry, while allowing your medical practice to accurately submit charges. At an extreme, ensure that your process does not permit charges to be denied for timely filing. If your charge submission fails to meet a payer's timely filing deadline, your medical practice will be forced to write off the charge.

Office and outpatient charges

Submit charges at the end of each patient visit and no later than day-end. The only exceptions are services awaiting a result, such as a laboratory test, which is needed to correctly code for the service. In this case, when the result is received, the charge should be submitted that day. All office and outpatient charges should be submitted within 24 hours of completion of the service.

Inpatient charges

Inpatient activity should be captured within 48 hours if possible. Some medical practices capture this activity on a monthly basis — for example, the attending of the month completes and submits the charge tickets at month end. However, this delay not only may prolong the time to revenue, it also does not permit the billing office to work in a systematic fashion or assist the physicians in identifying patients who may have inadvertently been overlooked during hospital rounds.

Conduct a Charge Capture Audit

Conduct a charge capture audit on a routine basis involving each type and place of service provided by the medical practice. This can be conducted on a quarterly rotational basis involving each type and place of service in order to ensure that the charge capture system that has been developed is working as intended. Or you can provide each physician with a list of what services were captured that month (date of service and date posted on the list) and the physician can help you audit. Most physicians are very aware of all the services they have performed. If they receive a timely report, they can often quickly identify if something is missing so you can close that loop sooner.

Many medical practices also have the clinical support staff conduct periodic audits to ensure that the billing office has billed the tests they have performed. For example, a nurse keeps a log of EKGs he/she performs and then queries the practice management system to determine if all of the EKGs have been billed. As another example, a technician performing pulmonary function tests maintains a log, and then on a monthly basis queries the accounts to ensure they have been billed. In this fashion, the "auditing" of charge capture is shared by other staff in the medical practice.

Record All Charges Received

The ideal state is to fully automate the charge capture process, which should be achieved by the electronic health record. However, if your medical practice is not automated, it is important to log in all charge documents received in the billing office, date the charge documents, and also keep a record of the timeliness of charge submission. This log can then be used to answer the following types of questions:

1. Did we receive charges for this date of service?
2. Did we receive charges for this date of service from each practice site?
3. What is the lag time between the date of service and the date the charge was received?
4. What volume of charges was received?
5. What services were included in the charges, for example, office only, procedures only, and others?
6. Have all the charges that were received now been entered?

The log helps identify missing charges and permits measurement of the lag time between the date of service and the date the charge is received in the billing office.

Conduct a Service Variance Analysis

A service variance analysis also serves as a verification to ensure the accounting of all charges. For each type of service, a projection is made regarding the number of encounters, tests, or procedures that are expected to be performed. Compare the projection to the actual volume of encounters, tests, and procedures that are performed. The variance between expected and actual should be reported at the level of physician to ensure that there are no missing charges. This analysis, which includes a volume target or goal, can be extended to the medical practice's management reports. The advantage of such a variance report is that the medical practice can learn early on in the process if patient volumes have fluctuated and can explore the reasons and/or plan for the change in resulting revenue performance. And importantly, such a report would alert the medical practice to missing charges.

Annually Review and Update Your Charge Ticket

Procedure and diagnosis codes change annually, and revisions to the bundling rules (rules related to services that are bundled or linked) are announced every quarter. Clarifications and revisions regarding procedure codes may also be issued throughout the year. Designate a coder or other staff member to monitor all changes applicable to your medical practice, based on specialty and nature of services rendered. Update all of the documents and software that you use to capture charges prior to the effective date of the changes; using invalid codes results in denied claims.

As we discuss throughout this chapter, the charge capture process should be formalized to include role delegation, timeliness, and the use of systematic tools. Closed-loop processes must be established to ensure that all charges are captured, with periodic audits conducted to ensure that the processes are working as intended.

STAFF WORKLOAD INDICATORS

Staff workload indicators for charge capture depend upon the type of systems and processes in place in the medical practice. For example, a charge capture process involving electronic health records requires a dramatically different staffing level than one that depends on investigating a paper trail to determine if all charges are captured. The keys to staffing for charge capture are to (1) identify the services that need to be captured, (2) determine a closed-loop system to ensure that the services are captured, and (3) delegate this work to a staff member who is focused on this task and who is held accountable to performance outcomes. The work process and tools for this work function should be developed by all involved parties in the medical practice, including physicians, the billing manager, and billing staff, to ensure a closed-loop process in which boundaries for responsibility and accountability are clearly defined and understood.

LEADING PERFORMANCE INDICATORS

Use the following indicators to assess the performance of your charge capture process. We refer to these measures as "leading" performance indicators. If your medical practice is successful in achieving these levels in the charge capture process, you are on the correct path to optimizing your revenue cycle.

Charge Lag Times

Date of service to date of documentation:	0 to 24 hours
Date of documentation to date of coding:	0 to 48 hours
Date of coding to date of charge entry:	0 to 48 hours
Date of charge entry to date of bill release:	24 to 72 hours
Missing charges for services documented:	0 percent

Note: Institute these lag times only if accuracy can be assured in this time frame. If not, you may need to increase the lag times to evaluate and remove errors.

© 2009 Walker, Woodcock, Larch. Reprinted with permission.

THE CHARGE CAPTURE DIAGNOSTIC TOOL

The charge capture diagnostic tool provided below helps ensure that the process, people, technology, and quality required for effective charge capture are in place in your medical practice.

Process:

1. What is the process for gathering charge tickets at the end of the day?
2. What is the process for obtaining charge tickets for services performed outside of the main practice site?
3. What is the process for capturing procedures and surgeries?
4. When are charges received by the billing office from each provider and site?
5. Is there a process to compare charge tickets to the schedule? Is a missing charge ticket report used?

6. What is the process for comparing source documents to the charge tickets?
    a. Office and outpatient
    b. Inpatient
    c. Procedures/surgeries
    d. Laboratory tests
    e. Radiology/imaging
    f. Non-physician services
    g. Supplies
    h. Other

People:

1. How many handoffs between people (or systems) are in the charge capture flow?
2. Who is responsible for capturing each type of charge?
3. Who is responsible for auditing charge capture to ensure all charges are captured?

Technology:

1. Has technology been leveraged to assist with charge capture?
2. Are charges "pushed" to the billing office or can charges be "pulled" to the billing office?
3. Are electronic tools used to log and track when charges are received and the dates and volume of charges received?
4. Is a service analysis report used to identify potential missing charges based on anticipated service volume?

Quality:

1. Who is "on point" for making sure all charges have been captured?
2. Does the charge capture audit used by your medical practice ensure that all charges are captured by type? For example, are inpatient charges for hospital visits, hospital procedures, and hospital consults captured?
3. What percentage of services arrive in the billing office with all required data elements?
4. How many resources could be saved if all charges were ready for entry when they arrived?
5. Are audits performed to ensure that the closed-loop charge capture processes are working as intended?

POLICIES AND PROCEDURES

At the end of each chapter, we provide policies and procedures to assist you in developing a policy and procedure manual for your medical practice. Below are four policies specific to the charge capture process.

Policy 9:   Manual Charge Ticket

Policy 10:   Charge Ticket Accuracy and Completeness

Policy 11:   Charge and Office Visit Reconciliation

Policy 12:   Charge and Service Reconciliation (Non-office services)

POLICY 9: MANUAL CHARGE TICKET

Policy:

It is the policy of the medical practice to ensure that charge tickets are user friendly and are routinely updated.

Procedures:

Charge tickets, which are also known as encounter forms and superbills, are very effective in saving time and assuring correct communication of services to be billed to the billing office. While most medical practices rely on paper charge tickets, electronic health record systems have allowed medical practices to automate the charge ticket. Whether manual or electronic, for best results, the charge ticket should be customized to the medical practice, including current procedure and diagnosis codes that are frequently used by the practice.

Physicians are responsible for the selection of the procedure and diagnosis codes relevant to the service that was rendered and documented. To ensure appropriate reimbursement, it is imperative to design a charge ticket with a layout that facilitates appropriate code selection with ease and accuracy.

The charge ticket is an internal document to communicate the codes for the services rendered between the provider(s) and the billing office. It is not a substitute for the documentation of the encounter. Chart documentation to substantiate the level of service provided, coded, and billed is crucial. Some examples of necessary documentation in the patient chart include the level of history taken, a description of the extent of the examination, the complexity of the decision made, counseling, and the time spent with the patient.

Charge tickets can also be used as receipts for patients, tracking documents for patient flow and/or orders, as well as a communication vehicle regarding the recommended follow-up appointments for patients. The form can also be used to capture patients' signatures to verify their presence in the practice and/or as their agreement to assign their benefits to the practice. If the form is used to capture signatures, a signature line should be added for patients. The medical practice should take into account these alternative uses when developing the charge ticket; accuracy and ease-of-use considerations should be made as well.

To ensure billing of all services, utilize an automated charge ticket tracking system provided by your practice management system or sequentially number all forms to provide an audit trail for daily reconciliation.

Layout:

The top of the charge ticket should include all the information required for charge entry. It should include information about the practice (name of medical practice, physicians, address, and telephone number) and other data fields including location of service. The formatting of this information should flow in the order of your charge entry screen.

Query the practice management system vendor for the layout that is compatible with your system. The specifications provided by the practice management system vendor for the patient's name, date of service, payer, and other relevant information that is printed by the practice management system should be accommodated. It is preferable that this information print together at the top or the bottom of the form, allowing the medical practice to use the remainder of the space to efficiently format coding choices.

The layout of the information regarding procedure and diagnosis codes on the encounter form should be set up in a logical order to facilitate ease of selection and immediate recognition of code selection by the provider. The subject areas should be in the same logical order as in the procedure coding books:

- Office visits;
- Consultations;
- Preventive medicine services;
- Surgical procedures;
- Pathology, laboratory;
- Injections, immunizations;
- Medical supplies; and
- Diagnosis codes.

After the code, brief descriptions (for example, "level-1 office visit") should be provided. For procedure codes, after the description, the fee — or a blank space for the fee — should be included. (If the practice uses the charge ticket as a receipt for the patient, it is recommended that fees not be pre-printed on the form.) The procedure codes should be listed in the order of level where appropriate (for example, 99211 followed by 99212, and so on). For the evaluation and management codes, include all code levels in the series (for example, 99211, 99212, 99213, 99214, and 99215). If only the higher level codes are pre-printed, this raises the suspicion of upcoding if an audit is performed by a payer.

Include on the form the most frequently used diagnosis codes (with appropriate level of specificity). Leave room for writing in seldom-used procedure codes and modifiers, as well as diagnosis codes. Use shading to highlight and/or delineate sections. Do not crowd the information. If there is too little space on the form for the practice to include all of the codes that need to be referenced, print some of the information on the back of the form or maintain a listing of the codes in each exam room on a laminated form.

If the medical practice has multiple specialties, develop and customize a charge ticket for each specialty (and, if appropriate, subspecialty). The layout should be consistent for all specialties to facilitate efficient processing in the billing office.

The medical practice should review and update the charge ticket when new codes and changes to existing codes are announced. If the practice offers a new service, immediately update the encounter form to reflect the codes associated with the service.

Offsite charge tickets:

Use separate charge tickets, with the same design format, for services provided out of the office (for example, hospital, ambulatory surgery center, nursing home, and all other places of service). If the physician is responsible for collecting demographic and insurance information at the offsite facility, allow ample room for the information to be stamped, recorded, or attached to the charge ticket. Since offsite forms may contain information for multiple dates of service, make sure that the format allows for recording multiple dates, as well as hospital discharge and admission dates.

When the billing office receives an offsite charge ticket, the patient's demographic and insurance information should be promptly reviewed. If no information can be located in the medical practice's registration system (for example, the patient has never been seen in the office or by the practice before), seek assistance from the registration department of the facility at which the patient was seen. Registration information should be confirmed within 24 hours of receipt by the billing office.

For offsite charge tickets, record the proper procedure and diagnosis codes (based on the physician's level of service and diagnosis). The physician who rendered the services or a designated coder may code these services. Batch the charge tickets and route to charge entry personnel for keying. These charges should be posted within 48 hours of receipt.

These procedures assure correct and complete charge capture and provide a convenient record-keeping method with accurate communication to the billing office.

POLICY 10: CHARGE TICKET ACCURACY AND COMPLETENESS

It is the policy of the medical practice that charge tickets will be accurate and complete at the time of service.

Procedures:

1. The provider will document all services rendered to the patient.

2. The provider will complete paper or electronic charge documents at the time the service is rendered.

3. Diagnosis "rule outs" are not permitted. A diagnosis must be made and coded based on the information available and the symptoms presented.

4. Providers will match procedure codes to the appropriate diagnosis codes using a numeric method and/or via the methodology provided by the practice management system for linking multiple procedures and diagnoses.

5. Illegible, un-scannable, incorrect, or incomplete charge tickets will be returned to the provider for correction within 24 hours so that timely charge entry can be performed.

POLICY 11: CHARGE AND OFFICE VISIT RECONCILIATION

Policy:

Charges for office and outpatient visits will be collected and entered throughout the day. Charges should be reconciled with the appointment schedule and sign-in sheet (if used), to ensure that all services are billed. A missing charge report will be generated to confirm that all charges have been entered for each patient that received medical services.

Procedures:

1. Staff will generate a charge ticket for all scheduled appointments. If a patient cancels or does not present for his/her visit, staff will mark this fact on the charge ticket and record the information regarding the cancellation or no-show in the practice management system. If a patient walks in without a scheduled appointment, staff will generate the appointment and a charge ticket at that time.

2. At the end of the day, the billing office will generate a missing charge report that will confirm all patients and charges for the day are included.

3. Staff will generate an appointment reconciliation report to compare the scheduled patients who kept their appointments to those patients with charges on their accounts.

4. All charge tickets will be sequentially numbered to provide an additional mechanism for monitoring missing tickets.

5. In the event that a missing charge ticket cannot be found, a supervisor must be notified. The supervisor will conduct a review of the search process, and will notify the provider immediately if the form cannot be located. The provider will be asked to generate a charge ticket to document the services that were rendered and select the appropriate procedure and diagnosis code(s).

POLICY 12: CHARGE AND SERVICE RECONCILIATION (NON-OFFICE SERVICES)

Policy:

It is the policy of the medical practice that a closed-loop process will be used to ensure that all charges are captured for billing purposes.

Procedures:

1. Formal logs will be developed to record all charges that are submitted to the billing office. In this fashion, missing dates of service and missing practice site data will be identified.

2. Logs will be developed for each key service in the medical practice. These logs will involve a comparison of source documents to the charges that have been submitted to ensure that all charges are captured. Source documents include hospital census reports, labor and delivery logs, operating room logs, echocardiogram (EKG) logs, and other similar documentation.

3. A service analysis report will be developed for each key service in the medical practice. The service analysis will be compared to projected service volumes to assist in identifying variation from expected productivity levels, which could signify missing charges.

4. In the event missing charges are identified, the staff will first check with the coding unit to determine if the charge has been pended. If the coding unit does not have the charge document, the staff will send an internal electronic communication to the provider(s) listed as performing the service, with a copy to the billing manager. Charges must be submitted within 48 hours of this notification. Before the charge is entered, documentation must be obtained and reviewed to ensure that the service was rendered, coded, and charged correctly.

CHAPTER 6

Pothole 4
The Coding Process

Professional services provided by physicians and other health care providers must be documented. The documentation — in the form of inpatient and outpatient notes, operative reports, procedure reports, and others — serves as the source for translating the services into diagnosis and procedure codes that are used to submit claims for reimbursement.

In this chapter, we discuss key issues associated with the coding process including the following:

- Coding conventions
- Coding responsibilities
- Internal coding competency
- Coding tools and technology
- The link between coding and reimbursement
- Regulatory compliance

A number of coding conventions are used in professional fee billing. They are often referred to by acronym. Figure 6.1 presents common, coding-related acronyms and their definitions.

STANDARD CODE SET

In the United States health care system, professional services are submitted for consideration of payment to government and private payers using a standard code set involving both procedure and diagnosis codes. Current Procedural Terminology (CPT®)* codes are used to describe the procedures and services performed, and International Classification of Diseases, Clinical Modification (ICD-CM) codes are used to indicate the diagnosis(es).

---

* CPT © 2009 American Medical Association. All rights reserved.

FIGURE 6.1 ■ Common Coding Terms in Physician Billing

CPT	Current Procedural Terminology
ICD-9-CM (or ICD-9)	International Classification of Diseases, Clinical Modification, 9th version
NCCI	National Correct Coding Initiative
HCPCS	Healthcare Common Procedure Coding System
NCD	National Coverage Determinations
LCD	Local Coverage Determinations
CMS	Centers for Medicare & Medicaid Services

Procedure Codes

The American Medical Association (AMA) authors the CPT® scale, and annually updates the scale. There are three categories of CPT® codes:

- Category I: Physician procedures and services;
- Category II: Performance management; and
- Category III: Emerging technologies

All CPT® codes are five digits; category I codes are numeric and categories II and III are alphanumeric with a letter in the last field.

According to the AMA, CPT® category I codes require:

- that the service/procedure receive approval from the Food and Drug Administration (FDA) for the specific use of devices or drugs;
- that the service/procedure is performed across the country in multiple locations;
- that many physicians or other health care professionals perform the service/procedure; and
- that the clinical efficacy of the service/procedure has been well established and documented.[1]

Category I codes are sequenced into ranges. For example, the CPT® codes for the integumentary system are 10000 to 19999, for the musculoskeletal system they are 20000 to 29999, and so forth.

Category II codes are a set of optional tracking codes for performance measurement, and category III codes are exclusively for emerging technologies.

---

[1] CPT® Background and Categories of CPT® Codes, American Medical Association, http://www.ama-assn.org/ama/pub/category/12886.html (accessed June 23, 2008).

Diagnosis Codes

Based on a system developed by the World Health Organization, the National Center for Health Statistics and the Centers for Medicare & Medicaid Services (CMS) are responsible for the modifications to the ICD-CM scale. The ICD is currently in its ninth version and is expected to transition to its tenth in 2013 to be referred to as "ICD-10-CM." ICD-CM consists of a numerical list of disease code numbers in tabular form; an alphabetical index to the disease entries; and a classification system for surgical, diagnostic, and therapeutic procedures. All health care settings, including hospitals, nursing homes, home health agencies, and other providers, use ICD-CM codes.

The CPT® and ICD-9-CM scales contain thousands of codes; choosing the appropriate codes to best describe every service provided to patients and the diagnoses that are applicable requires sophisticated knowledge and skill.

In addition to the basic scales, there are several other critical components of the coding process. Although not meant to be a comprehensive review of the professional coding process, the following should be regarded as integral components of the coding process. Physicians and staff recording codes should familiarize themselves with the details of each component.

Healthcare Common Procedure Coding System (HCPCS)

Established in 1978, HCPCS, pronounced as "hick-picks," comprises two sub-systems: Level 1, which are the CPT® codes, and Level 2, which are the products, equipment, and supply codes. Level I CPT® codes, which are described above, are the primary scale for medical services that are performed by physicians and health care professionals. Level II codes, which, in industry parlance, are referred to as the "HCPCS codes," are five-digit, alphanumeric codes. This subsystem of codes is used for products, equipment, and supplies, such as durable medical equipment, and ambulance services. CMS maintains and updates Level II HCPCS codes.

Modifiers

The AMA established several dozen modifiers that can be used in conjunction with CPT® codes. The two-digit alpha or numeric modifiers, which are added to the end of the CPT® code with a hyphen in between, are intended to allow coders to better define the services being rendered, particularly when a CPT® code applies but does not fully describe the nature of the circumstances. Use of a modifier is warranted if the service was increased or decreased, has both a technical and professional component, only part of the service was performed, or if an unusual event occurred. Modifiers can also be used to indicate site of service (for example, left hand, second digit). Some payers maintain rules about the use of modifiers; some require modifiers on certain services, others refuse to pay for services with modifiers. The AMA makes modifications and updates to modifiers on an annual basis, and payers change their expectations about their usage periodically.

National Correct Coding Initiative (NCCI)

In the mid-1990s, CMS commissioned a study to "promote national correct coding methodologies and to control improper coding leading to inappropriate payment in Part B claims."[2] The result of that study was the National Correct Coding Initiative (NCCI). The NCCI, which applies to claims submitted beginning January 1, 1996, determines what services are considered as integral parts of other services, and therefore not separately payable. Commonly referred to as "bundled with" or "incident to" another service, the NCCI lists the codes that are not reimbursed when billed with another code. Unless a modifier is appended to one of the codes to indicate that the services are distinct, CMS does not pay for the services considered bundled. Many of the codes on the NCCI edit list, which is updated quarterly, describe procedures or surgeries. However, all physicians and staff involved in the coding process should familiarize themselves with NCCI, review the quarterly updates, and become knowledgeable about any service they render that is featured on the list. The list is annually updated and published in the National Correct Coding Initiative Coding Policy Manual for Medicare Services.

Global period

When a surgical procedure is billed, many of the procedure codes also include all necessary services performed by the physician before, during, and after the procedure. Reimbursement for a given surgical procedure code includes applicable pre-operative, intra-operative, and post-operative care. Physicians cannot bill separately for these services in addition to the surgery or procedure. CPT® codes are assigned a period of time in which all services are expected to be included with the reimbursement for the surgery or procedure. CPT® codes with 90 follow-up days are considered major surgeries; procedure codes with zero or 10 follow-up days are considered minor surgeries. In the case of a service that is performed on a patient in the global period but does not relate to the surgery or procedure, a physician can use a modifier to indicate that the service falls out of the global and should be paid separately. CMS maintains a list of the global periods for all CPT® codes.

National Coverage Determinations (NCD) and Local Coverage Determinations (LCD)

Although standard lists of procedure and diagnosis codes exist and can be used when services are performed and documented, the usage of these codes does not necessarily result in payment. Indeed, there is a distinction between "coding" and "reimbursement." CMS assists physicians and staff in understanding when a service that is performed and coded will not be paid by publishing a list of coverage determinations. CMS, for example, decided that it will pay for a certain lab test with a specific diagnosis, but it won't cover another lab test for the same diagnosis. Understanding the list allows the physician to tell patients that the service about to be rendered won't be paid, and to acknowledge that they will receive the service but will be responsible for payment themselves. CMS provides a standard form to use for services that

---

[2] NCCI Overview. http://www.cms.hhs.gov/NationalCorrectCodInitEd/ (accessed September 9, 2008).

will not be covered called the advance beneficiary notice (ABN). CMS publishes national coverage rules called "national coverage determinations;" it also allows its carriers to establish and promulgate "local coverage determinations" specific to coverage in their jurisdictions. CMS maintains NCDs and LCDs, local policy articles, and proposed NCD decisions in an online Medicare Coverage Database.[3] Similarly, commercial payers maintain policies regarding the payment of services. Often called "payment policies," these may be published or unpublished. Some payers provide waiver forms to use for their beneficiaries if a service won't be covered; others do not have any such requirement and medical practices use a standard waiver form to indicate that the service won't be paid by the payer and that the patient is responsible for the bill.

Physician Quality Reporting Initiative (PQRI)

Medicare has initiated a Physician Quality Reporting Initiative intended to capture quality data related to a defined set of clinical measures. Those medical practices that effectively participate receive an increase in professional fee (Medicare Part B) reimbursement based on a percentage of their Medicare payments, subject to a cap. (The percentage and the cap are both established by CMS for each reporting period.) A set of codes has been identified to capture the PQRI indices for participating medical practices; participants should consult the instructions for PQRI, as well as any pay-for-performance program, to determine how to code to appropriately capture the work performed by participating physicians.

The coding process forms the basis for a successful revenue cycle. Carelessness, ignorance, or malfeasance in the coding process cannot only damage cash flow, it can result in the medical practice running afoul of state or federal law. The consequence of inattention to the coding process is truly a pothole in the road to getting paid.

In addition to the above recommendations to ensure efficient and effective coding processes, we present the following proven strategies to enhance your revenue cycle.

ADVANCED PRACTICES: THE CODING PROCESS

Identify Who Is Responsible for Coding

As services are rendered, they are documented by the person providing the service (for example, the physician or other health care professional) or a staff member directly observing the services being rendered (for example, a scribe). Regardless of who records the documentation, the record must accurately reflect the services that were rendered.

Based on this documentation, codes can be chosen to best describe the services that were rendered to the patient. The choice of codes may be made in the course of several processes:

- Physician or health care professional: The clinician who provided the care may choose the procedure and diagnosis codes based on the services performed and documented.

---

[3] NCD decisions are available via the online Medicare Coverage Database at https://www.cms.hhs.gov/mcd. (Link active as of September 9, 2008.)

- Credentialed coder: Licensure for coding is available from professional organizations, including the American Academy of Professional Coders and the American Health Information Management Association. Using coding sourcebooks, experience, and professional training, a licensed coder can choose procedure and diagnosis codes based on the services performed and documented. The coder may utilize the documentation to choose the codes, or the coder may have served as a scribe in the exam room. In the case of using documentation from which to choose the codes, the process is commonly referred to as "chart abstraction." Whether the coder was involved in the process of recording the service or not, the documentation must support the codes chosen. The coder may exclusively serve the medical practice or be employed by a company contracted by the practice to code its services. As documentation and codes can be transmitted electronically, companies that offer professional fee coding can be found around the world.

There may be a combination of coding methods used at the medical practice, and the coding process may be supplemented by the medical practice's electronic health record. Many clinicians select their own codes, which are later reviewed by a staff member or credentialed coder. The review may include all services, a subset of services (for example, surgeries), or occur on an audit basis. Furthermore, the electronic health record may be equipped with coding support. Based on the services documented, the system may guide the user to choose a code(s). If automation is available, be alert to the fact that the system should reflect services rendered and documented and should not be recommending or inserting codes for billing purposes only.

Create Internal Coding Competency

Regardless of who is selecting the codes to be used for billing purposes, the individual should be educated to the coding process. Not only is general coding education required, but a coder must be skilled in the specific specialty(ies) of the physicians and other health care professionals rendering services in the medical practice. A coder who works in a primary care office, for example, is not likely trained to code the complexities associated with medical specialty or surgical specialty practices. Similarly, a coder for neurosurgery, for example, would not be equipped without additional education and competency assessment to code other surgical disciplines, for example, cardiovascular surgery. Furthermore, although coding conventions exist on a national level, payers may have specific rules and regulations for their participating providers related to coding of services rendered to their beneficiaries. In sum, each person involved in coding in the medical practice must have specialty-specific knowledge and payer-specific knowledge in order to code appropriately for services that have been provided and documented.

Education and training are available from many sources:

- The Centers for Medicare & Medicaid Services (CMS): CMS offers the Medicare Learning Network, Medicare Coverage Database, National Correct Coding Initiative, Resource-based Relative Value Scale, memoranda, and documents posted on its Website.

- The American Medical Association (AMA): The AMA offers books, manuals, training courses, annual coding convention, and documents posted on its Website.

- Specialty societies: Most specialty societies offer written materials and training courses focusing on coding issues relevant to their members.

- Professional coders' associations: The American Academy of Professional Coders and the American Health Information Management Association offer credentialing for coders, educational programming, documents posted on their Websites, and opportunities for networking with other coders.

- Publishers: Health care publishers have coding resources and manuals available, including those focused on all professional fee coding or by specialty; the resources may be online or in written form.

- Institutions of higher learning: Many universities and colleges offer onsite or online courses to students.

- Other: Recognizing the importance of the coding process to clinicians, medical centers, malpractice carriers, state and local medical societies, payers, and others sponsor coding material and courses for their medical staff, members, or interested persons.

In summary, there are many ways that a person who is interested in coding can receive training and education. The key is to recognize that coding requires more than just one course. Professional fee coding is not only complex, but also ever-changing. To code successfully, ongoing training and education is critical, as is the specialty- and payer-specific knowledge required to translate the service performed and documented into a correct code.

Develop Coding Tools and Leverage Technology

Besides ongoing training and education, tools should be developed to facilitate coding by physicians, other health care providers, and coders in the medical practice. These tools can take various forms and range from the very basic to electronic coding tools. For example, a number of medical practices use a laminated pocket card of common codes to aid the coder in identifying appropriate codes. Now, however, more medical practices deploy automated tools to assist the provider or coder in determining the appropriate code for the service that has been provided and documented and/or have embedded tools in the electronic health record. Coding rules are "built into" the medical practice's practice management system. For example, using software loaded onto a personal digital assistant designed to capture charges, the physician is alerted to a coding rule or convention at the time the codes are entered. Problem linkages between the procedure and diagnosis codes, missing modifiers, improper global periods, and other coding rules can be identified electronically, and coding corrections can then be performed in real time. Mistakes can be corrected prior to claims submission, thereby reducing denials. It is important to recognize that when coding aids are developed, they must be (a) formalized (versus an informal "cheat sheet" or multiple Post-it® notes), (b) accurate, and (c) routinely updated.

Recognize the Link between Coding and Reimbursement

Although a code may exist and be appropriately used for a service, it does not require the payer to reimburse you. In other words, just because a clinician has performed and documented a service, and the right code is chosen, the party responsible for payment may not always choose to pay.

Following is a list of common reasons that services are coded properly but not paid:

1. *Medical necessity.* As noted above in the discussion of coverage determinations, payers make choices regarding the services that they determine are medically necessary to their beneficiaries. These determinations are not consistent among all payers, nor are they always consistent within the payer. Payers may have varying policies for different health plan products they have in the market. Some payers, including Medicare, make their medical necessity determinations publicly available; others do not. When an insurer determines that a service is not medically necessary, the physician may not then bill the patient. There are certain circumstances in which the patient may acknowledge that the service is not medically necessary and not covered but may elect to pay for the service directly (see non-covered services below). Most recently, some payers refuse to reimburse hospitals and physicians for certain medical errors that they deem "preventable." This is an extreme example of denials due to medical necessity. While the coding may be correct as billed, the claim is simply not paid by the payer, nor can the balance be shifted to the patient's financial responsibility.

2. *Non-covered services.* Patients often choose health care insurance from their employer or insurance agent. Thousands of plans are available for purchase. Each plan may offer a different financial package, networks of facilities and providers, as well as coverage. Regarding coverage, some plans pay for certain services; others do not. If a patient does not have coverage for a service rendered at your medical practice, even if it is documented, coded, and billed appropriately, the claim will not be paid by the payer. For non-covered services, the payer directs your medical practice to collect from the patient. This is why we recommend that a waiver be secured when there is even a question as to whether the payer will cover the service. Notably, some payers do not allow participating providers to bill patients for non-covered services without obtaining an approval — via a waiver — prior to the service being rendered.

   As discussed in Chapter 4: The Patient Check-in and Check-Out Processes, it is ideal for your medical practice to identify services that are not covered and collect payment from the patient at the time of service. If this does not occur, the medical practice needs to follow its normal patient account follow-up process in order to secure payment unless contractually obligated to write off the expected payment.

3. *Global, bundled, or package services.* Out of necessity, there are codes to describe various parts or components of a service. If the party responsible for payment determines that the code submitted for reimbursement is part of a service for which they have already paid or expect to pay, the

party may refuse to pay. Obstetrical services, for example, can be billed in part (for example, a prenatal visit only) or in whole (for example, from the confirmation of pregnancy to the postpartum appointment).

4. *Local or proprietary codes.* The payer publishes a code(s) for its participating providers to use in the instance that a specific service (per its definition) is rendered. Once ubiquitous, the number of payers that maintain codes specific to their companies is diminishing. However, these local codes are still used by some payers. In this case, the standard code is denied for payment, and the medical practice must resubmit the claim with the proprietary code.

5. *Inability or unwillingness to pay.* If a patient has no means to pay or refuses to pay, a properly coded service may never be reimbursed. Furthermore, an insurance company that declares bankruptcy may never pay for services rendered to its beneficiaries, even if coded appropriately.

As you submit claims for payment to payers and patients, you will recognize that a properly coded service does not always equal the payment that you expected. For other reasons that claims and statements are not paid and what to do about them, see Chapter 12: The Denial Management Process and Chapter 13: The Patient Collections Process.

The actual reimbursement your medical practice receives depends on the diagnosis and procedure codes that are submitted for payment. The Medicare Physician Fee Schedule (MPFS) is a case in point. Depending on the CPT® code that is selected and the geographic practice cost index (GPCI) that has been designated for your local area, reimbursement levels will vary. Different GPCIs are identified for each of the components of the relative value unit (RVU) as follows: (1) work RVU, (2) practice expense RVU, and (3) facility RVU. The GPCIs make payment adjustments based on geographic location. A published conversion factor that typically changes on an annual basis is then applied in order to convert the relative values to payment amounts. The basic payment formula currently followed by Medicare is:

$$[(\text{Work RVU} \times \text{Work GPCI}) + (\text{Practice Expense RVU} \times \text{Practice Expense GPCI}) + (\text{Malpractice RVU} \times \text{Malpractice GPCI})] \times \text{Conversion Factor}$$

In recent years, a budget neutrality adjustor has also been applied to the work RVU portion (with the product rounded to two decimal places) prior to calculating the reimbursement level.

As this demonstrates, the selection of the CPT® code, which then explodes to the RVU levels associated with that CPT® code, dictates the amount of payment that is allowed for treating Medicare patients.[4]

For other payers, the amount that is reimbursed may tie to the selection of the diagnosis code, as well as the procedure code, necessitating careful attention to coding processes. In pay-for-performance plans, in particular, the diagnosis code has taken on heightened importance in the algorithms used to identify expected services to be provided, and hence, differential payment levels.

---

[4] Medical practices can access the Medicare Physician Fee Schedule via http://www.cms.hhs.gov/apps/pfslookup/step1.asp. (Link active as of September 9, 2008.)

FIGURE 6.2 ■ Place-of-Service Codes for Professional Claims

Place-of-Service Codes for Professional Claims
(partial listing)

11	Office
12	Home
13	Assisted living facility
20	Urgent care facility
21	Inpatient hospital
22	Outpatient hospital
23	Emergency room — hospital
24	Ambulatory surgery center
31	Skilled nursing facility
34	Hospice

Source: CMS[5]

There are a number of other links between coding and reimbursement that demonstrate the inherent complexity of the coding process. The place of service often signals a different level of reimbursement depending on payer requirements. See Figure 6.2 for a list of commonly used place-of-service codes. As another example, a frequency limit placed on a service may also lead to a denied claim, even though the service was performed and has been appropriately documented and coded. Finally, if the procedure codes are listed but not linked properly to the diagnosis(es) codes, there may be a denial as well.

Due to the frequent changes to coding conventions — including the annual changes to codes and the many payer interpretations and requirements that lead to claim denials — as well as the changes in the services provided by physicians because of new technologies and innovations, many medical practices seek external coding expertise. Internal billing staff can then contact the external expert with questions and concerns related to coding nuances of their particular specialty or to seek training updates related to new procedures. Such outside experts may be secured on either a retainer or per-contact basis and often serve as an important resource to the medical practice.

Order Procedure Codes Properly

While the order in which you submit procedure codes for payment should not technically matter, because payers process the service that is listed first, the second one next, and so forth, the order does matter for the purposes of payment. Report your codes in descending order by RVU, with the highest RVU value first, the second value listed next, and so forth. Although this rule of thumb normally applies, some medical practices may find that the payer

---

[5] A complete listing of place-of-service codes is available at: www.cms.hhs.gov/ medhcpcsgeninfo/downloads/place_of_service.pdf. (Link active as of September 9, 2008.)

may not reimburse according to RVUs. Therefore, your billing office may recommend that the order be changed for a particular payer to support optimal
reimbursement.

Link the Diagnosis Code to the Procedure Code

Often, patients receive multiple services from their physicians during a single
encounter. Furthermore, those services may be rendered for multiple medical conditions. For example, patients may be sent for a pulmonary function
test (PFT) to evaluate their pulmonary condition and a treadmill test for their
cardiac condition. In the case of multiple services being rendered for more
than one diagnosis, it is critical that the codes be linked appropriately. In
this example, the diagnosis of chronic obstructive pulmonary disease should
be linked to the PFT, while the diagnosis of cardiovascular disease should be
linked to the treadmill test. The link must be keyed into your practice management system as the system instructs. Furthermore, the link must be recognized by the system when a claim form is created and submitted to the payer.
Discuss the issue of appropriately linking procedure codes and diagnosis codes
with your practice management system vendor.

Be Specific When Coding

There are thousands of procedure and diagnosis codes. Moreover, there are
dozens to describe conditions like diabetes, cardiovascular disease, and so
forth. It is critical to use the most specific code available to describe the service
rendered to the patient, as well as the diagnosis of his/her condition. Without
specificity, the payer may deny payment for the claim.

Make Use of CMS-1500 Field 19

Although there are thousands of procedure codes that describe professional
services, there may be a service that your physician provides for which there is
no procedure code. In most sections of the CPT® coding book, there is a code
at the end of the section marked "unlisted." (For example, 43999 is marked as
"unlisted procedure, stomach."[6]) Most of these codes have a "99" at the end of
them. When an unlisted code is billed, pay particular attention when submitting the claim. Each of the fields on the CMS-1500 claim form has a specific
purpose. Field 19, however, offers flexibility in its use. Denoted as "Reserved
for Local Use," Medicare specifically indicates that you can "enter a concise
description of an unlisted procedure code or a NOC [not otherwise classified]
code if one can be given within the confines of this box." A complete list of
the uses of Field 19, as well as instructions to complete the rest of the fields,
can be found in the Medicare Claims Processing Manual.[7] If your description
exceeds the size of the field on the claim form, you should attach documentation about the procedure to the claim form.

---

[6] On the 2008 CPT scale.

[7] http://www.cms.hhs.gov/manuals/downloads/clm104c26.pdf (accessed September 9,
2008).

Comply with Regulations

Because the coding system provides the infrastructure for which physicians are reimbursed for their services, the potential for fraud, abuse, and waste is significant. Neither government nor private insurance companies can or want to be present in the exam room when services are rendered, so they must rely on the health care provider or his/her staff to properly use the coding systems to be paid. Unfortunately, there have been instances whereby services have been miscoded — knowingly and unknowingly — to the provider's financial benefit.

In order to protect patients, insurance companies, and law-abiding health care professionals, regulations have been established by state governments, the federal government, and insurance companies. As a stakeholder in the revenue cycle, familiarize yourself with any regulations mandated by your state and the insurance companies with which you participate.

Regardless of your locale, specialty, or participation status, all medical practices must comply with the regulations issued by the Office of the Inspector General (OIG), a division of the United States Department of Health and Human Services (HHS). The OIG's mission is to protect the integrity of HHS programs, as well as the health and welfare of the beneficiaries of those programs. The OIG's duties are carried out through a nationwide network of recovery audits, investigations, inspections, and other mission-related functions performed by OIG components. Each year, the OIG publishes a work plan regarding issues on which it will proactively focus. These may include the use of a particular modifier, a certain code, or the place of service the care was rendered. Persons involved in the coding process should pay particular attention to the OIG Work Plan to review compliance with the issues being audited. Compliance plans are further discussed in Chapter 20: Regulations Impacting the Revenue Cycle.

As part of a formal compliance plan, each medical practice should arrange for coding audits involving a sampling of each physician's coding based on the type and place of service. In this fashion, opportunities to provide enhanced education and training to the physician and/or coder are identified. Typically, medical practices conduct prospective audits, auditing claims that have not yet been submitted to the payer. The audits are performed by internal coding staff or the audits are outsourced to a coding vendor. If coding errors or discrepancies are found, the coding can then be corrected prior to claims submission. The alternative to this approach is to conduct coding audits retrospectively — after the claim has been submitted for payment or after the claim has been adjudicated and paid. In these instances, we recommend that a medical practice secure the services of a coding vendor through its legal counsel. Any discrepancies noted as part of the coding audit are then subject to appropriate disclosure requirements that can be facilitated by the medical practice's legal experts.

Another tool used by medical practices to identify opportunities to improve coding education is to benchmark the practice's coding levels to industry coding levels. For example, CPT® codes and the volume billed during a specific period of time are compared to levels reported by CMS. CMS publishes data regarding codes that physicians across the country have submitted during a specific period of time. A graph outlining evaluation and management (E/M) coding frequency by physician is compared to CMS-reported levels (often reflected in a bell-shaped curve). The data may also be internally benchmarked among the medical practice's other physicians. In this fashion, opportunity to identify any outliers and to then determine why there may be valid or invalid differences in coding selection can be explored.

It is not uncommon for equipment vendors to communicate information regarding the procedure and diagnosis codes that should be used with their products and the ensuing payment to expect. Be sure to verify the accuracy of this advice, as correct coding is your responsibility.

The coding process may seem daunting, but mastering the basics is essential to avoid the potholes in the road to getting paid. Coding experience and knowledge are needed not only to ensure effective compliance, but also to optimize your practice's billing performance.

STAFF WORKLOAD RANGES

The staff workload ranges for coding that we typically expect are provided below. The ability to perform within these ranges may vary due to internal practice-specific factors, as well as the scope of work delegated to the staff. The workload ranges are based on a staff member performing these functions approximately seven hours of productive time per day (allowing one hour for breaks, interruptions, and other down time). Note that the workload ranges reflect quantitative performance levels. Qualitative performance — accuracy, completeness, appropriateness, and quality of these functions — should also be measured. When issues of quantity versus quality arise, we strongly recommend that quality be emphasized, even if the performance workload ranges for a particular function need to be relaxed from these levels. The complexity of coding varies significantly by subspecialty, which needs to be taken into account when analyzing staff workload ranges.

Staff Function	Encounters per hour	Encounters transaction time
Evaluation and management coding	15 to 20	3 to 4 minutes
Surgery/procedure coding	6 to 12	5 to 10 minutes

Note: Institute these workload ranges only if accuracy can be ensured in this time frame. If not, you may need to increase the time to perform the function in order to avoid mistakes.

© 2009 Walker, Woodcock, Larch. Reprinted with permission.

LEADING PERFORMANCE INDICATORS

Use the following indicators to assess the performance of your coding process. We refer to these measures as "leading" performance indicators. If your medical practice is successful in achieving these levels in the coding process, you are on the correct path to optimizing your revenue cycle.

Charge corrections due to coding errors:	Less than 1 percent
Claims denied due to coding:	Less than 2 percent
Date of documentation to date of coding:	0 to 48 hours

Note: Institute this lag time only if accuracy can be assured in this time frame. If not, you may need to increase the lag time to evaluate and remove errors.

© 2009 Walker, Woodcock, Larch. Reprinted with permission.

THE CODING DIAGNOSTIC TOOL

The coding diagnostic tool provided below helps you ensure that the process, people, technology, and quality required for an effective coding process are in place in your medical practice.

Process:

1. What written documentation will be used as the source for the coding?
2. What is the expected lag time between providing the service and coding the service?
3. Are you monitoring and disseminating information regarding coding and reimbursement updates?

People:

1. Who is responsible for identifying each type of code?
2. What education and training is required for physicians, other health care providers, and coders?
3. Are your staff members trained in both coding and payer reimbursement policies?

Technology:

1. Has technology been leveraged to provide coding tools to physicians, other health care providers, and coders?
2. Are you automatically editing your codes to ensure accuracy and consistency with payer guidelines?
3. Have edits been built into the practice management software to signal problem coding, for example, inappropriate CPT®/ICD-9 coding linkages and need for modifiers?
4. Does your practice management system allow you to report the CPT® codes billed by each provider per time period to evaluate CPT® utilization as compared to benchmarks?

Quality:

1. What audit plan have you developed to ensure coding quality?
2. Are you editing your CPT®, modifiers, and ICD-9 codes to ensure accuracy based on payer guidelines (assuming you document appropriately)?
3. Have you identified an expert coder with specialty-specific knowledge either via internal resources or externally?

CHAPTER 7

Pothole 5
The Charge Entry Process

The charge entry process is often taken for granted, given the demands of other areas of the revenue cycle, yet it is crucial to ensuring a "clean claim" and avoiding claim denials.

In this chapter, we discuss the following areas:

- Charge entry responsibility
- Timeliness of charge entry
- Electronic charge entry
- Pre-adjudication edits
- Charge entry audits
- Fee schedules

Charge entry involves entering the diagnosis and procedure codes that have been used to document the service that was performed. The charge entry process simply transfers this information from one medium to another. For example, charges that were recorded on a charge ticket are keyed into the practice management system for billing. For many medical practices, some or all charges are electronically transferred without manual intervention. The process sounds simple, but there are a number of potholes in the transfer of charge information. Whether on paper or via electronic means, judgments must be made by the charge entry staff in order to ensure that the charge is "clean" prior to it being submitted.

The charges themselves need to be entered correctly as coded, in a timely manner. Furthermore, they need to be compliant with coding guidelines and payer policies.

Many medical practices require outpatient charge entry to be performed at the location of service (distributing this function to multiple practice sites, as appropriate). Outpatient charge entry is conducted by physicians via electronic health records or by practice site staff who enter this information to the practice management system via written charge tickets.

Inpatient charge entry is more typically performed in a central billing office; however, physicians are increasingly performing this function themselves. Smart phones, electronic hand-held devices, and electronic health records permit physicians to complete their documentation and then select procedure and diagnosis codes, with the charge automatically entered to the practice management system. Inpatient charge entry may also be delegated to the physician's primary outpatient location, to a staff member who travels to the hospital or other place of service to capture the charges for services rendered, or to staff based at the hospital (for example, the practice employs a nurse to round with the physicians at the hospital).

To ensure efficient and effective charge entry processes, we present proven strategies to enhance your revenue cycle.

ADVANCED PRACTICES: THE CHARGE ENTRY PROCESS

Ensure Complete and Accurate Registration Data

If the registration data for the patient has not been entered, it will be necessary to perform this function before the charges are entered. We expect that front-office staff will have entered and updated patient demographic and insurance information for services performed in the office. For non-office services, responsibility for registration may reside with a staff member delegated this task or with the charge entry staff and/or the coding staff. Regardless of who is registering the patient, it is important that the registration information be accurate. This may require staff to access the hospital system for registration information, query payers' Websites for information, contact the payer or patient by telephone, or other similar steps to ensure that the data are accurate and complete.

Make Sure All Charges Are Entered

It seems obvious that all charges should be entered into your practice management system. But sometimes not all charges are entered. Beyond human error, the reasons practices don't enter charge tickets as they are received include:

- The charge ticket is incomplete;
- The physician providing the service is not credentialed with that payer; and
- The service was not documented appropriately.

A formal procedure is needed for each of these situations to ensure that all charges are in fact billed. If there is one practice site that submits incomplete charge tickets, sit down with the staff involved in this process and explain what is missing and why you need the information. The handoffs back and forth between the billing office and this front office are costly in terms of time and resources. They also can lead to "controllable" account adjustments, such as timely filing.

Leverage technology to ensure that these unbilled charges are worked. Edits can be built into your practice management system that will hold your claim until the outstanding information is obtained. This "account on hold" report should be reviewed at routine intervals to ensure that accounts do not remain "on hold" for prolonged periods of time. If the service cannot be billed, then you will need to write off the charge with a write-off code specific to the reason (for example, "no documentation" or "not a credentialed provider"). These write-offs can be monitored, reported, and analyzed so that you can take action to improve collections. We will discuss claim scrubbing software to identify pre-adjudication errors and adjustment codes more in later chapters, but for now the key is to develop and follow procedures to ensure all of your charges are correctly entered into your system.

Develop a Rational Fee Schedule

Regardless of who performs charge entry or where it is performed, be sure that your medical practice's fee or charge schedule is designed in a systematic fashion and is "rationally" based. Your fee or charge schedule is what your medical practice has determined as its gross charges for each CPT® code that it bills. (This is not to be confused with a payer fee schedule, which is the reimbursement schedule used by the payer to pay you that which is contractually determined.) By rational, we mean that fees are not haphazardly determined, but are based on a quantifiable and systematic approach.

Many medical practices have established their fees based on the Resource-based Relative Value Scale (RBRVS), which involves multiplying the total relative value units (RVUs) of the procedure code by a multiplier. The multiplier may be a function of the current year conversion factor, as established by the Centers for Medicare & Medicaid Services (CMS) for professional fee payment or a multiplier accepted by the practice as reflective of current market rates. Because RBRVS is the system used by the CMS to establish Medicare rates, this method of fee setting is essentially setting fees as a percentage of the Medicare allowed. (As discussed further in Chapter 10: The Payment and Denial Posting Process, the "allowed" is the price for each procedure code that a payer agrees to reimburse your practice.)

Most medical practices set their fees within a range of 200 to 400 percent of the Medicare allowed. (See Figure 7.1 for an example of this fee-setting approach.) This type of consistent approach to establishing a medical practice's fee schedule enhances your ability to analyze payer reimbursement levels, update the fee schedule, efficiently establish fees for new services, and study the impact of changes in reimbursement levels by payer on a normalized scale.

Some medical practices have decided that it is no longer worth the trouble to keep their fee schedule current. They believe their payer contracts dictate what they are paid regardless of what they charge. But almost every practice has some percentage of commercial payers that pay a percentage of the charge,

FIGURE 7.1 ■ Sample Fee Schedule Determination

Office Visit, Established Patient

CPT®	RVUs[1]	Payment[2]	200%	250%	300%	350%	400%
99211	0.52	$18.75	$37.51	$46.89	$56.26	$65.64	$75.02
99212	1.03	$37.15	$74.30	$92.87	$111.45	$130.02	$148.59
99213	1.70	$61.31	$122.63	$153.28	$183.94	$214.60	$245.25
99214	2.56	$92.33	$184.66	$230.83	$276.99	$323.16	$369.32
99215	3.46	$124.79	$249.58	$311.98	$374.37	$436.77	$499.16

[1] 2009 transitional, non-facility total relative value unit (RVU).
[2] Conversion factor of $36.0666 (2009) applied, with no geographical adjustment.
Source: www.cms.hhs.gov/PhysicianFeeSched/PFSRVF/.

often referred to as "indemnity plans." Even if these payers make up only 2 percent of your patient volume, your revenue performance will be healthier if you keep your fees at competitive market levels.

Increases to your fee schedule will affect your self-pay population, and this is often considered a reason not to alter charges. Consumers are more price sensitive to changes in evaluation and management fees than other parts of your fee schedule. If this is a concern, maintain competitive fees but establish a policy and procedure regarding discounting for financial hardship (as discussed in Chapter 13: The Patient Collections Process), permitting your medical practice to extend a discount to uninsured patients without compromising your fee schedule.

It is crucial to understand the impact of changes to your fee schedule on receivables management reports. In particular, your gross collection rate will be affected by a change in fees. In the past, under the traditional "usual, customary, and reasonable" (UCR) reimbursement system, an increase in fees resulted in an across-the-board increase in revenue. As noted above, indemnity plans continue to operate, but they now represent a small minority of commercial payers. Today, an increase in charges will inflate the gap between charges and collections, thereby lowering your gross collection rate. Importantly, this should not be considered a negative reflection of the performance of the billing office, but rather a function of the fee schedule change. Remember to use the net collection rate (NCR) when you want to evaluate billing office performance. The NCR tells you how you are doing collecting what is truly collectible. Performance measures to be used to assess your revenue cycle are further discussed in Chapter 19: Measuring and Analyzing the Revenue Cycle.

Establish One Fee Schedule

Some medical practices have elected to develop separate fee schedules based on payer, for example, a Medicare fee schedule and a commercial fee schedule. The reason they do this is to reduce the contractual adjustments that must be applied and to permit the payment posters to recognize the expected reimbursement level from the payer, in this case, Medicare's allowable. We do not recommend that medical practices adopt fee schedules by payer for two reasons: (1) the practice would not want to be in the position of justifying why it is charging Medicare patients different rates than commercial patients (particularly if the fee schedules are not well coordinated) and (2) the use of different fee schedules will negatively impact the medical practice's ability to benchmark against peer groups due to the variable gross charges that are entered and reside in the accounts receivable.

A large medical practice may want to have separate fee schedules for its various specialties. In these instances, we believe it is important to standardize the fees used for "shared" procedure codes, such as evaluation and management codes, and others so that patients perceive a group practice, rather than individual physicians simply co-located and practicing medicine within the same facility. This will also ensure that internal competition for patients based on price does not ensue.

Recognize the Impact of Modifiers on Your Fees

Often your fee schedule will be determined first without modifiers. For specialties that utilize many modifiers, your practice management system needs to adjust the fee when certain modifiers are applied. There are times when the modifier should cause the fee to increase or decrease and you will expect the payment to be similarly adjusted. When analyzing your payments against your fee schedule, having an alternative fee for a modifier will increase data accuracy, both in terms of gross charges and in terms of payer reimbursement management. (See Chapter 14: The Contract and Reimbursement Management Process for a discussion of reimbursement management tools.)

Avoid "Netting the Charge"

The process of entering the charge at the level of what is expected from the payer is commonly referred to as "netting the charge." When participating with a payer, the medical practice agrees to accept a reimbursement level typically reduced from the gross charge. Industry standard is to bill the gross charge on the claim form and take the adjustment — whether it is a contractual adjustment or a non-contractual adjustment — at the time of payment posting. When "netting the charge," the medical practice takes the adjustment at the time of charge posting. Instead of entering a standard fee for each service, the staff member enters the expected payment (referred to as the "allowance" or "allowable").

This procedure of netting the charge prior to claim submission is inconsistent with the industry standard and is not recommended for the following reasons:

1. *Guessing payer payment levels may reduce revenue.* Too often, payers either fail to disclose or try to hide allowable amounts from physicians. Or, payers commonly make changes to their fee schedule, often with no notification to the medical practice at all. Because contracts are typically

written such that the reimbursement is the "the lesser of the allowable or the charge," a medical practice does not want to take a chance that its guess — even if it's based on an historical fee schedule — will be less. Because the payer may not alert a practice to the fact that the "lesser" was indeed the charge, the medical practice that nets the charge prior to claim submission will be none the wiser to missed reimbursement.

2. *Accounts receivable reports are compromised.* When a medical practice nets the charge to the allowable at the time of charge entry and prior to payment posting, its receivables are significantly reduced. Consider billing a charge to one payer at the practice's full charge and another at the allowance (typically, 10 to more than 50 percent less than the full charge). The challenge, from a management perspective, is that the accounts receivable are no longer normalized. This makes it nearly impossible to truly judge the performance of the billing office. Consider these scenarios: one month, patients covered by a payer in which the charge is netted to 50 percent receive services; the next month, patients covered by a payer that is not netted receive services. The receivables — days in receivables outstanding, percentage of total receivables outstanding over 90 days, and so forth — appear to jump from month to month. The problem is that the data are jumping, not the performance.

3. *Payers gain leverage on the prevailing rate.* Finally, and arguably most importantly, the reduction of the charge gives the payers tremendous leverage. With medical practices billing at this rate, the payer "justifies" its reduced fee internally or blatantly during negotiations as paying at the prevailing industry rate. A medical practice holds no credibility in requesting a higher level of reimbursement if it has been billing at a reduced fee equivalent to the payer's rate so marked as the practice's charge. Payers use the "usual, customary, and reasonable" charge submitted to propagate future fees. By, in essence, reducing physician charges across the country, this process gives license to the payers to ratchet down fees for medical services.

Systematically Review and Update Your Fee Schedule

Review your medical practice's fee schedule at least annually to ensure that it is appropriate based on reimbursement levels, your local market, and other factors. A sure means of identifying fees that are too low is to watch for explanation of benefits (EOB) and/or electronic payment remittance (EPR) in which the payers reimburse at 100 percent of your medical practice's charge. This should alert you to the need to update your fees. No insurance company will offer the alert to your medical practice, as they establish their payment schedules based on the price they allow — or you charge — whichever is lower.

Use Tool 11 to examine your fee schedule for update opportunity.

Do Not Bill Unless Documentation is Complete

Medical practices should not be entering charges to the practice management system unless they have determined that the physician has documented the visit (to include an interpretation, in the case of an imaging or laboratory

TOOL 11	Fee Schedule Review

This is an example of a tool that can be used to evaluate your current fee schedule to determine whether changes are warranted. The first column in this table lists the procedures provided in your medical practice. The next four columns reflect the CPT® code associated with the procedure description, the total charges this practice has for that procedure, the frequency with which the procedure is performed by the medical practice, and the current fee for the procedure, respectively. These columns are in charge order, with the highest charges listed first followed by the next highest, and so forth. Following this practice-specific data, the allowed reimbursement rates for each of your key payers would be reflected so that you can examine each of the payer reimbursement levels. At minimum, you should evaluate reimbursement levels by payers that make up 80 percent of your charge volume. Once these data are compiled, you can then determine if a new fee is warranted and record this new fee in the far-right column of the table.

Services Sorted by Charges	CPT®	Charges	Volume	Fee	Allowed Rates by Payers	Proposed New Fees for Practice
Office Visit, Est. Patient	99213	$1,101,600	8,160	$135		
Office Visit, Est. Patient	99214	$1,045,330	4,862	$215		Fees may remain the same or change based on relationship to payer-allowed amounts, RVUs, or some percentage of the Medicare fee schedule
MRI Brain w/o Contrast	70553	$783,900	268	$2,925		
Subsequent Hospital Care	99232	$712,530	3,393	$210		
Office Consultation	99244	$609,425	1,283	$475	To be filled in for each CPT® code for payers that make up 80 percent of volume	
Critical Care, First 30–74 Mins	99291	$459,000	680	$675		
Subsequent Hospital Care	99233	$294,000	980	$300		
Emergency Department Visit	99285	$249,310	466	$535		
Emergency Department Visit	99284	$217,200	600	$362		
CT Abdomen w/Contrast	74160	$207,900	189	$1,100		
Tissue Exam by Pathologist	88305	$131,355	417	$315		
Office Consultation	99243	$115,500	385	$300		
Subsequent Hospital Care	99231	$112,815	981	$115		
Office Visit, Est. Patient	99212	$86,475	1,153	$75		

© 2009 Walker, Woodcock, Larch. Reprinted with permission.

Note: Sample data.

service). Thus, a charge ticket alone should not signal that the payer or patient is ready to be billed. The medical practice needs to develop a formal policy and procedure, along with physician expectations, related to service documentation and ensure that documentation has taken place before charges are submitted to the payer or patient.

Perform Pre-adjudication Edits

Due diligence must be given to ensuring that charges are submitted correctly. Due to the complexity of the coding and reimbursement process, the poten-

---

FIGURE 7.2 ■ Pre-adjudication Tools

Physician Performs, Documents, Codes, and Submits Charges for the Service

Pre-adjudication edits (also referred to as "errors" and "rejections")

Tools:

- Mobile, point-of-care charge capture devices
- Charge capture module of electronic health record
- Charge entry function in practice management system
- Claims clearinghouse

© 2009 Walker, Woodcock, Larch. Reprinted with permission.

---

tial for errors is high. To avoid mistakes, develop a pre-adjudication review of charges. "Pre-adjudication" refers to reviewing and editing the charge before it moves into the payer's adjudication process. This can be a manual review of charges by a practice biller or a more sophisticated evaluation by an automatic pre-adjudication editing tool. (See Figure 7.2 for examples of pre-adjudication tools.) Whether performed manually or electronically, the edits should be pre-defined and payer-specific. In addition to pre-defined payer edits, which may include incorrect diagnosis codes identified for the procedure, global period edits, and missing modifiers, many medical practices deploy editing systems that are loaded with practice-specific rules. Automated systems, which essentially become "smarter over time," can be programmed with rules based on the medical practice's common denial trends. Functionality differs between devices, but a claim edit or rejection alerts the medical practice to take the steps needed to ensure that a clean claim is submitted.

In contrast to pre-adjudication edits, post-adjudication errors are also known as claim denials. The payer refuses payment and transmits this information to the medical practice typically on the EOB form. A medical practice also must exercise due diligence in managing claim denials, as they represent a high cost to the medical practice, not only in terms of the rework involved in researching issues and resubmitting the claim, but also in terms of delayed cash flow. (For more information about post-adjudication denials, see Chapter 12: The Denial Management Process.)

Institute Electronic Charge Entry

Electronic charge entry can be conducted via scannable charge tickets, physicians using a mobile device to capture charges, an electronic health record, or a charge interface with another entity (for example, a hospital). If you have these capabilities, be sure to leverage the technology to permit automated charge entry. If the software is interfaced with your practice management system, this download posts the charges electronically, thereby minimizing errors and reducing lag time from date-of-service to date-of-charge entry.

A medical practice may still want to institute a review of the charges prior to claims submission to ensure accuracy. However, the automated entry saves time and staff resources by eliminating the need to post each charge into the practice management system.

Establish Point-of-Care Charge Entry

Medical practices can delegate charge entry to the person who provides the service at the point of care. This is facilitated by an electronic health record. So, for example, if the nurse performs a nurse visit or if the technician performs a pulmonary function test, the charge can be entered at the point of care. (As discussed above, the charge should not be released until the service is documented and completed.)

Establish Expected Timelines for Charge Entry

Late submission of charges not only contributes to problematic staffing workload, but to fluctuating revenue streams. Some medical practices find that their physicians submit the majority of their charges in the last few days of the month. This not only delays revenue to the medical practice, it requires an extraordinary amount of work for the staff, often taking them from other responsibilities such as account follow-up, which then get delayed, and often generates staff overtime, which then increases the practice's overhead. Define a cut-off date by which no more charges will be entered for that month, with all late charges entered the next month. This policy improves the quality of charge entry (because staff are not rushing to finish). It also lets your staff perform the important work of reviewing charges and claims and responding to pre-adjudication claim edits to ensure the claims are correct the first time.

Batch Charges to be Entered

The medical practice needs to ensure that the charges that are ready to be entered are indeed entered to the system. One way to assist in this effort is to perform charge entry via a batch mode. In this case, the number of charges that are in the batch are totaled; once entered to the practice management system, the system total is calculated and confirmed with the batch total. This ensures that the same number of charges in the batch are in fact entered to the system. Note that this does not ensure that charge entry is accurate, it only serves as an edit system to ensure that the number of charges available for charge entry is indeed the number of charges that was entered to the system.

Embed Charge Entry Edits into Your Practice Management System and Electronic Health Record

Many practice management systems and electronic health records permit real-time recognition of charge entry errors via edits that are built into these systems. As charges are entered, the physician or charge entry staff are immediately alerted to correct missing or inconsistent information. For example, the procedure code may be inconsistent with the diagnosis code or there may be a missing modifier. In this fashion, the physicians and/or charge entry staff are able to correct charges as they are entered to the system in real time (or work these edits when taking the charge from an "unbilled" to a "billed" status) rather than submit a claim and wait for the clearinghouse or payer to reject it due to charge entry errors. The ability to correct edits or errors at the point of charge entry is a form of pre-adjudication of the claim. Every effort should be made to edit the charges on this pre-adjudication basis by leveraging your technology.

Determine if Charges are "Clean"

If the important billing steps discussed in earlier chapters of this book, particularly those discussed in Chapter 3: The Patient Financial Clearance Process, have not been conducted, it will be necessary for charge entry staff to perform expanded services beyond "heads down" charge entry.

The staff will need to expend additional time and effort to ensure a "clean" charge and therefore a clean claim if these steps have not already been performed. This could include the following:

- Enter and/or update patient registration information;
- Verify active insurance coverage and benefits eligibility;
- Ensure that the diagnosis code meets local and national coverage determinations for the service performed and communicate discrepancies to the physician;
- Query the hospital database and investigate data discrepancies;
- Ensure that missing information is completed;
- Obtain missing authorizations; and/or
- Verify charges with source documents (as discussed in Chapter 5: The Charge Capture Process).

If staff involved in charge entry are also performing these tasks, recognize that charge entry will involve a longer process than if the staff are simply entering procedure and diagnosis codes.

Conduct Quality Assurance Review of Physicians and Staff Involved in Charge Entry

A detailed review of charge entry should occur for all new physicians and staff for at least a three-month period, combined with education and feedback so that any errors can be corrected for the future. During this initial period, the billing staff should review each charge that is entered for accuracy and completeness before the claim or statement is submitted.

If staff enter charges at the practice site, be sure to audit the work of staff involved in charge entry for practices that have recently been acquired or upon the opening of a new practice. During this training period, the billing staff should review each charge ticket and the data entered into the practice management system for accuracy of registration, posting of time-of-service payments, and charge entry. While this may result in an increased workload over regular billing and collection functions for a specific time period, the opportunity to respond and resolve data capture and charge entry problems early in the employee's tenure with the practice reduces billing rework and ensures that staff are educated to perform the work correctly so a clean claim can be generated.

Tool 12 provides an example of a competency assessment you can customize for your medical practice as you assess the performance of your staff in performing charge entry.

TOOL 12   **Competency Assessment: Charge Entry**

Demonstrate the following activities involved in the charge entry process:

	Competency Level	
	Satisfactory	Unsatisfactory
1. Creating accounts	_____	_____
2. Following up on missing demographic information	_____	_____
3. Verifying insurance coverage and benefits eligibility	_____	_____
4. Understanding coverage determinations	_____	_____
5. Linking charge to appointment/visit	_____	_____
6. Interpreting the charge ticket	_____	_____
7. Posting office/outpatient charges	_____	_____
8. Posting non-office charges	_____	_____
9. Linking procedure and diagnosis codes	_____	_____
10. Applying modifiers as needed	_____	_____
11. Resolving pre-adjudication charge edits	_____	_____
12. Balancing payments received at the time of service	_____	_____
13. Balancing charges keyed to source documents	_____	_____

© 2009 Walker, Woodcock, Larch. Reprinted with permission.

Provide Appropriate Separation of Duties for Charge Entry and Changes to Charges

Make sure that you have developed a policy regarding changes to charges. (A sample policy is provided at the end of this chapter.) It is important that appropriate internal controls be established for any changes to charges that are made. Many medical practices go beyond a standard policy to restrict the staff who are able to change incorrect charges. Instead, they institute a formal method by which charges for correction are identified and designate the charge correction process to a specific staff member or manager. Such a separation of duties supports charge entry internal controls.

Link Coding and Charge Entry

When certified coders are used to code procedures and surgeries, they are at times also asked to perform charge entry. This permits the coding and charge entry work to be conducted in one step, rather than insert a process handoff. However, this benefit must be weighed against the cost of coding support staff, as their wage rates are significantly higher than charge entry staff. If coders also enter charges, it is recommended that the coders first code all of the procedures and then perform charge entry on all of the procedures, rather than code-enter-code-enter, as this increases the efficiency of the coders involved in the charge entry process.

Be Savvy Regarding Patient Deductibles

Some medical practices delay their charge entry in an attempt to ensure they are paid by the payer rather than the patient. For example, if the patient has a hospital bill and physician bill, the practice may delay charge entry of the physician services so that the hospital bill is the one that is denied due to patient deductible. If a medical practice elects to adopt this type of strategy, it needs to be clear regarding the many health products of its patients. For example, if a majority of patients have a high-deductible health plan coupled with a health savings account, this type of strategy could backfire. In this scenario, the patient would pay his/her hospital bill and may or may not have sufficient funds to pay the physician. Other medical practices have adopted the opposite approach to the above scenario. In these medical practices, the focus is to collect the patient's portion of the bill, whether it be co-insurance, deductible, or copayment, and thus be "first in line" for payment. In these medical practices, revenue is received prior to or at the time of service, significantly shortening the time to payment.

Initiate Audits of Charge Entry

Conduct charge entry audits on a monthly basis involving a sample of charges. We recommend that 2 to 10 percent of charges be audited. This permits identification of problem areas, which may include improper linkage of diagnosis and procedure codes, data accuracy, and other errors. These instances should be used as an educational opportunity for staff in order to prevent future errors.

As we have discussed in this chapter, your fee schedule should be rationally based and subject to systematic review. Make sure that your charges are entered timely and accurately and leverage your technology to capture and correct pre-adjudication errors. Your charge entry process is critical to ensuring that a clean bill is submitted to your payers.

STAFF WORKLOAD RANGES

The staff workload ranges for charge entry that we typically expect are provided below. The ability to perform within these ranges may vary due to internal practice-specific factors, as well as the scope of work delegated to the staff. The workload ranges are based on a staff member performing these functions approximately seven hours of productive time per day (allowing one hour for breaks, interruptions, and other down time). Note that the workload ranges reflect quantitative performance levels. Qualitative performance — accuracy, completeness, appropriateness, and quality of these functions — should also be measured. When issues of quantity versus quality arise, we strongly recommend that quality be emphasized, even if the performance workload ranges for a particular function need to be relaxed from these levels.

	Line Items	
Staff Function	**per day**	**per hour**
Charge entry (without registration)	375 to 525	55 to 75
Charge entry (with registration)	280 to 395	40 to 55

Note: Institute these workload ranges only if accuracy can be assured in this time frame. If not, you may need to increase the time to perform the function in order to avoid mistakes.

© 2009 Walker, Woodcock, Larch. Reprinted with permission.

LEADING PERFORMANCE INDICATORS

Use the following indicators to assess the performance of your charge entry process. We refer to these measures as "leading" performance indicators. If your medical practice is successful in achieving these levels in the charge entry process, you are on the correct path to optimizing your revenue cycle.

Date of coding to date of charge entry:	0 to 48 hours
Charge corrections due to charge entry errors:	0 percent

Note: Institute this lag time only if accuracy can be assured in this time frame. If not, you may increase the lag time to evaluate and remove errors. If you rely on the hospital registration system, for example, it may be totally appropriate to suspend charges within your practice management system until the hospital patient accounts department has completed its updates to insurance and authorizations.

© 2009 Walker, Woodcock, Larch. Reprinted with permission.

THE CHARGE ENTRY DIAGNOSTIC TOOL

The charge entry diagnostic tool provided below helps you ensure that the process, people, technology, and quality required for effective charge entry are in place in your medical practice.

Process:

1. When are charges entered with respect to date of service:
   a. By practice site
   b. By physician
   c. By place of service
   d. By service type
2. Is a systematic approach used to determine and update your fee schedule?
3. What process is used to identify and work charge entry errors?

People:

1. Are the appropriate parties entering charges?
   a. Role of health care providers
   b. Role of practice site staff
   c. Role of coders
   d. Role of billing office staff
2. How many charges are entered by each party?
3. Are staff fully trained in charge entry?

Technology:

1. Does your practice management system alert you to edit charges when entering them?
2. Have you built in charge entry edits that can be resolved at the time charges are entered (for example, diagnosis code does not match procedure code)?

Quality:

1. Have you conducted an audit of charge entry to evaluate quality?
2. Do you have systems in place to ensure that all charges are entered?
3. Do you track charge entry errors and provide feedback to staff so they can improve the quality of their work?

POLICIES AND PROCEDURES

At the end of each chapter, we provide policies and procedures to assist you in developing a policy and procedure manual for your medical practice. Below are five policies specific to the charge entry process.

Policy 13:   Fee Schedule

Policy 14:   Outpatient Charge Entry

Policy 15:   Timeliness and Accuracy of Data Entry

Policy 16:   Lag Time: Date of Service to Date of Bill Release

Policy 17:   Charge Correction

POLICY 13: FEE SCHEDULE

Policy:

It is the policy of the medical practice to maintain a consistent and current schedule of fees for all services it renders.

Procedures:

1. The medical practice will establish its fee schedule based on the resource-based relative value scale (RBRVS). The relative value units will be multiplied by a conversion factor. The conversion factor will be chosen in order that the result (unit times a conversion factor) will be higher than all expected reimbursement from payers. The medical practice may choose to utilize a separate conversion factor for sets of services, such as procedures, surgeries, lab, imaging, evaluation and management, and so forth. The methodology will be clearly documented and filed in the medical practice's permanent records.

2. The fee schedule will be analyzed and updated, if necessary, annually, on or about November 1. Changes to fees will be effective January 1.

3. The billing manager will alert the administrators and providers to the change in fee schedule, which will increase the accounts receivable. An alert should be provided, as this change in receivables should not be considered a reflection of poor billing and collection performance. To the extent possible, the billing manager shall identify the expected impact on the receivables indicators (for example, days in receivables outstanding).

4. At the time of the fee schedule analysis, the medical practice will analyze its reimbursement from all payers to (1) ensure that the payer is making payments based on expected reimbursement and (2) determine if the medical practice should renegotiate and/or discontinue a relationship with a payer based on reimbursement and/or administrative hassle. This detailed analysis should also ensure that the fee schedule is higher than the medical practice's expected reimbursement.

5. Practice staff engaged in payment posting will promptly alert the billing manager or his/her designee for any claims adjudicated at 100 percent of the medical practice fee. At that time, the billing manager and the administrator will confer to decide if raising the fee is appropriate. If so, the fee will be raised consistent with the methodology listed above (using units times a conversion factor).

6. For all new services performed, the medical practice will utilize the RBRVS units for that particular procedure code multiplied by the conversion factor. If the service has never been billed before, medical practice staff will communicate the new service and designated fee to the administrator or his/her designee for review.

7. The medical practice will utilize its fee schedule for all physicians and providers without exception. Fees may be discounted according to agreements with participating payers, prompt payment at the time of service, and financial hardship. See related policies on patient financial responsibility waiver and financial hardship.

POLICY 14: OUTPATIENT CHARGE ENTRY

Policy:

Charges for outpatient services will be accurately posted in the practice management system at the point of service and balanced at the end of the day that services are rendered.

Procedures:

1. Staff will post charges to unique batch-control groups at the time of service. Staff members will be assigned individual control groups. They will be responsible for posting the financial transactions.

2. Health care providers will document charges and corresponding procedure and diagnosis codes on pre-printed charge tickets. These tickets will be created for each unique patient visit.

3. All charges will be posted to a batch control group assigned to each staff member.

4. Staff will post accurate charges to the patient account.

5. The staff member to whom the batch is assigned will balance each batch control group at the end of each day.

6. Staff will generate an audit report and balance the batch control group.

7. Staff will resolve all batches with conflicting balances or notify a supervisor regarding inability to balance.

8. Staff will return charge tickets with incomplete charge data to the originating provider for completion to ensure expedient billing and collection. This process must occur on the same day as the service. The practice management system's charge entry suspense function will monitor return of the incomplete charge tickets sent to the providers.

POLICY 15: TIMELINESS AND ACCURACY OF DATA ENTRY

Policy:

All demographic, clinical, and financial data entry will occur in a timely and accurate manner.

Procedures:

1. Staff will enter data according to the following time frames:

   ▪ Registration and patient demographic data will be entered at the time the patient schedules the appointment, with updates entered at the time of service;

- Clinical data and all medical chart documentation will be recorded on the date of service or within 24 hours of the date of service;

- All charges will be entered into the system within 48 hours of the completion of the coding of services performed; and

- All payments will be entered into the system at the time of service or within 24 hours.

2. Staff must achieve a 99 percent accuracy rate for data entry. Staff not achieving this goal will be assigned to complete a day of training in charge entry and related tasks. If a staff member is not able to achieve accuracy during this additional training, the employee will be considered for transfer to another work area or dismissal from employment.

POLICY 16: LAG TIME: DATE OF SERVICE TO DATE OF BILL RELEASE

Policy:

It is the policy of the medical practice to facilitate a timely and efficient billing and collections process. To that end, the medical practice will comply with pre-determined lag times for key billing processes.

Procedures:

1. Medical practice providers will be responsible for documenting all services within 24 hours of the date of service. Providers will submit all procedure and diagnosis codes within 24 hours of rendering services in the office, and 48 hours for services out of the office. If coding is not performed by providers, the coding process performed by medical practice staff may consume a maximum of 48 hours from the completion of documentation.

2. Staff will be responsible for entering charges, whether by keying, scanning, or interface with the electronic health records system, within 48 hours of the date of coding.

3. Staff will be responsible for reviewing and editing the charges before they are submitted. This process may consume up to the 48-hour period allowed between the date of coding and the date of charge entry. Exceptions, such as causing a charge ticket to be returned to a provider for further review, will not exceed three business days.

4. Staff will submit claims within 72 hours of charge entry.

5. Staff will submit claims on a daily basis.

6. The lag times for the following key processes will be tracked and monitored by the billing manager every week. Outliers will be reported to the practice executive, and a performance improvement initiative will commence.

    - Date of service to date of documentation: 0 to 24 hours

    - Date of documentation to date of coding: 0 to 48 hours

    - Date of coding to date of charge entry: 0 to 48 hours

    - Date of charge entry to date of claim release: 24 to 72 hours

POLICY 17: CHARGE CORRECTION

Policy:

It is the policy of the medical practice that a charge cannot be deleted. For management purposes, an audit trail is necessary.

Procedures:

1. Only designated staff will be permitted to correct a charge that has been entered into the practice management system.

2. If a correction to a charge is necessary, the charge must be written off to the appropriate adjustment code as per the practice management system, and then the correct charge entered.

3. A note of explanation regarding the charge correction will be documented in the notes section of the patient's account to include the staff's initials and date.

4. Charge corrections may occur due to the following errors:
   - Charge posted to the incorrect account
   - Incorrect amount of charge
   - Duplicate posting
   - Incorrect charge code and fee
   - Other

5. Charge corrections will be audited at least monthly by the billing manager to ensure compliance with this policy and procedure.

CHAPTER 8

Pothole 6
The Claims Management Process

The claims management process is the translation of all the work completed earlier in the revenue cycle into a standardized document known as the "claim form." The claim form outlines the services for which the payer is supposed to pay the physician, the charges for those services, and the supporting information required by the payer to adjudicate the claim. In order to receive payment, the medical practice must submit claims in a timely manner and with all of the information precisely as the payer requires it. Proactively managing the claims process leads to improved revenue outcomes for your medical practice.

In this chapter, we cover:

- Claims clearinghouses
- Electronic claims submission
- Claim review and scrubbing
- Tracking and resolving claim edits
- Claim filing deadlines
- Suspended claims
- Secondary claims
- Real-time claims adjudication
- Payer Websites

A claim is a request-for-payment form that payers have agreed to accept and use to adjudicate services rendered by health care providers. In the past, medical practices were required to manually record charges on a standard claim form and submit this written form to the payer. Today, medical practices post the charges to the patients' accounts in the practice management system, and the system generates a claim form known as the CMS-1500. The right information must be recorded in each field consistent with the requirements by the Health Insurance Portability and Accountability Act (HIPAA) and by each payer. The claims can be printed and mailed to a payer or transmitted electronically. The electronic transmission can be directed to a payer or through a clearinghouse. At what may be multiple steps along the way, quality review of the claims takes place and claim edits are worked to ensure that, to the extent possible, a clean claim is submitted in order to successfully negotiate each step along its journey to the payer.

Whether transmitted on paper or electronically, a medical practice can submit claims as often as the practice elects. Most medical practices batch their claims, combining the most recent date of service with rebills and secondary claims (further defined below), and submit them daily.

REBILLS

Rebills are claims that are resubmitted because there was an error on the first submission. With a rebill, the medical practice requests a reconsideration of the original claim, or it has discovered that the original claim was never received by the payer and thus must be resubmitted. Rebills are different from appeals (discussed in Chapter 12: The Denial Management Process) because a rebill involves resubmitting a claim accompanied by no additional explanation or supporting documentation.

SECONDARY CLAIMS

Secondary claims are claims that are submitted to secondary payers. This occurs when the patient has a second insurance carrier in addition to a primary insurance carrier, and the medical practice agrees to submit a claim to the patient's secondary payer after it has received the allowed portion of the payment from the primary payer.

The primary payer — for example, Medicare — either indicates on the explanation of benefits (EOB) that the claim should be printed and submitted to the secondary payer, or the primary payer automatically "crosses over" the claim. (An EOB is the payer form that accompanies the payment. On this form, important information is recorded regarding payments, denials, adjustments, and reasons for particular actions taken by the payer. We discuss EOBs further in Chapter 10: The Payment and Denial Posting Process.)

The payers can automatically cross over claims because they maintain a database with information regarding their beneficiaries' coverage. If a beneficiary is listed with a secondary insurance in their database, they automatically transfer the residual financial responsibility to the secondary payer they have on file. Not all payers maintain such a database, and the database is not always correct. There are times when your medical practice must submit a claim for the residual financial responsibility to the secondary payer. In this case, the secondary payer requires a copy of the primary payer's EOB. If your medical practice is required to submit the secondary claim, you must attach the primary EOB to it. Depending on the payer, the EOB is mailed or transmitted electronically. This is most frequently performed immediately after the receipt of the primary EOB because that is the point at which the primary EOB is available for duplication and attachment to the secondary claim. You print the secondary claim, attach the primary EOB, and submit the documents to the secondary payer together.

If the primary payer automatically crosses over the claim to the secondary payer, in what is termed an "automatic crossover," the medical practice does not need to generate a secondary claim because the primary payer has already sent it to the second payer. The relationship between the primary and secondary payer is referred to as the coordination of benefits (COB). It can be complex and may require communication with both payers to determine which is considered the primary carrier and which is considered the secondary carrier. Some patients maintain tertiary coverage, and this third insurance payer must also be considered in the journey to get paid.

CLAIM EDITS

Whether you submit the claims manually or electronically or whether the claims are initial submissions, rebills, or secondary claims, the billing staff should review the information on the claim to ensure its accuracy. If there is a concern about the accuracy of the information that is being submitted, the claim should be held or suspended until it is corrected. The billing staff are alerted to potential claim errors by conducting a manual review of the claim or by deploying technology to assist in evaluating whether claims comply with the payer rules. The software that is used to identify "problem" claims is often referred to as a "charge scrubber" or "claims scrubber," which we discuss in Chapter 7: The Charge Entry Process; more information is provided in Chapter 18: Leveraging Technology to Enhance the Revenue Cycle. A clearinghouse will also edit claims and report on any claims that have inaccurate or missing information. Some clearinghouses may just review your claims for missing fields; others have more robust editing tools. Your medical practice must correct and resubmit the claims that do not pass this edit process. Although there is work involved if a claim must be corrected at this stage, it is much better to work a claim before the payer adjudicates it. If a claim is denied, the delay is at least 30 to more than 100 days, and the cost to appeal a denial is considerably greater than working a claim edit.

The payer claims process varies from company to company, but all payers follow key steps to process their claims. This process, which is referred to as the "adjudication" process, is described in Figure 8.1.

FIGURE 8.1 ■ Payer Claims Adjudication Process

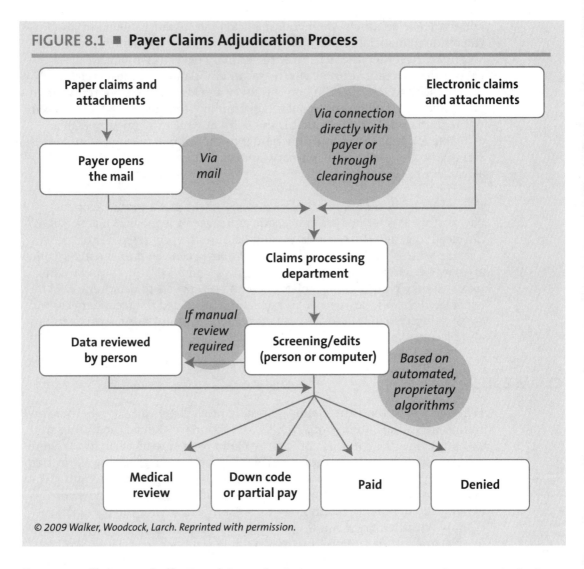

© 2009 Walker, Woodcock, Larch. Reprinted with permission.

To ensure efficient and effective claims submission processes, we present proven strategies to enhance your revenue cycle.

ADVANCED PRACTICES: THE CLAIMS PROCESS

Submit Claims on a Daily Basis

Your medical practice should generate and submit claims on a daily basis. If you submit them once a week, it delays your payments by one to four days. Over time, this delay may significantly impact your cash flow.

Monitor Claim Filing Deadlines

Claims must be filed in a timely fashion, and the claim filing deadlines vary by payer. Currently, most payers maintain 45- to 90-day filing deadlines from the date of service. That is, the payer requires that the claim for payment be submitted no later than 45 to 90 days after the service is provided. Based on current guidelines, the submission of Medicare claims ranges from 15 to 27 months, as determined by the date of service. For services rendered January 1 through September 30, the submission must be made by the end of the following calendar year; for services rendered October 1 through December 31, the submission must be made by the end of the second calendar year. If the date of service is February 1, 2010, for example, the filing deadline is December 31, 2011. If the date of service is November 1, 2010, the filing deadline is December 31, 2012. Most Medicaid plans follow Medicare guidelines. Make sure you know the initial claim submission filing deadline and the appeals filing deadline for all of your payers. Some states have passed legislation that requires payers to extend their claim filing timelines to six months. Your medical practice's revenue cycle performance will be stronger if you stay current on legislation that affects billing and claims submission.

Submit Electronic Claims

Payers are installing more sophisticated technology that lets you submit claims electronically. This saves the medical practice costs and typically reduces the turnaround time for payment of the claim. Figure 8.2 demonstrates the amount of money a medical practice can save by switching from paper claims to e-claims.

FIGURE 8.2 ■ From Paper to E-claims

If you process 15,000 claims per year, you can save $1.70 per claim!

- $174 claim forms (six boxes @ $29 each)
- $120 envelopes (six boxes @ $20 each)
- $600 for 600 long-distance calls to payers
- $1,260 on 3,000 stamps @ $.42 each (five claims/envelope)
- $400 supplies (ink, pens, electricity, overhead)
- $22,880 salaries (20 hours per week @ $22/hour for salary and benefits)

Total savings for 15,000 claims? $25,434.

© 2009 Walker, Woodcock, Larch. Reprinted with permission.

America's Health Insurance Plans (AHIP) reports that the frequency of electronic submission of health insurance claims has more than tripled in the last decade. AHIP also reports that electronic claims are less costly to process than paper claims and that electronic claims are processed faster than paper claims by the payers. The survey finds that 69 percent of electronic claims are processed in seven days and only 29 percent of paper claim are processed within that seven-day window.[1]

---

[1] AHIP Center for Policy and Research: *An Updated Survey of Health Care Claims Receipt and Processing Times,* May 2006.
http://www.ahipresearch.org/pdfs/PromptPayFinalDraft.pdf

CMS instituted a deadline by which e-claims are expected for all Medicare and Medicaid services; new participating providers have no choice but to submit claims electronically. Many other payers are developing systems to accept e-claims. Tool 13 is an e-claims checklist to help you avoid e-claim rejections.

TOOL 13   **E-claims Checklist**

Sending e-claims is cheaper than sending paper claims. These e-claims also get paid faster, but you need to avoid data errors. Some of the most frequent problems found in e-claims are the easiest to correct. This tool provides you with some of the most frequent reasons e-claims are rejected; use this as a checklist to evaluate the accuracy of your e-claims.

■ **Name mismatch:** This means the name was not entered exactly as written on the insurance card. The name on the claim must exactly match what is on the card, which is what the payer has on record.

■ **Gender mismatch:** This indicates a discrepancy in the gender associated with the records of the payer and what was entered on the claim.

■ **Payer Insurance Certificate Number mismatch:** Verify that the number on the patient's insurance card exactly matches the number on the claim. Include all numbers/alphas (prefix/suffix).

■ **Invalid assignment agreement:** Indicate your assignment choice – either assigned or non-assigned.

■ **NPI missing:** National Provider Identifier (NPI) is not included on the claim for the provider and referring physician.

© 2009 Walker, Woodcock, Larch. Reprinted with permission.

Keep Updated on Claim Formats

If your medical practice's physicians participate with payers, you must stay current on changes from the payers regarding how they require claims to be submitted. Participating with payers means that your physicians have agreed to a contractual relationship with the payer. Payers communicate claim-specific changes in their newsletters and e-mails. Be sure to keep updated on these changes and communicate them to the appropriate staff involved in charge entry and claims generation.

At minimum, you should establish "required fields" to ensure that all information requested by the payer is provided. By integrating a required field, the claim is not released until the field is properly populated. Many payers can provide you with their claims specifications. There are different field requirements for paper claims and e-claims, so be sure to ask for both formats. HIPAA was intended to standardize the electronic format of claims, but the paper-claim formats continue to vary by payer.

Know Your State's Regulations about a Clean Claim

Many states now have laws or regulations in place that help medical practices succeed in getting paid what they are due. One area that is still evolving is the definition of a clean claim. In some state statutes, the definition of a clean claim is so vague that it provides little help to a medical practice. Contact your state Medical Group Management Association (MGMA) or state medical society for information on your state's laws and regulations related to the submission of clean claims.

Make Wise Use of Your Clearinghouse

Many medical practices submit some if not all of their claims through a clearinghouse. A clearinghouse serves as a data broker between the medical practice and the payer. Typically, the medical practice submits claims electronically to the clearinghouse, and the clearinghouse is responsible for routing the claims to the payer. It is critical that you receive acknowledgment from the clearinghouse and the payer that your claims were received. Most clearinghouses have filters that evaluate the claims for missing information. The clearinghouse lists any rejected claims on an error report and sends the report to the medical practice. From your payer and/or your clearinghouse, you should receive acknowledgment that:

- Claims sent from your practice management system were received by the clearinghouse;
- Claims sent from the clearinghouse were received by the payer; and
- Claims received by the payer were accepted into the payer's adjudication system.

At each of these stages, you should receive a number and list of claims not received and the reason. In your contracts with your clearinghouse and payers, you should also require these acknowledgment reports. Figure 8.3 provides an example of these necessary acknowledgment reports.

Although the clearinghouse filtering process allows medical practices to correct claims before submitting them to the payers, the filters can't identify every payer's requirement. Errors and mistakes are inevitable. Recent technological advances have enhanced the ability of medical practices to submit clean claims. Typically the electronic clearinghouse — and, increasingly, applications for the practice management software used by the practice — includes "scrubbing" software to identify problems with claims *before* they are transmitted to the payer for adjudication. These pre-adjudication claim edits help you increase the number of clean claims you submit and thus increase the percentage of claims paid correctly the first time.

In addition to using a clearinghouse, many medical practices now relay claims directly to payers. This saves money, but it is currently limited to those payers that have the technology to accept a direct transmission.

FIGURE 8.3 ■ The Electronic Claim Journey

	# of Claims	Date	Notes
Claims to clearinghouse	100	June 15	
Clearinghouse acknowledges receipt	100	June 16	
Clearinghouse sends claims to payer	100	June 16	
Payer acknowledges receipt	98	June 18	Two claims hit error report — insurance # doesn't match payer format
Payer acknowledges claims hit adjudication system	92	June 20	Six claims rejected — cannot identify patient

Practice Tips: The electronic claim journey outlined above is sometimes not known by the practice. This practice needs to receive three acknowledgment reports to track this claim batch, as well as two error/rejected claims lists. Not all clearinghouses and payers provide timely acknowledgment of reports. Few provide error/rejection reports with much detail other than number of claims received. In this scenario, you know that eight claims will never be paid unless you take action to correct the claim and resubmit it. This is one of the reasons payers state, "we don't have a record of your claim" – and they don't in this case.

© 2009 Walker, Woodcock, Larch. Reprinted with permission.

Review Your Relationship with Your Clearinghouse

Many clearinghouses set their fees based on the number of claims that a medical practice transmits. Cost savings may be realized by pursuing a set fee for clearinghouse activity, or by transmitting claims directly to payers. In addition to considering a change in your clearinghouse fees, add a penalty clause in case the clearinghouse does not perform its functions within certain agreed-upon parameters. If all the claims are going through the clearinghouse, all of the medical practice's revenue could be disrupted if the clearinghouse has a glitch in its processes. Obviously we'd like the clearinghouse to share the risk and be prepared to provide the medical practice with compensation if cash flow is disrupted for more than a certain number of days.

When considering your partnership with clearinghouses, determine whether the clearinghouses can provide functionality your medical practice may not be able to receive elsewhere. Some clearinghouses offer sophisticated edits to medical practices that have practice management systems that cannot provide that functionality.

Conduct a Quality Review of Claims

Some better-performing medical practices find that printing and reviewing each claim (or charge ticket, if reviewed prior to keying) before its submission are cost effective. Although resource-intensive, reviewing the information allows a staff member to recognize and fix problems that would likely result in claim denials. The person assigned to review the claim is typically knowledgeable in payer requirements. While the review of the information takes time, each claim denial that can be avoided represents a gain of approximately $15 (see Chapter 2, Figure 2.6 for the calculation of the cost to work a denied claim). In addition, the cash flow for the medical practice is significantly improved by avoiding the denial.

Institute an Edit Function for Paper Claims

Consider a manual edit function for paper claims to ensure they are accurate and complete before they are mailed. In the past, many medical practices focused on the time it took to get claims out. But now, medical practices need to focus on the completeness and accuracy of the claim. As we noted earlier, it takes less time and money to correct the error before the claim is released than to fix the error after the claim has been processed, adjudicated, and denied by the payer.

Another benefit to this review of paper claims is to reduce the number of claims that are submitted on paper. Review your paper claims, asking, "Why does this claim have to go on paper?" Then determine how you can submit it electronically. Many medical practices are not aware that some payers will accept attachments, documentation, and authorizations electronically or via fax, without sending a paper claim. Ask each of your top payers about which claims need to be sent on paper. Some medical practices follow payer claim processes that are outdated or they duplicate the work performed via automatic crossovers, both of which add extra work to the billing office and also result in duplicate billing to the payer, which can lead to business risk.

Investigate Scrubbing Software

Investigate scrubbing software for your practice management system. Scrubbing software allows your practice to apply pre-adjudication edits to the claims, giving you the chance to identify and correct the error before the claim is submitted. Your medical practice's denial data is an excellent source of edits that need to be added to the scrubbing software. If your current practice management system does not have such an application, then you need to designate more "required" fields for charge entry to ensure that the claim is complete before it is transmitted. Stand-alone software that requires double key entry (once into the software for scrubbing and once into the practice management system for charge submission) is also available. Although integration with your existing system is preferable, catching the errors may be well worth the extra keying. As these tools continue to evolve, edits will include not only the procedure and diagnosis coding rules, but also medical necessity algorithms, bundling edits, and medical review and coverage policies for national payers. Make sure the scrubbing system is updated at least quarterly to stay current with payer requirements. You want a claim scrubber system that allows you to customize it to individual payer rules. In addition to edits that notify staff of errors, you also want your claim scrubber system to alert you to possible missed revenue opportunities.

Finally, some medical practices recognize the value of claim scrubbing but cannot find an appropriate automated solution. Therefore, they assign someone the responsibility of manually reviewing all claims. (For example, Medicare claims are reviewed by the Medicare account representative.) This ensures that problems with the claims are identified and corrected before the claim is submitted. Tool 14 is a checklist you can use to help you ensure a clean claim.

TOOL 14   Clean Claims Checklist

This tool is a checklist to ensure your claims are clean. Completing a clean claims checklist, building pre-adjudication edits into your practice management system, and making maximum use of required fields help you submit a clean claim, requiring less rework and improving the timeliness of reimbursement.

The following are common reasons that claims are not "clean":

- Assignment: "Accept assignment" box checked inappropriately.
- Authorization: Claim form did not list the mandatory authorization number or referral form is missing.
- CPT®:   Invalid CPT® code.
- Contract number: Subscriber's contract number missing or invalid.
- Dates: Missing or incorrect dates, such as admission and discharge dates, duplicate dates of service for same procedure code, or dates of first symptom.
- Diagnosis: Diagnosis code missing or invalid.
- Group number: Missing group number on claim form.
- ID number: Physician's national provider identification (NPI) number missing on claim form.
- Insurance information: Subscriber's name, gender, Social Security number, group, and/or plan number missing or invalid.
- Modifiers: Missing modifier on procedure that mandates usage of one.
- Patient information: Patient's gender missing or invalid, patient's address invalid, birth date missing.
- Place: Place of service incorrect.
- Provider: Provider (physician) information missing or incorrect (for example, NPI).
- Referral: Referring physician's name and/or NPI missing on claim form.
- Service type: Type of service listed incorrectly on claim form.

© 2009 Walker, Woodcock, Larch. Reprinted with permission.

Track and Resolve Claim Edits

Whatever method your medical practice chooses for reviewing the claim information prior to its submission, you should develop a protocol that outlines the steps and the extent to which changes or corrections of problems should be undertaken. For example, if there is a coding problem, how and to what extent does the physician who rendered the service need to be involved? Maintaining these protocols in writing ensures that you consider all aspects of the problem and outline the process steps to be taken.

We recommend that you implement a claims scrubber tool, preferably integrated into your practice management system. If you track and resolve claims that are "suspended or edited" in a timely manner, this tool helps you reach your goal of getting claims paid the first time.

Your claims scrubber system creates reports to provide information regarding the number of claims edited and the dollar value of the pending claims. Make sure the report also tracks when the claim hits an edit and how long it has been sitting unresolved. You want to measure the lag time associated with an unresolved claim. For claims that are suspended (often termed "pended") in order to correct an error, compare the date they are suspended to the date that they are released. Untimely resolution of these edits is another delay in getting paid for the service already provided.

Look at the claim edit report example in Figure 8.4. The report offers a snapshot of a medical practice that has a significant challenge. A significant number of this medical practice's claims are "dirty." In the first 30 days, 52 claims require resolution. Those 52 claims, worth $7,800, are not going to be paid. Not only will the medical practice lose the interest on that money, but the medical practice may also be forced to write off the accounts because it missed timely filing deadlines. In total, this medical practice has 89 accounts, worth $13,350, suspended because the claims are not clean.

FIGURE 8.4 ■ Claims Edit Report Example

Reason	0–30 days Count	0–30 days Dollars	31–60 days Count	31–60 days Dollars	>60 days Count	>60 days Dollars	Total Count	Total Dollars
Coding	15	$2,250	4	$600	1	$150	20	$3,000
Provider Numbers	25	$3,750	20	$3,000	10	$1,500	55	$8,250
Referring Physician	12	$1,800	2	$300	0	$0	14	$2,100
TOTAL	52	$7,800	26	$3,900	11	$1,650	89	$13,350

© 2009 Walker, Woodcock, Larch. Reprinted with permission.

Resolving claim edits can be simple or complex. Depending on the originating cause, your staff can resolve an edit in five minutes or it might take several days or weeks if the resolution depends on others in your medical practice.

Let's walk through several edit scenarios to familiarize ourselves with how to resolve pending edits.

Scenario 1 — Coding edits

Charge entry staff enter data from the charge ticket. Claim scrubbing software determines if a modifier is needed. These edits appear on an electronic work file for the coder, and they are reviewed and resolved within a day.

The charge is entered without a CPT® code and, obviously, hits an edit due to "missing CPT® code." The coder reviews the medical record and has a question for the physician about his/her documentation. The coder is not ready to assign the CPT® code. This edit will be resolved when the coder hears back from the physician. Once the physician responds, the coder keys the code and forwards the charge onto the charge entry team so it can be entered and tracked.

Scenario 2 — Provider number edits

Before a new physician joins your medical practice, it is important to complete all payer credentialing applications prior to the physician's arrival. Even though you have successfully submitted all of the required applications and supporting paperwork, you may still experience payer delays in enrolling a provider. The enrollment process of some payers may take six months or longer. These delays cause many medical practices' claims to sit on edit lists for a long time. (Note: your contract with the payer dictates the extent to which your practice can bill for a physician's services before he/she is successfully enrolled.) When the credentialing paperwork is finished and approved by the payer, the missing data are entered into the system and the claim is released for payment.

Scenario 3 — Referring physician edits

Scrubbing systems can store complex edits. You can store payer rules, such as which medical service requires the referring physician to be noted on the claim form. In your claim scrubbing system, you can define the procedure codes by payer that require a referring physician. When a charge is entered with those data elements, the claims scrubber looks to see if the referring physician is indeed on the claim. If not, it suspends the claim and reports the reason as "missing referring physician." In many practice management systems, your staff can see these edits in real time as they enter the charge (and then can enter the referring physician information if they have it), or they can continue on and the edit will hit a work file to be queued for action by the appropriate staff at a later time.

Referring physician information is most often stored in the patient's medical record. Thus, staff need to query the record electronically, or one of the medical records, billing, or practice site staff need to be assigned to review the manual record and resolve these edits. As staff enter the referring physician information on the claim, the claim automatically clears and queues up for the next electronic claim submission.

Assign Edit Work Files for Timely and Effective Resolution

Opinions differ on the best way to assign claim edit work files. Like other areas of this book, we recommend that you look at the most efficient workflow for your medical practice. Analyze your edits to determine where the information is located that the claim needs and assign it to that work area. Train the staff on resolving the edits that they are assigned. Each edit category requires a written protocol on how it will be resolved; include expectations regarding who is responsible for the work, as well as the time frame of resolution. Maintaining these protocols in writing ensures that you consider all aspects of the problem, that staff understand their role in the process, and that all of the required process steps are taken to resolve the claim edits before the claims are submitted to the payer.

Resolve the Root Cause of Claim Edits

Reduce the number of claims hitting an edit. Track the originating cause of the most frequent errors. Work with staff to make changes to process performance to prevent future occurrences. Many claim edits are due to errors or omissions in the data that populate your claim forms. Your provider's name, the location of the service provided, and other required data elements are entered at the charge entry process and then need to appear on the claim form in the correct formats and fields. In order to reduce your claim edits, it is important that your staff understand the basic claim fields. When your staff select the site at which the service was performed in the practice management system, for example, it must have the correct "place-of-service" code assigned to it.

Reduce the Time Frame During which Claims are Suspended

As demonstrated on the Claims Edit Report Example presented in Figure 8.4, it is important to measure how long the claims queue in your system without being released to the clearinghouse or the payer. As shown in the previous scenarios, some edits can be resolved in a couple of minutes and your claims are ready to be released. Others require more work and time. Initially when you implement a claims scrubber, you may be surprised how many edits you receive each day. Although edits may be frustrating, they point out the claims that will be denied by the payer and give you the opportunity to fix them. Identifying these claim errors and omissions reduces costly rework on the back end, as well as the days to initial payment.

Establishing a performance target for the volume and age of claim edits ensures your medical practice applies the necessary resources to resolving all edits. We recommend that edits be worked as they are identified with no edits aging past one week. If you have edits that are beyond your staff's control (for example, a credentialing delay), exclude these from your target. If your edits sit for a long time, monitor your claims' timely filing limit requirements to ensure that these deadlines are not missed.

Work Suspended Claims

Many practice management systems are able to hold or suspend a claim to obtain additional information or to verify the accuracy of information. Your medical practice should regularly track, resolve, and release accounts put into this category. Establish thresholds to identify the number of claims in suspense, as well as the dollar value of those claims. Your billing manager should monitor accounts in this category.

When a billing staff member leaves the medical practice, be sure to check any accounts that may have been suspended and assigned to the departed staff member. Reassign these so they are worked in a timely fashion.

Be Efficient in Processing Secondary Claims

Process as many secondary insurance claims as automatic crossovers as possible to avoid the need for manual intervention. If the payers do not permit crossovers, or if the secondary volume is otherwise high, scan all of your EOBs into a database that is accessible through your practice management system or by toggling to it from the employees' desktops. Easy access at staff workstations to print EOBs or automatically attach them to an electronic claim allows secondary claims to be processed more efficiently. You can achieve this process through a document management system.

Some payers allow electronic submission of secondary claims. In order to provide the secondary payer with required information, you often need to modify your practice management system's claim specifications so that additional information can be provided on that claim form (this eliminates the need to send a copy of the primary EOB) or invest in a software product that can automate the secondary claim process.

Implement Real-time Claims Adjudication

Some payers now offer real-time claims adjudication (RTCA). RTCA enables a medical practice to bill for a service before the patient leaves the office and to receive a fully adjudicated response back — *at the time of service*. With this technology, a provider can print out the response, displaying total and allowable charges, as well as the patient's financial responsibility (co-insurance, deductible, and copayment). Providers can be certain of the amount the patient should pay at the time of service. Some medical practices utilize their own practice management system with a designated claims clearinghouse to accomplish this; others use payers' Websites.

Even though medical practices want to reduce the time to be paid, RTCA currently has limitations. For some payers, the practice staff need to manually key charges into the payer's entry screen. This requires the medical practice to key all information related to the services twice — to the payer's Website and to the medical practice's practice management system — including registration and charge data. In addition, the charge must be ready to be submitted as the patient departs the medical practice. Figure 8.5 depicts the RTCA process and contrasts it with the more traditional claims process.

FIGURE 8.5 ■ Real-time Claims Adjudication (RTCA)

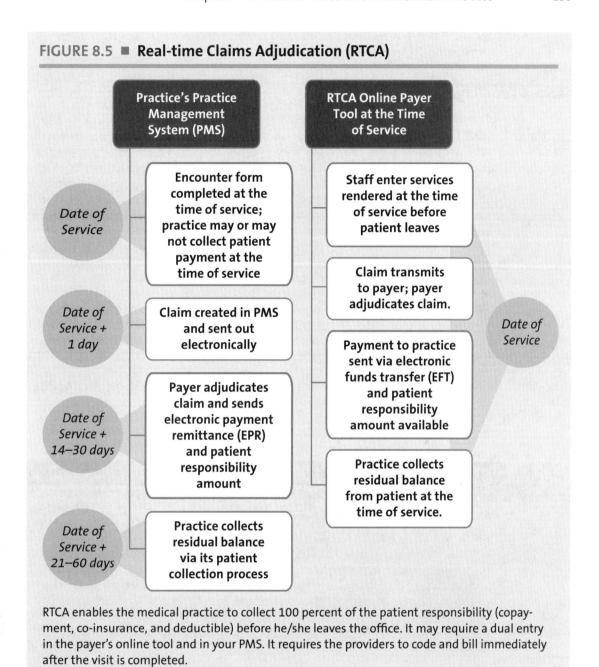

RTCA enables the medical practice to collect 100 percent of the patient responsibility (copayment, co-insurance, and deductible) before he/she leaves the office. It may require a dual entry in the payer's online tool and in your PMS. It requires the providers to code and bill immediately after the visit is completed.

© 2009 Walker, Woodcock, Larch. Reprinted with permission.

When implementing RTCA, your medical practice may need to adjust staffing as there is more work involved in front-end billing and less work in back-end billing. Medical practices that have embraced RTCA realize significant gains. They experience increased collections from patients because they can tell the patient exactly what is owed before the patient leaves the medical practice. Medical practices have also had reduced days in receivables outstanding (DRO) for the RTCA payers. (Find additional information about RTCA in Chapter 18: Leveraging Technology to Enhance the Revenue Cycle.)

Access Your Payer Websites

The Websites developed by your payers offer a wealth of information. In the past, you likely maintained a copy of the provider manual and three-ring binders full of payer newsletters. Now, everything you need is on payers' Websites. In addition to general information found in the provider manual, you can also find patient and claim-specific information that can eliminate many telephone calls. Insurance eligibility and claim status are offered at all major payer Websites. The functionality that a billing staff needs from a payer's Website requires an application to gain access to the site. Assign a manager or supervisor to apply for access on behalf of the medical practice. Managers should request login and password information for all applicable staff members from all payers.

Assign responsibility to a staff member to review all major payers' Websites for new information and/or new functionality on at least a monthly basis. Communicate findings to the billing office manager, and disseminate new information to all impacted staff members through electronic mail or during a staff meeting.

The claims management process is an important function in the revenue cycle. Submitting timely, accurate claims establishes the groundwork for receiving payment on the first claim submission — without being forced to dedicate additional resources to work claim denials.

STAFF WORKLOAD RANGES

The staff workload ranges for the claims process that we typically expect are provided below. The ability to perform within these ranges may vary due to internal practice-specific factors (such as facility layout, telephone system, and practice management system). Note that the workload ranges reflect *quantitative* performance levels. Note that *qualitative* performance — accuracy, completeness, appropriateness, and quality of these functions — should also be measured. When issues of quantity versus quality arise, we strongly recommend that quality be emphasized, even if the performance workload ranges for a particular function need to be relaxed from these levels.

Staff Function	Transaction Time
Resolving pre-adjudication edits	2 to 10 minutes

Note: Institute these workload ranges only if accuracy can be assured in this time frame. If not, you may need to increase the time to perform the function in order to avoid mistakes.

LEADING PERFORMANCE INDICATORS

Use the following indicators to assess the performance of your claims management process. We refer to these measures as "leading" performance indicators. If your medical practice is successful in achieving these levels in the claims management process, you are on the correct path to optimizing your revenue cycle.

Claims submission:	Daily
Percentage of claims billed electronically:	> 90 percent
Meeting claims filing deadlines:	100 percent
Date of charge entry to date of claim release:	0 to 72 hours
Resolution of pre-adjudication edits:	0 to 48 hours
Number of claims pending on edit/suspense report:	< 1 percent of claims

Note: Institute these lag times only if accuracy can be assured in this time frame. If not, you may need to increase the lag times to evaluate and remove errors.

© 2009 Walker, Woodcock, Larch. Reprinted with permission.

THE CLAIMS MANAGEMENT DIAGNOSTIC TOOL

The claims management diagnostic tool below helps you and your medical practice ensure that the process, people, technology, and quality required for effective claims management processes are in place in your medical practice.

Process:

1. Are claims being submitted on a daily basis?
2. What happens to claims that drop to paper?
3. Do you receive acknowledgment and rejection reports from payers and clearinghouses?
4. Do you review or "edit" your claims prior to submission?
5. Do you have a process for resolving edits in a timely manner?
6. Do you have a system in place to monitor the number, type, and source of edits on a daily, weekly, and monthly basis?

People:

1. Who is responsible for submitting claims?
2. Does the staff know how to identify and correct the claim edits so that claims are submitted?
3. Do you have enough staff dedicated to working the edits?

Technology:

1. Are you submitting claims electronically to all payers that accept this format?
2. Do you directly submit claims to payers that allow it?
3. Does your practice management system hold the entire batch of claims awaiting edits or does it discriminate and only hold claims that have been placed in suspense?

Quality:

1. Do you maintain documentation of claims submission to timely filing denials?
2. Do you follow up on open claims to ensure that your payer received the claims?
3. Are automatic crossover claims submitted correctly, ensuring no duplicate claim submission?

POLICIES AND PROCEDURES

At the end of each chapter, we provide policies and procedures to assist you in developing a policy and procedure manual for your medical practice. Below are two policies specific to the claims management process.

Policy 18: Timely Submission of Claims

Policy 19: Billing Primary and Secondary Insurance Claims

POLICY 18: TIMELY SUBMISSION OF CLAIMS

Policy:

Payers will be billed in a timely manner in order to ensure timely payment for services rendered.

Procedures:

1. Payers will be billed via electronic claims process when available.

2. Claims that cannot be billed electronically due to payer's inability to accept e-claims or other requirements such as the need for attachments or for other reasons will be billed using the standard CMS-1500 claim form.

3. Claims will be generated and forwarded to payers on a daily basis to expedite reimbursement.

4. Every effort will be made to eliminate errors in registration, charge coding, and charge entry to ensure timely reimbursement. Pre-adjudication claim edits will be worked in real time or via edit lists within 48 hours.

POLICY 19: BILLING PRIMARY AND SECONDARY INSURANCE CLAIMS

Policy:

It is the policy of the medical practice to submit clean claims to payers in a timely manner and to receive expedient payment for services rendered to their beneficiaries.

Procedures:

1. Prior to submitting claims, charges will be reviewed automatically or manually for accuracy. Every effort will be made to eliminate errors in registration, procedure and diagnosis coding, and charge entry to ensure timely reimbursement. During the review process, any discrepancies will be resolved immediately. If necessary, the provider rendering the service for which the charge is being billed will be contacted in person, via a standard form or an internal e-mail communication regarding the charge. Providers will have three business days to respond to questions about charges.

2. Following the edit process, clean claims will be electronically sent on a daily basis.

3. Exception reports generated from the submission will be worked on a same-day basis.

4. Claims will not be suspended unless absolutely necessary. An electronic log of suspended claims will be maintained and monitored in order to ensure that they are resolved expediently.

5. The medical practice will submit secondary claims in the event that a patient maintains a secondary insurance policy and the primary insurance payer does not pay the full amount of the charge. The secondary insurance payer will be billed for the remainder of the balance. The medical practice will make best efforts to work with payers to cross over secondary claims automatically. If not, the primary explanation of benefits (EOB) will be flagged manually or electronically and submitted to medical practice staff to bill the secondary. Secondary claims will be submitted within 24 hours of notification of the responsibility of the secondary payer.

6. The full balance of primary and secondary claims submitted to payers with whom the medical practice does not participate will be transferred to patient responsibility at 45 days, or another time period for which the billing office may designate.

7. For services covered under a capitated plan, charges will be automatically adjusted by the practice management system. If a patient receives a service for which the patient is covered but which is not included in the capitation agreement, a claim will be sent to the payer. If a patient who is a beneficiary under a capitated plan receives a service that is non-covered or carved out under his/her policy, the charge will be the patient's responsibility and billed according to the medical practice's policies and procedures for patient billing.

CHAPTER 9

Pothole 7
The Patient Statement Process

Patients receive notification of the amount they owe on their account via patient statements, which are essentially invoices for payment. In reality, the party that truly owes the outstanding amount is the guarantor; however, by convention, we typically refer to this process as the patient statement process since the patient is often also the guarantor. Unlike claims that are usually sent electronically to payers, the patient statement process is conducted via the United States Postal Service (USPS). More recently, however, better-performing medical practices have initiated electronic submission of statements to patients through their Web portal or via other electronic means.

In this chapter, we discuss the following key issues involved in the patient statement process:

- Statement cycles
- Patient-friendly statements
- Online bill payment
- Dunning cycles and statement messages
- Returned mail

Statements are sent to inform patients of the status of their account and notify them of the amount that is outstanding and owed the medical practice by the patient. As we discussed in Chapter 3: The Patient Financial Clearance Process, the patient collection process should commence before the patient is seen. If all of the money owed the medical practice by the patient is collected at the time of service, then statements would not be necessary.

However, even for better-performing medical practices that optimize their face-to-face interactions with patients and maximize their time-of-service collections, there is typically a residual balance on a high percentage of patient accounts. Patients who have a financial responsibility after their insurance has paid or patients who have an insurance with which the medical practice does not participate often receive statements, as do patients who carry no insurance at all.

Thus, even with optimal time-of-service collections, a medical practice still needs a thoughtful, consistent patient statement process.

For a patient who has insurance that the medical practice accepts, a statement is sent to the patient after both the primary and secondary insurances have paid their portions of the bill. For a patient who owes the entire bill (they are not insured or their insurance does not cover the service), a statement is sent to the patient directly after services are rendered. (As discussed in Chapter 3, in either case, time-of-service collections efforts are encouraged to capture full or partial payment before the service is rendered.) The statement informs the patient of the activity that has occurred on the account and the account balance that is the patient's responsibility.

If your medical practice mails statements to patients each month for 12 months, accompanied by a series of letters and telephone calls, and then makes a decision to send the patient to the collection agency if payment has not been received, you're not investing wisely in your patient collections cycle. In addition to bearing a high cost, your patients learn that your practice tolerates long payment delays. In turn, your patients delay sending payment for as long as possible. Your medical practice also increases its cost to collect because statements and letters run at least $.75 each, and inbound and outbound billing-related telephone calls can cost more than $5.00 when factoring in staff time and resources.

Due to changing health plan designs, a greater portion of the amount owed your medical practice is patient responsibility, as a result of higher deductibles, co-insurance, and copayment levels. Thus, it is important for medical practices to analyze their patient statement process and determine opportunities to not only shrink the patient collections cycle to permit more timely payments (discussed in detail in Chapter 13: The Patient Collections Process), but also to reduce the cost of this back-end billing function.

To ensure an efficient and effective patient statement process, we present proven strategies to enhance your revenue cycle.

ADVANCED PRACTICES: THE PATIENT STATEMENT PROCESS

Tighten Your Statement Process

Historically, medical practices paid little attention to their patient statements. The majority of revenue was collected from payers, so patient collections was not given high priority. Although revenue from payers still constitutes the majority of the revenue stream of most medical practices, medical practices cannot afford to ignore patients' financial responsibility. Thus, better-performing medical practices scrutinize their statement process to ensure that outcomes and costs are optimized.

The majority of medical practices send three statements to patients, with many practices moving toward a two-statement cycle. Some medical practices are justifiable in extending their cycle by one or two statements, particularly if they have never had the opportunity to ask for payment from the patient at the point of care (for example, a pathologist). Otherwise, several contacts at the time of service, followed by three statements, enable a medical practice to optimize outcomes without spending too much money on the process. If a patient has been asked in person twice and via mail three times, for a total of five requests, and he/she still doesn't pay, a sixth request of the same ilk is not likely to elicit payment.

For more information on patient collection cycles, including statements, letters, and using a collection agency, see Chapter 13: The Patient Collections Process.

Adopt an Optimal Statement Process

Regardless of the patient collections cycle that your medical practice has adopted (involving some combination of statements, letters, and telephone calls), follow these recommendations regarding your patient statements:

- Send the statement as soon as it becomes the guarantor's responsibility. Statements are typically sent in a monthly cycle alphabetically by the patient's last name. So, for example, at set days of the month, various alpha ranges determine which patients are sent a statement. In contrast to waiting for the appropriate alpha cycle, which may consume an extra three weeks, drop the statement into the next cycle as soon as the patient payment is due.

- Note a specific due date on the statement, in contrast to stating "due in 30 days."

- Do not show an aging on the patient statement, for example, 30 days, 60 days, 90 days, and so forth. This implies that you will send statements for each of these time periods. The goal is to get paid with one statement if possible, not to encourage patients to simply watch the aging of the statement each month.

- Do not state "amount enclosed" with a blank box next to it for patients to populate the amount they are paying. State the full amount you expect them to pay rather than imply that you will accept a lower amount.

- Follow your dunning cycle with due diligence; if the dunning cycle indicates that the patient account may be sent to a collection agency if there is no response within 10 days, take action.

- Provide a telephone number for the patient to call; assign a staff member to answer it during all regular business hours.

- Establish a Web portal or e-mail address and publicize this avenue for patient billing inquiries.

- Offer the option for patients to submit their credit or debit cards on your statements.

Adopt Patient-Friendly Billing®

Patient-Friendly Billing®, an initiative to develop a statement that patients can easily read and understand, is supported by many professional organizations, vendors, and other health care management stakeholders. The Patient-Friendly

Billing® project strives to provide patients with financial communications that are clear, concise, correct, and patient friendly, which is generally defined as follows:[1]

Clear: Documents should be easily understood and clearly communicated.

Concise: Documents should contain the correct language and detail necessary to communicate the intended message.

Correct: Documents should be accurate and complete.

Patient friendly: Documents and processes should be patient-centric.

One of the easiest ways to determine if you need to improve your statements is to ask your staff and physicians for input and/or solicit a group of patients to read a statement and see how well they understand it. Commonly, the feedback is that statements are difficult to read and comprehend. In addition to delivering poor customer service, a poorly formatted and worded statement means your medical practice won't be paid.

Avoid "Information-only" Statements

Do not send statements to patients until the account becomes their responsibility. "Information-only" statements often confound patients. Not only does it increase the volume of telephone calls to your billing office and increase the volume (and cost) of statements, but it also results in patient confusion about when the payment is really due. For insured patients, send statements after your medical practice has billed their insurance and received payment or an indication from the payers that the patients are responsible for the charges. Avoiding "information-only" statements minimizes the cost to the medical practice related to statement mailing, the telephone inquiries associated with these informational statements, and the chance that patients won't pay because they didn't realize that the statement switched from "information only" to "patient payment due."

Send a Consolidated Statement

If your medical practice has multiple physicians, to include those practicing different specialties, send a single statement to your patients regardless of who renders the services. Not only is this the most cost-effective process, a single statement is patient-centric.

Maximize the Use of Statement Notes to Communicate with Patients

Use patient statement notes as a method to communicate with patients rather than initiating formal letters. This reduces the patient inquiries to the billing office, as well as billing expenditures. Refer to Tool 15 for tips to improve statement messages.

Incorporate dunning notices on statements to communicate with patients and to avoid the cost of mailing separate letters. Tool 15 provides samples of notices that can be placed on patient statements to enhance communication with patients regarding their balance due.

---

[1] Source: http://www.hfma.org/library/revenue/PatientFriendlyBilling/purpose.htm (accessed December 2, 2008).

TOOL 15   **Sample Statement Notes**

- Your insurance company has paid its share of your bill. This statement is for the amount due from you.
- In order to process your claim, your insurance company needs information. Please call the company or send us payment now.
- Account seriously overdue. Please send payment immediately.
- The bank has returned your check marked "insufficient funds." Please call today!
- Payment has been received from your insurance company. This amount remaining is now due from you.
- Can we help you? We can make payment arrangements with you to help clear up your balance. Please call or stop in today.
- Second notice: Your account is past due. Please pay today.

© 2009 Walker, Woodcock, Larch. Reprinted with permission.

Send a Statement to the Practice Executive

Create a fictitious "open" patient account with the practice executive's (or billing manager's) address so that he/she receives the same mailings as the patients receive. Then the executive can track the performance of statement mailing. It is a great way to be assured that your statement vendor is getting statements out in the mail according to their contract.

Show Patients How to Read the Patient Statement

Provide an instructional notice that explains how to read the patient statement. Present the notice to new patients; send it with the statement or include text on the bottom or back of statements to be sure patients understand it and to minimize questions about bills. If patients are likely to receive more than one bill (for example, a bill from the hospital), explain that fact in the beginning to minimize confusion (and possibly reduce telephone calls). Better-performing medical practices present samples of their bills — and the other parties' bills — to enhance patients' understanding of the process. If your medical practice has a Website, you can create a sample patient statement that explains the different parts of the patient statement.

Follow Up on All Patient Correspondence

Patients may respond to statements by paying the balance due, providing additional insurance information, giving credit/debit card information, or clarifying previous information provided via patient correspondence. Make sure that staff act on the patient's correspondence and incorporate the information provided by the patient into the patient's account in the practice management system before the next statement mailing cycle.

Be Distinctive in Your Final Letter

Print your final collections letter on orange paper and place it in an orange envelope that reads "FINAL NOTICE." Handwrite the patient's address, and place a stamp (that is, a postage stamp not a meter) on the envelope. This bright color signals an alarm, and is more effective at getting a patient's attention than a regular envelope and letter. Because this recommendation requires manual intervention, limit your efforts to high-dollar accounts if resources do not allow you to process all letters in this regard.

For more information on post-statement collection efforts, see Chapter 13: The Patient Collections Process.

Offer Online Bill Payment on Your Web Portal

Offer patients an online bill payment option. Gather permission and e-mail addresses in writing at the time of patient registration. When a balance becomes due, send the patient a link to your online bill payment system, and specifically, to his/her account. On your Website, establish a secure, encrypted, password-protected system so that patients can submit updates to their demographic or insurance information, be informed about their balances, set up payment plans and make payments on them, review and print the detail behind their balances, and make payments securely via credit cards. In addition, provide information on insurance, billing policies, a glossary of billing terms, answers to frequently asked questions, and resources to help patients manage their health care billing, including how they can assist in appealing an insurance denial. Be sure to have forms and materials that you post available in other languages, if applicable for your patient population.

Online bill payment allows patients to access their accounts 24 hours a day, seven days a week. During business hours, a special section can also provide patients with the option of chatting "live" with one of your billers.

Patients are interested in (and are increasingly demanding) online billing information and bill payment options due to the following advantages of this option:

It is convenient.
Patients can view account information on all recent encounters with open balances in a consolidated, simplified format. They can pay bills anytime and anywhere.

Patients can easily get help.
They can send an e-mail to ask about their account, update their mailing address, or update insurance information online. They can find answers to the most frequently asked questions about medical billing.

It is secure and private.
Access to financial account information is limited to authorized individuals. Sophisticated encryption technology protects account information and payments.

It empowers them.

As employers place more responsibility in the hands of employees to manage their own health care accounts, information about the cost of health care is increasingly important to patients. An online billing option can assist your medical practice in supporting your patients in the era of consumer-directed health care.

It reduces patient telephone calls.

Assuming a cost of $5.00 per call, any decrease in calls is significant from a financial perspective, as well as a customer service plus for patients.

It increases cash flow.

Patients who review their bills online are very likely to also pay them online. This results in reduced days in accounts receivable and improved cash flow.

Establish a Billing E-mail for Your Medical Practice

Establish an e-mail address specific to the billing office to correspond with patients regarding billing issues. Some medical practices send their patients one statement that notifies them of this resource and they conduct further correspondence — including reminders of patient payment plans and other functions — electronically. Correspondence with the patient is faster and the medical practice saves money. If your medical practice uses an e-mail address, establish protocols regarding who is responsible for responding to the e-mails and how often the e-mail account is checked.

Recognize Your Statement as a Useful Patient Communication Tool

Because statements are already being sent to patients, they can be a useful, cost-effective communication tool for medical practice matters. If you want to announce new office hours, new services, or other practice announcements, include a mailer in your statements. This offers a communication vehicle that has no additional cost to your medical practice (that is, you were already mailing the envelope).

Process Returned Mail Expeditiously

If statements (and other correspondence) are sent to patients at incorrect addresses, the mail is returned to your medical practice. Processing returned mail can be handled internally by your medical practice staff or outsourced to the vendor who is mailing statements and other mail for you. (Using a statement vendor can reduce the internal resources that are required, as well as allow your medical practice to capture savings through bulk mail.)

The reason for the returned mail is recorded on the front of the envelope by the USPS. Review returned mail soon after it arrives to ensure that the mail is not returned again in the following billing cycle (that is, 30 days). The longer the delay in attempting to locate a patient, the harder the chances are of collecting the balance due.

To prevent bad addresses, integrate an automated address verification process when you perform registration, as discussed in Chapter 3: The Patient Financial Clearance Process. The address verification process allows your medical practice to validate the address listed on the account as an existing address in the USPS database. Furthermore, the process can match the guarantor listed on the account in your practice management system to the current resident listed in the USPS database for that address.

Sign up — or contract with your vendor — to use USPS' "Address Service Requested" service.[2] Follow USPS guidelines regarding the marking on the envelope. Using the time frame defined by when the USPS receives an address change notification, statements sent to an address at which the patient no longer resides are treated as follows:

- *Months 1 through 12*: Piece forwarded and separate notice of new address provided;
- *Months 13 through 18*: Piece returned with new address attached; and
- *After month 18*: Piece returned with reason for non-delivery attached.

A nominal fee is charged for the service, but an account can be established at the post office by your medical practice or vendor to which the fees can be posted. The USPS invoices you for the fees incurred.

If your medical practice outsources the mailing of statements to a vendor, ensure that the vendor matches your patient statement addresses to the USPS database prior to statement submission.

To manage mail that is returned to the medical practice as undeliverable, collect cellular telephone numbers during patient registration. In the case of returned mail, dial all telephone numbers listed on the patients' account, including the cellular number. Cellular telephone numbers can be valuable in locating patients, as compared to an address or home telephone number. If this attempt to reach the patient fails, subscribe to a free or fee-based Internet skip-tracing search tool to identify correct contact information for these accounts. Alternatively, contract with your collection agency to manage this process for you. With access to sophisticated skip-tracing tools and up-to-date consumer databases, a collection agency is an effective partner in this laborious process.

Regardless of the outcome of your efforts, record an alert such as "bad address — correct address needed" on the patient's account. This permits staff to obtain updated information from the patient if he/she contacts the medical practice for any reason, such as to request an appointment or obtain a prescription renewal. Also suspend statement distribution to the invalid address.

Patient statements formulate the cornerstone of your patient collections process. Review the construction of your statements, as well as the nature of when and how they are distributed to improve patient collections and reduce your billing costs.

---

[2] See http://pe.usps.gov/text/qsg300/Q507d.htm#wp1020177 for more information about all USPS ancillary service endorsements. (Link active as of May 17, 2008.)

LEADING PERFORMANCE INDICATORS

Use the following indicators to assess the performance of your patient statement process. We refer to these measures as "leading" performance indicators. If your medical practice is successful in achieving these levels in the patient statement process, you are on the correct path to optimizing your revenue cycle.

Statement release time based on determination   0 to 24 hours
   of patient financial responsibility:

Statement suspended due for account   < 2 percent
   investigation (for example, bad address):

Investigate and resolve return mail: 0 to 48 hours

Mail returned due to bad address: < 2 percent

Note: Institute these lag times only if accuracy can be assured in this time frame. If not, you may need to increase the lag times to evaluate and remove errors.

© 2009 Walker, Woodcock, Larch. Reprinted with permission.

THE PATIENT STATEMENT DIAGNOSTIC TOOL

The patient statement diagnostic tool provided below helps you ensure that the process, people, technology, and quality required for an effective patient statement process are in place in your medical practice.

Process:

1. What is the medical practice's patient collection cycle? Is it in writing and consistently followed?
2. Can steps be taken to reduce the number of statements sent to patients by collecting more at the time of service?
3. Can steps be taken to reduce the number of statements, while maintaining the same results, by changing the collection cycle?
4. Is the medical practice tracking the reason for inbound calls related to statements to determine if there is an opportunity to improve the statements sent to patients?

People:

1. Are staff assigned to answer telephone calls and e-mails generated from patient statements?
2. Is there an adequate number of staff to handle these inquiries?
3. Do staff have the tools to research returned mail?

Technology:

1. Are statement addresses verified with the USPS prior to submission?
2. Are statements automatically generated when the party responsible for payment changes to the guarantor?
3. Is there a systematic review of accounts in which the statements have been suppressed?
4. Have online bill options been developed for patients?
5. Can patients initiate questions regarding their statements online to the medical practice?

Quality:

1. Are statements easy for patients to interpret and understand?
2. How many patient statements are returned due to incorrect address?
3. How many statements do patients receive? Is it consistent with your patient collections cycle?
4. Is there a quality review of the patient statements?

CHAPTER 10

Pothole 8
The Payment and Denial Posting Process

The payment and denial posting process is one of the most frequently underrated and overlooked processes in the revenue cycle. Posting a payment is highly complex, yet rarely do we see medical practices devoting appropriate resources to this function. It is not sufficient to simply post the money received in an accurate and timely fashion. Payment posters play a key role in the revenue cycle by determining contractual and non-contractual adjustments, posting denials, and recognizing underpayments by payers.

In this chapter, we cover:

- Reading an explanation of benefits (EOB)
- Payment posting methods
- Denial posting methods
- Electronic payment remittance (EPR) and electronic funds transfer (EFT)
- Remote deposit and lockbox services
- Account adjustments and their classifications
- Credit balances and refunds
- Prompt payment
- Payment variance analysis

PAYMENT POSTING ELEMENTS

Once a medical practice receives payment for services, it posts the payment to the patient's account. If it is an insurance payment and the EOB is transmitted to the practice manually, the medical practice enters the payment reported on the EOB to the patient's account. If the EOB is transmitted electronically, the information is included in the electronic payment remittance (EPR) and the payment is automatically posted to the practice management system. In this chapter, we refer to the information as being received on an EOB whether it is manually or electronically transmitted.

Regardless of how the payment is remitted, the payment should be posted to the charge that was billed. Posting payments to individual invoices, often referred to as line-item posting, is critical to ensure that all payments are accurate.

POSTING OF INSURANCE PAYMENTS

If the EOB is transmitted manually, the payment is typically made via check and attached or included in the envelope with the EOB. If the EOB is transmitted electronically, the check either arrives in an envelope or the funds are directly routed to the medical practice's bank account (assuming, of course, that the practice has set up the bank routing correctly) through an electronic funds transfer (EFT) process. To ensure that the payment process is automated, make sure your payment EOBs are being posted electronically and the money is deposited directly into your bank account. Most payers require an EPR and an EFT enrollment and approval process.

The payment and accompanying information (for example, the reason for a denial) are keyed or transmitted through an interface to the appropriate line item on the patient's account in the practice management system. In addition to providing payment information, the EOB includes the details of the payment — and what may be further due from the patient or another responsible party, such as a secondary payer. A skilled and experienced staff member needs to read and interpret the EOB. Each payer's EOB format is different, and each uses varying EOB remark codes.

See Figure 10.1 for a sample explanation of benefits. In this example, payment was denied because the payer regarded the appendectomy as included in the payment for a surgery that has been billed a few weeks prior. The example demonstrates how critical it is to understand the remark codes, be familiar with reimbursement policies, and have access to the patient's entire account. If any of this data is missing, the denial can easily translate into lost revenue.

The Health Insurance Portability and Accountability Act (HIPAA) Transaction and Code Sets regulation is intended to standardize EOB content. But at the writing of this book, medical practices continue to handle various, non-standard transaction code sets. (See Chapter 20: Regulations Impacting the Revenue Cycle for a further discussion of HIPAA.)

Until standardization of the EOB is achieved and/or the process is totally automated, employ a skilled payment poster. Payment posters need advanced education in insurance and account follow-up and should have direct access to the payers so they can ask questions about the EOB. Payment posting must be highly accurate, so your poster must be diligent. If your poster makes mistakes in posting payments or posting the accompanying EOB information, your medical practice may fail to appeal under-profile payments and/or fail to bill patients for balances due after their insurance has paid.

ELECTRONIC PAYMENT POSTING

As we already discussed, payment posting is a complex function. Interpreting EOBs and accurately posting payments requires skill and experience. More and more, payers are improving their information systems to offer EPR

FIGURE 10.1 ■ Sample Explanation of Benefits

ANYWHERE INSURANCE COMPANY
EXPLANATION OF BENEFITS

Please retain for future reference

Dr. Test MD/NPI 11111111

Page 1 of 1
Date printed: 6/1/10

Tax ID number: 11111111   Check number: 1111111111   Check amount: $0.00

Dr. Test, MD
One Hospital Drive
Anytown, Any State 55555

Patient name: Sally Jones

Patient account number: 112223333300

Patient ID number: 1110020020000

Relation: Mother
Member: Jane Jones
Group name: Acme Electric Company
Claim ID: EL6Q7U29I00

Diag:........................ 540.0
                            Acute appendicitis with generalized peritonitis
Service dates: 5/01/10
POS:........................ 21
Code: 44960
                            Appendectomy; for ruptured appendix with abscess or
                            generalized peritonitis
Submitted charges: $752.00
Negotiated amount: $395.00
Coinsurance amount: $77.00
Not payable:................. $395.00 *See Remarks*
Patient responsibility:........ $0
Payable amount:............. $0
Issued amount:.............. $0

For questions regarding this claim, call 800-666-6666.

TOTAL payment to Dr. Test: $0

Remarks: Service is bundled.

and EFT. Payers send an electronic file that the medical practice loads into its practice management system, and the payers transfer funds directly into the financial institution identified by the medical practice via EFT. Alternatively, medical practices can consider scanning technology to replace manual payment posting. The medical practice scans EOBs upon receipt, having already mapped EOB fields to payment posting screens/fields using optical character recognition technology. An electronic remittance advice (ERA) is the electronic equivalent of the EOB. To set up an ERA, contact the payer and follow its ERA application process.

Those medical practices that have converted to electronic posting realize real savings in staff time and reduced payment error rates. Both manual and electronic systems require a staff member to review any exceptions that are not posted or transferred. For more information on these technologies, see Chapter 18: Leveraging Technology to Enhance the Revenue Cycle.

POSTING OF PATIENT PAYMENTS

If it is a patient payment, posting of the payment is typically performed at the practice site (for those payments received at the time of service) or at the billing office (for those payments received via mail, e-mail transaction, or telephone). Some medical practices utilize a lockbox service to produce an electronic file of patient payments. The file is then loaded onto the practice management system and the patient payments are electronically posted, typically, in a "first in, first out" (FIFO) mode.

REMOTE DEPOSIT AND LOCKBOX SERVICES

Medical practices can use remote deposit and/or lockbox services to process payments. These services, which interface directly with the medical practice's bank account, are offered by financial institutions.

Remote deposit. Remote deposit, a service provided by banks since a 2004 federal law, the Check Clearing for the 21st Century Act, permitted such deposits, allows medical practices to accept checks at their site and scan a digital image of the check. The scanned image is then transmitted electronically to the bank, and the funds are deposited consistent with the amount on the check, essentially treating it as if it is a "live" check.

Lockbox. A lockbox service can be designated to receive payments paid to the medical practice. The lockbox service opens the mail, copies or scans the check and backup information, and deposits the check to the medical practice's bank. Remote deposit and lockbox services allow medical practices to improve cash flow by taking advantage of the float based on accelerating the deposit. Remote deposit and lockbox services also provide enhanced internal controls because the live check is immediately scanned, or it is received by the bank directly from another party, bypassing the billing office altogether. In addition, checks with insufficient funds, also known as bounced checks, can be discovered faster when processed through remote deposit. A further advantage for medical practices that use remote deposit and lockbox services is that they no longer must send an employee or a courier to take their checks to the bank. Avoiding couriering money to the bank by hand further reduces their internal control risk. (See additional information on internal controls in Chapter 16: Internal Controls for the Revenue Cycle.)

These services cost money, so you'll want to evaluate the return on investment carefully. Require an explanation for any delays that occur between the deposit and posting of the funds. If patients send in their payments in a timely manner, for example, but the payments aren't posted prior to the next set of statements being released, this creates another statement — and very likely a call from an angry patient. Most medical practices utilize remote deposit and/or lockboxes without any delays in the processes, but you need to choose a bank experienced in health care transactions.

ACCOUNT ADJUSTMENTS

When the medical practice receives a payment from a payer, the EOB includes notification of the "allowance" or "allowable" per procedure code. The allowance or allowable is what the payer has agreed the service is worth, not the fee that you charged. It is the total amount that you are allowed to collect from the payer *and* the patient.

Because the payer often requires the patient to pay for a portion of the service in the form of a copayment, co-insurance, or unmet deductible, the check submitted by the payer typically does not reflect the amount of the allowable. Furthermore, the payer may state that the payment is due from another payer that provides insurance coverage to the patient. Ideally, as we discussed in Chapter 4: The Patient Check-in and Check-out Processes, a medical practice will have already determined the patient's responsibility level and will have collected this payment at the time of service.

Contractual Adjustments

In addition to the allowable, the EOB also notes the amount of the contractual adjustment, which equals the practice's charge minus the allowable. If the medical practice participates with the payer and has agreed to accept its allowables, the practice must write off the difference between the charge and the allowable as a contractual adjustment.

Many practice management systems allow the medical practice the ability to maintain the allowance schedules at the line item level for some or all payers. Thus, when payments are received, the system automatically writes off the contractual allowance. If there is a discrepancy (for example, the payment is lower than the allowable recorded in the system's database for that payer, that plan, or that procedure code), the system alerts the payment poster.

Non-contractual Adjustments

On occasion, the EOB contains no payment or only a partial payment. In industry parlance, these are called "denials," "rejections," "zero-pay EOBs," or "correspondence." The EOB indicates that the payment was reduced or not paid for a particular reason. If the reason is outside of the allowable that has been entered into by the medical practice and the payer, these are called "non-contractual allowances." That is, your medical practice did not agree to accept that level of write-off as part of the amount that the practice is allowed to collect. The issue at hand could be the fault of the medical practice — or the payer. For example, a common reason for a non-contractual allowance is that the claim filing deadline was missed. That means that your medical practice did not submit the claim for its services within the payer's designated time frame for submission of claims. Therefore, the payer denies payment for the service. Learn more about managing denials in Chapter 12: The Denial Management Process.

DENIAL CODES

The payment denials are posted to the practice management system via denial codes, which are also referred to as adjustment codes. Three different methods are used to post denials in the practice management system. They include:

1. Don't post the denial on the invoice, then flag the EOB for follow-up action;
2. Post the denial and adjust the invoice balance accordingly, then flag the EOB for follow-up action; and
3. Post the denial and maintain the invoice balance, then flag the EOB for follow-up action.

We recommend that medical practices adopt strategy number three outlined above, ideally scanning the EOB and flagging it in an electronic work file.

At the time the denial is posted to the invoice, the following types of non-contractual adjustments should be reported into your practice management system like other adjustment transactions:

- Untimely filing;
- Lack of authorization/referral;
- Not a covered benefit;
- Out-of-network or non-credentialed provider;
- Non-covered service/diagnosis;
- Not medically necessary; and
- Not eligible on the date of service.

Importantly, some of these denials may be billable to the patient, so your staff need direction as to how to take action on the denial. (More information about account follow-up is included in Chapter 11: The Insurance Follow-up Process.) You may find it helpful to also categorize the denial reason codes by "controllable" or "uncontrollable" adjustments, based on whether or not the denial is under your medical practice's control. An example of a controllable adjustment would be failing to have a required referral or authorization for the service that was performed; an example of an uncontrollable adjustment would be a payer bankruptcy. The uncontrollable adjustments and the amount sent to the collection agency typically form what is known as "bad debt" adjustments.

When dollars are adjusted off of an account for contractual or non-contractual adjustments, an adjustment code is selected and entered to denote the action. Each practice management system has a different database of adjustment codes and sometimes even refer to them by different terminology. It is important to work with your practice management system vendor to establish a discrete set of adjustment codes and then educate staff as to their use so that each staff member who is permitted to adjust the invoice uses the codes in a consistent fashion.

By creating codes for non-contractual adjustments — including denials — and posting the adjustments accurately in your practice management system, you create information that you can utilize to improve revenue performance. Every action taken to reduce these adjustments creates increased collections and reduces rework by the billing staff.

Posting Denials

As the poster is posting payments, he/she enters denials into the practice management system on a line-item basis. If some services have been paid but others have not, the services that have not been paid should be denoted. The poster marks denials manually or electronically for further research.

The billing office can establish the workflow to take action regarding the EOB denials at the time of payment posting, batch this work for the poster to handle later in the day, or submit it to another responsible party, such as the staff member assigned to account follow-up for a particular payer. The staff who are responsible for researching the accounts can then take action using information gleaned from the EOB directly, from the practice management system reports, or from an electronic work file.

The denial codes can also have reporting categories, which can provide a breadth of information. In some practice management systems, the denial codes are in a special rejection module that automates subsequent actions, such as transferring the account balance to the patient and sending a statement. As you formulate these denial codes, you'll find that some are not really "denial" codes. Instead, they are EOB "remark" codes providing information about why the payer did not pay the entire allowed amount. Obviously, we want to capture this information so that it will drive the next action on the account, for example, appeal the denial, transfer the balance to patient responsibility, or bill the account to another payer.

If you pre-load all the Medicare, Medicaid, and Blue Cross Blue Shield denial codes into your system and then accept electronic payment files, not only will you have all these payer payments posted electronically, but you will also have all of these payer denials posted as well. If those denial codes have been categorized and set up for certain actions, those actions can be triggered at the time of electronic payment posting, too.

Example: Payer ABC pays its portion but denies the remaining balance as "patient responsibility for annual deductible." If that denial code (patient responsibility for annual deductible) has been set up correctly, when that is posted on the invoice, it will automatically move the remaining balance to self pay and a statement will be generated and sent to the patient.

Example: Payer XYZ pays its portion, but a 20 percent co-insurance remains. That EOB remark code signifies that the balance should be billed to the next responsible party — a secondary payer or the patient, which is then performed automatically.

Before you establish your denial codes, think about what information you want to know about your denials. By identifying the data you want to know about your denials, you can then set up the appropriate codes and processes to ensure you receive this data on a routine basis.

In Chapter 12: The Denial Management Process, we discuss tracking and evaluating denial reasons in much more depth. After reading that chapter, you may want to revisit the formulation of denial codes. Appropriate establishment and use of denial codes determine how much information you can obtain from your management reports.

IMPORTANCE OF ACCURACY IN PAYMENT POSTING

If your medical practice uses denial codes inconsistently or inappropriately, your practice cannot determine the effectiveness of its revenue cycle. In particular, it is not possible for you to calculate a correct net collection rate or a legitimate "bad debt" rate due to the need to correctly isolate contractual adjustments from non-contractual adjustments. (See Chapter 19: Measuring and Analyzing the Revenue Cycle for a further discussion of these revenue cycle performance indices.)

We have often found that medical practices adjust accounts incorrectly, by either writing them off as a contractual adjustment (confusing the legitimate contractual adjustment that has been recognized via contract terms) or writing them off as bad debt, again confusing data interpretation. These inappropriate treatments of non-contractual adjustments could mislead a medical practice into thinking that billing and collection performance has been optimized, when in fact, the medical practice may not be pursuing opportunities to enhance its revenue potential.

Figure 10.2 depicts three payment posting scenarios to illustrate the importance of payment posting accuracy. In the first scenario, staff have posted the adjustment codes correctly; in the following two, they have posted the codes incorrectly. Notice how much less the medical practice collects when staff post the adjustment incorrectly and how the net collection rate responds. In this example, as summarized below, improved payment posting accuracy results in $315.00 more in cash and an accurate (real) net collection rate!

Scenario one: Posted correctly

Result: cash received = $475.00

Net collection rate: 100 percent

Scenario two: Posted incorrectly

Result: cash received = $160.00

Net collection rate: 100 percent

Scenario three: Posted incorrectly

Result: cash received = $160.00

Net collection rate: 38 percent

FIGURE 10.2 ■ Payment Posting: Three Scenarios

Charge is $900.
Patient pays copayment of $10.
Payer allows $475, applying $85 to patient responsibility as deductible.
Payer remits $150.

How should this be posted?

SCENARIO 1: Payment posted correctly

	Payment Received	Contractual Adjustment	Other Adjustment	A/R	Formula	NCR
Charge = $900	—	—	—	$900	$\frac{0}{900}$	0%
Patient pays copayment = $10	$10	—	—	$890	$\frac{10}{900}$	1%
Claim transmitted to payer EOB received ($150 paid)	$150	—	—	$740	$\frac{10 + 150}{900}$	18%
Allowed amount on EOB = $475 ($85 applied to deductible)	—	$425	—	$315	$\frac{160}{900 - 425}$	34%
Staff notices payment is low Low payment appeal filed EOB received (remaining $230 paid)	$230	—	—	$85	$\frac{160 + 230}{475}$	82%
Statement to patient to collect remaining balance ($85)						
Patient pays	$85	—	—	0	$\frac{390 + 85}{475}$	100%
Result	**$475**	$425	$0	$0		**100%**

SCENARIO 2: Payment posted incorrectly

	Payment Received	Contractual Adjustment	Other Adjustment	A/R	Formula	NCR
Charge = $900	—	—	—	$900	$\frac{0}{900}$	0%
Patient pays copayment = $10	$10	—	—	$890	$\frac{10}{900}$	1%
Claim transmitted to payer						
EOB received ($150 paid) Allowed amount on EOB = $475 Staff member adjusts off balance as contractual	$150	$740	—	$0	$\frac{10 + 150}{900 - 740}$	100%
Result	**$160**	$740	$0	$0		**100%**

(continued on next page)

FIGURE 10.2 ■ Payment Posting: Three Scenarios *(continued)*

SCENARIO 3: Payment posted incorrectly

	Payment Received	Contractual Adjustment	Other Adjustment	A/R	Formula	NCR
Charge = $900	—	—	—	$900	$\frac{0}{900}$	0%
Patient pays copayment = $10	$10	—	—	$890	$\frac{10}{900}$	1%
Claim transmitted to payer						
EOB received ($150 paid) Allowed amount on EOB = $475 (staff posts wrong contractual)	$150	$475	—	$265	$\frac{10 + 150}{900 - 475}$	38%
Statement to patient ($265)	$0	—	—	$265	$\frac{160}{425}$	38%
Patient calls – payer owes more and patient refuses to pay						
18 months later, account written off to bad debt	$0	$0	$265	$0	$\frac{160}{425}$	38%
Result	**$160**	$475	$265	$0		**38%**

$$\text{NCR (net collection rate)} = \frac{\text{Collections} - \text{Refunds}}{\text{Charges} - \text{Contractual Adjustments} + \text{Debits} - \text{Credits} - \text{Discounts}}$$

© 2009 Walker, Woodcock, Larch. Reprinted with permission.

Payment Variance

Are you being paid what you are due? This question is obviously critical, but the answer is not at all intuitive. Some payers do not publish their fee schedules, and a medical practice must often guess if the payer is paying at appropriate levels. At times, the payer reimburses at variable levels on the same procedure code due to different employer-defined plans, making an accurate estimate particularly challenging and certainly frustrating. In addition, medical practices often do not provide payment posters with appropriate tools to determine if the practice is being reimbursed at the expected levels. Many payment posters essentially eyeball the payment on the claim and make a quick decision about whether to manually or electronically flag the EOB for additional internal review. If there is a payment on even one line item, some payment posters consider this "good enough" and write off the remaining balance to a contractual adjustment. As these examples suggest, the knowledge and tools required for payment posting accuracy are vital to ensuring that you optimize your revenue performance.

In addition to the above discussion of payment and denial posting, we present the following proven strategies to enhance payment posting processes.

ADVANCED PRACTICES: THE PAYMENT AND DENIAL POSTING PROCESS

Establish Payment Receipt Logs

Maintain a running log of the date and amount of payments from payers. In this fashion, the medical practice can determine at a glance the amount of money that has been received by a payer and the date of each check or EFT. This is a method by which a medical practice can track remits and follow up with a payer that may be delaying payment. If your practice management software does not permit this to be performed electronically, maintain this information in a spreadsheet by month (for example, columns reflecting each payer and rows reflecting date the check was received, with the field indicating the dollar amount paid). A further discussion of internal controls and cash management is provided in Chapter 16: Internal Controls for the Revenue Cycle.

Post Payments Promptly

As the payments come in to the billing office — from payers or patients — it is important that payments are posted into the practice management system promptly. Most medical practices post payments within 24 hours of receipt. Typically, payments received at the time of service are posted immediately upon receipt. If payment posting is delayed for more than 24 hours, it could allow patient statements to be mailed without reflecting the patient's payment. Additionally, your account follow-up staff will not know the payer has already paid and may contact payers unnecessarily.

Develop a Policy for Handling Pre-paid Monies

If you collect monies prior to services being rendered, you need a consistent policy for how to post these monies and ultimately link the pre-payment with the actual charge. Some medical practices post pre-paid monies and enter a "dummy charge" equal to the payment to avoid creating a false credit balance. Others delay posting the payment until the charge is entered. We recommend that you post pre-paid monies to a zero invoice and reconcile the payment to the charge once it is posted.

Explore advanced capabilities within your practice management system to determine if you have auto-linking capabilities. If you link the pre-payment to the encounter or visit and then enter the charge days or weeks later and link it to the same encounter or visit, the pre-payment should link to the charge and be correctly reported.

Utilizing a specific pre-paid payment code and financial class allows your medical practice to monitor the age of these pre-payments. If the charges do not appear within an established time frame and the credits are not systematically applied, work with your practice management system vendor to rectify this problem or, alternatively, resort to a manual reconciliation process.

Actively Manage Unidentified Payments

When you deposit checks daily, you need a separate process to record unidentified payments. Post the checks that are unapplied or require research to a separate account, and make controlled transfers of this account once you have established proper identification. Undertake a bounded search process that defines the research steps the employee should make to attempt to identify the payment. This could involve gaining access to the hospital information system, searching appropriate potential databases, and/or communicating with the payer or patient. If your staff has followed this defined search process and the payment remains unidentifiable, prepare a refund and return the money to the payer or patient in a timely fashion. Identify and refund these unidentified payments within 60 days.

Investigate Insurance Take-backs

At times, the payer reduces the amount paid for the date of service on the current claim by a level that it deemed to be an overpayment on a prior claim. This requires the payment poster to readily identify the "take-back" and post this to the system so that both dates of service are accurately reconciled with the EOB and the payment level. Investigate the source of take-backs to ensure that the payer is appropriate when applying them and that the take-backs are consistent with your current contract and state law. Some state laws and payer contracts limit the length of time a payer can alter a prior payment and perform a take-back, so be sure to monitor the timeliness in case you can appeal the take-backs with the payer.

Create Separate Tracking of Capitation Funds

If your medical practice maintains a capitated contract with a payer, delineate that book of business. You should book the revenue, but set up your practice management system to report it separately. In addition, set up your system so you can track the utilization of your capitated business without carrying the accounts receivable *ad infinitum*. Instead, book the charges to track the utilization and write off the accounts receivable at minimum, each month, or maintain these receivables in a separate report.

Set up a Hierarchy of Payment Codes

When you implemented your current practice management system, you made decisions about what payment codes you would utilize. Payment codes define the source of the payment so that you can track and monitor payments by payer category, payer, and even plan type.

Every payment will ultimately be part of your revenue cycle analysis data. Answer the questions below to determine if it is time to update the payment codes you utilize.

Type of payment

Are you able to determine if the cash that is posted during the time of service came in via cash, check, or credit/debit card? Would this data be useful to your medical practice?

Payer categories

Have you established a payer code hierarchy that tells you the payer category (for example, commercial or HMO) or the actual payer (for example, Aetna or Medicare)? Would knowing this information help you in identifying an opportunity for your medical practice?

The payment code structure in Figure 10.3 shows examples of different payment codes your medical practice may utilize. Structuring payment codes properly helps a medical practice analyze and run its business.

FIGURE 10.3 ■ Payment Code Structure

Payment Code #	Examples of Payment Codes	Reporting Category
1	Collection agency	Bad Debt
2	Blue Cross/Blue Shield Indemnity	Blue Shield
3	Blue Cross/Blue Shield HMO	Blue Shield
4	Aetna PPO	Commercial
5	Traveler's of Ohio	Commercial
6	Write off — no referral	Controllable Loss
7	Aetna HMO	HMO FFS
8	Medicaid Managed Care	Medicaid
9	Medicare	Medicare
10	Cash collected	Patient Responsibility
11	Check collected	Patient Responsibility
12	Credit card collected	Patient Responsibility
13	Cash at the time of service	Patient Responsibility
14	Check at the time of service	Patient Responsibility
15	Credit card at the time of service	Patient Responsibility
16	Write off — payer bankruptcy	Uncontrollable Loss

© 2009 Walker, Woodcock, Larch. Reprinted with permission.

The case example below illustrates the use of payment codes to reflect different billing situations. Be certain that you record the payments in the correct category.

Case example: The use of payment codes

The charge was $200.00.

The patient is a beneficiary of Blue Cross/Blue Shield (BCBS) as primary and Aetna as secondary.

The patient pays a $20.00 copayment at the time of service.

BCBS pays $65.00 on the account.

Aetna secondary pays $15.00 on the account.

Depending on how your practice management system is set up and based on how you pull the data, you may obtain different results.

When you posted the $20.00 copay, the patient's financial class was BCBS. If you posted it with a generic payment code, then all you will know is that you received $20.00 on a BCBS account. If you posted it with a "cash at the time of service" payment code, then you know more information about the transaction.

We recommend that you use payment codes as follows:

Total payments. Total payments to an account that was BCBS = $100.00 ($20.00 + $65.00 + $15.00). This total payment is the amount you would compare to the allowable from BCBS based on your contract. The total payment is the allowable, regardless of which party paid (patient, primary payer, or secondary payer).

Payments at the time of service. Payments received at the time of service = $20.00 (the patient copayment).

Payments by payer. Payments received from BCBS = $65.00. You would not want to compare this payment to the contract you have with BCBS for expected reimbursement as it would look like an under-profile payment.

Payments by payer. Payments received from Aetna secondary = $15.00. You would not want to compare this payment to the contract you have with Aetna for expected reimbursement as it would look like an under-profile payment.

This example demonstrates the choices your medical practice should consider when establishing your payment codes. You don't want to make the categorization overly complicated, but on the other hand, the classification system needs to have enough complexity to support your business analysis needs. If your practice management system allows financial type and payment code reporting categories, we recommend that you formulate them. Reporting categories are established in your practice management system's dictionaries and are available for reporting purposes. This is a great way to obtain more information without making the charge entry and payment posters' jobs too complex. If your practice management system does not allow for this level of detail, create additional payment codes to which to post payer products.

The following example illustrates the payer category designations that can be set up for reporting purposes.

Payer Financial Class = HMO ABC (a health plan)

Three reporting categories are available for the financial class:

Reporting category 1 = HMO FFS (need to know if the HMO is FFS or capitated)

Reporting category 2 = Anytown Insurance Company (because HMO ABC is owned by Anytown Insurance Company and we want to analyze our total Anytown Insurance Company book of business)

Reporting category 3 = HMO (used to create major payer mix charts where data is rolled up to a higher level)

Payment Code = HMO ABC

Two reporting categories are available for the payment code:

Reporting category 1 = Payment/Contractual (this tells us we have a contract and expect to see a contractual adjustment)

Reporting category 2 = HMO FFS (this tells us which HMO ABC fee schedule to which to compare it)

Assign Payment Posting to Account Follow-up Staff

In the past, many medical practices instituted a focused payment posting unit within their billing office. Today, with the complexities of medical insurance and the technology that permits payments to be posted electronically (with only exceptions being flagged for manual posting), many medical practices delegate payment posting to account follow-up staff and/or assign a dedicated payment poster to a specific payer account follow-up team. Co-locating this function with accounts receivable follow-up lets staff research and resolve the account simultaneously with payment posting because account follow-up staff are skilled in payer reimbursement strategies. It also reduces the number of process handoffs and the cycle time to resolve payment discrepancies. Accounts receivable staff post the payment and/or denial, perform necessary follow-up, process secondary claims, transfer financial responsibility to patients, and make appropriate adjustments. These payer teams are responsible for resolving the account once the EOB has been received until the account balance is zero. See Chapter 15: Staffing the Revenue Cycle for further discussion of staffing deployment models.

Provide Tools to Payment Posters

Give payment posters tools so they can recognize low reimbursement levels and flag accounts for appeal. For example, make sure that the maximum number of payer reimbursement schedules (also known as payer "fee schedules," these reflect the allowables from the payer pursuant to your contract) are loaded into your practice management system and produce exception reports on a daily basis to recognize payments that fall outside of defined ranges.

The checklist in Tool 16 helps you make sure that payment posters have the tools and education needed for this important billing function.

Develop Performance Reviews for Payment Posting Staff

Payment posting accuracy and interpretation are learned over time, but there are key competencies that all payment posters must master from the beginning. Managers should evaluate staff performance against a list of key competencies. Use Tool 17 to evaluate key competencies for your payment posters and to identify potential training opportunities. On an ongoing basis, managers need to perform performance audits to evaluate how staff are interpreting EOBs. In Tool 17, we provide a sample audit form. We recommend that you evaluate 10 payments for each payment poster on a quarterly basis, at minimum, to determine if the staff member is performing at optimal levels. After a period of time to which all work is subject to audit, we recommend weekly audits for the first quarter to assess the performance of new staff.

TOOL 16	Payment Posting Checklist

This tool is a checklist for payment posting to ensure that your medical practice has appropriately delegated the payment posting function and educated staff in this function.

Yes No

Yes	No	
___	___	1. Are payment posters familiar with accounts receivable follow-up and/or assigned to payer-specific account follow-up teams?
___	___	2. Have staff been given tools and resources to permit identification of low reimbursement?
___	___	3. Is the maximum number of payer fee schedules loaded on the practice management system?
___	___	4. Are exception reports by payer produced daily to be worked?
___	___	5. Are payments posted within 24 hours of receipt?
___	___	6. Is there a streamlined handoff from payment posting to billing of secondary claims and statements?
___	___	7. Are EOBs appropriately flagged for appeal?
___	___	8. Are there sufficient adjustment codes for non-contractual adjustments?
___	___	9. Do payment posters understand the use of payment and adjustment codes?
___	___	10. Is there an appropriate separation of duties between individuals who receive the mail, open the mail, post the payment, deposit the payment, and reconcile bank ledgers?
___	___	11. Are zero payments posted and worked the day of receipt or no later than 24 hours?
___	___	12. Is the small balance write-off set at an appropriate level?
___	___	13. When credits are generated, are they worked the same day or no later than 60 days from the date of discovery of the problem?

© 2009 Walker, Woodcock, Larch. Reprinted with permission.

Leverage Data from HIPAA Code Sets

As discussed earlier, EOBs inform you of your payments and your reasons for non-payment. The HIPAA Code Sets define "claim adjustment" codes to help group the EOB remark codes. If your staff understand how these codes were established, they can ensure that their account follow-up strategies are appropriate. Not all, but many payers use these standard formats.

Consider this the "secret decoder" to the HIPAA EOB remark codes:[1]

- Patient Responsibility (PR): If the group code "PR" is in the EOB remark, the amount not paid is the patient's responsibility. Thus, the medical practice should be billing the patient for this amount.

- Contractual Obligation (CO): If the group code "CO" is in the EOB remark, the amount adjusted is not the patient's responsibility under any circumstances either due to a contractual obligation between the provider and the payer or a regulatory requirement.

[1] *Source:* http://www.cms.hhs.gov/EducationMaterials/Downloads/Whateelectronictransactionsandcodesets-4.pdf (accessed December 22, 2008).

- Payer Initiated (PI): If the group code "PI" is in the EOB remark, in the payer's opinion, the amount adjusted is not the responsibility of the patient, unless the payer contract states otherwise.
- Correction and Reversals (CR): If the group code "CR" is used, the claim is considered a reversal of a previously reported claim or claim payment.
- Other Adjustment (OA): Usage of group code "OA" should be rare, except when reporting pre-determination of benefits or the impacted amount of the prior payer.

Safeguard Checks and Credit/Debit Card Receipts

Unless your medical practice uses remote deposit for all checks, immediately endorse and deposit checks daily. This may require you to develop courier services for outlying practice areas. Maintain all cash, checks, and credit and debit card receipts in a locked drawer or safe until deposit. For a complete discussion of internal controls, see Chapter 16: Internal Controls for the Revenue Cycle.

TOOL 17   **Payment Posting Audit Tool**

PAYMENT POSTING QUALITY REVIEW

Select 10 payments posted to patient accounts.
Review the EOB and other back-up for proper research.
Access the account in the practice management system and review for errors.
Discuss the results of the quality review with the employee.
Log results into performance management file.

	1	2	3	4	5	6	7	8	9	10
Account number										
Applied payment to correct account										
Applied the correct payment amount										
Applied in a timely manner										
Used correct payment code										
Used correct rejection code										
Correctly made contractual adjustments										
Took correct action on under-reimbursed procedures										
Account in appropriate payer after posting										
Comments:										
Action taken on accounts:										

This sample indicates payment posting performance at the following level:
_____ Unsatisfactory _____ Needs improvement _____ Satisfactory _____Exceeds expectations
_____ Significantly exceeds expectations

_____   _____   _____
Supervisor's Signature   Employee's Signature   Date

© 2009 University Physicians, Inc. Reprinted with permission.

Make Sure Payers Have Updated Information on Your Medical Practice

When your medical practice submits group and individual provider applications to payers, provide accurate information for payers to submit payment to you. If and when you move your medical practice or change the name of your medical practice, submit the new information to each payer and monitor payments carefully for at least 6 months to ensure that the payers acted on your change request.

Monitor Your State's Prompt Payment Laws

Most states have passed prompt payment laws. These laws outline the maximum time allowed for payment of a clean claim. Typically, when a payer misses this payment deadline, either penalties or interest accrues and is due to the medical practice. The current problem with these laws, however, relates to the definition of a clean claim, which can vary considerably from state to state and often requires subjective interpretation. Moreover, there is no federal law related to prompt payment.

The Employee Retirement Income Security Act of 1974 (ERISA) established governance over private-sector employee health plans. ERISA plans can be a challenge in the billing office. Because these plans, which include employer self-funded plans, are not regulated by the state, these health plans need not comply with state prompt payment laws that govern commercial payers. This often means a frustrating cycle of delays, leaving your billing staff with no apparent recourse.

ERISA plans are, however, regulated by the United States Department of Labor. ERISA requires plans to provide participants with important information about plan features and funding. In addition, it provides fiduciary responsibilities for those who manage and control plan assets, requires plans to establish a grievance and appeals process for participants to receive benefits from their plans, and gives participants the right to sue for benefits and breaches of fiduciary duty.

According to the federal code, ERISA plans must notify your medical practice of a claim rejection within 30 days after their receipt of the claim — or their intent to spend another 15 days evaluating your claim. Although the law does not offer a payment time frame per se, your medical practice can use the fact that the plan has a 30-day period to communicate with you to prompt action on your claim.

Script your appeal letter as such:

> We believe that failure to release information about the claim regarding [offer details about your claim] may be a violation of United States Federal Code Title 29.[2] This portion of the Pension and Welfare Benefits law prohibits self-funded group employer-sponsored health plans from unnecessarily delaying claims processing.

---

[2] http://www.dol.gov/dol/allcfr/Title_29/Part_2560/29CFR2560.503-1.htm (accessed June 26, 2008).

The United States Federal Code of Regulations, 29 CFR 2560.503-1 — Claims procedure, states: "(B) Post-service claims. In the case of a post-service claim, the plan administrator shall notify the claimant, in accordance with paragraph (g) of this section, of the plan's adverse benefit determination within a reasonable period of time, but not later than 30 days after receipt of the claim. This period may be extended one time by the plan for up to 15 days, provided that the plan administrator both determines that such an extension is necessary due to matters beyond the control of the plan and notifies the claimant, prior to the expiration of the initial 30-day period, of the circumstances requiring the extension of time and the date by which the plan expects to render a decision. If such an extension is necessary due to a failure of the claimant to submit the information necessary to decide the claim, the notice of extension shall specifically describe the required information, and the claimant shall be afforded at least 45 days from receipt of the notice within which to provide the specified information."

Based on this federal mandate and the fact that this is a "clean claim," we ask that this claim be adjudicated immediately.

Send an appeal letter for ERISA claims for which you have received no response within 45 days of submission. Demonstrating your knowledge of the regulation will engender prompt action — and hopefully get you paid what you deserve.

If you have problems getting paid, report the non-compliant party to the Employee Benefits Security Administration of the United States Department of Labor, which oversees these ERISA plans. A listing of the regional offices resides on the Department of Labor's Website.

Please note that this strategy does not guarantee payment or even action on the part of the ERISA plan. It is, however, another weapon in your medical practice's arsenal to get paid.

Glean information regarding your state's prompt payment law by downloading a list at www.elizabethwoodcock.com/resources.html. If your state allows for remuneration for delayed payments, be sure to pursue payments owed to you, including interest.

Generate and Review Payment Exception Reports

Generate a payment exception report by payer. If a particular payer is to reimburse you, for example, 180 percent of Medicare allowable levels, produce an exception report with reimbursement levels that fall outside of these limits. When you're armed with this data, a meeting with the payer can produce excellent results.

Resolve Credit Balances Within 60 Days

Your medical practice should regularly research and resolve outstanding credit balances generated by the payment posting process. Staff can work these daily by producing an ad hoc report after they post payments; however, medical practice staff typically work a credit balance report each week to correct payment posting errors, as well as to ensure appropriate refunds are sent to the patient and/or payer. Many payers, including the Centers for Medicare & Medicaid Services (CMS), require medical practices to repay overpayments within a specified time period, and many legal experts have outlined an "affirmative duty" on the part of medical practices to report overpayments within a timely fashion.

Verifying Reimbursement Level by Payer

To ensure that your medical practice is being paid what it is due, analyze reimbursement levels by payer. Tool 18 is an example of this analysis. It outlines the top 25 procedure codes and reimbursement levels by the top 6 payers of a medical practice. If you cannot load all of the payer reimbursement schedules into your practice management system, this tool provides a manual method to review reimbursement levels to ensure consistency with contract terms. Your medical practice should develop this report for the top 25 procedure codes by frequency and the top 25 procedure codes by dollar level.

TOOL 18 Verify Reimbursement Level by Payer

| CPT® | Description | Practice Charge | Reimbursement by Payer | | | | | |
			Payer 1	Payer 2	Payer 3	Payer 4	Payer 5	Payer 6
11200	Removal of skin tags	$175.00	$70.19	$66.68	$94.76	$77.21	$73.70	$112.31
45330	Diagnostic sigmoidoscopy	$300.00	$120.23	$114.22	$162.31	$132.25	$126.24	$192.36
71010	Chest X-ray	$70.00	$27.63	$26.25	$37.30	$30.39	$29.01	$44.21
73090	X-ray exam of forearm	$71.00	$28.38	$26.96	$38.31	$31.21	$29.80	$45.40
99202	Office/outpatient visit, new	$161.00	$64.59	$58.13	$87.20	$77.51	$61.36	$103.35
99203	Office/outpatient visit, new	$240.00	$95.96	$86.36	$129.54	$115.15	$91.16	$153.53
99204	Office/outpatient visit, new	$340.00	$135.53	$121.98	$182.97	$162.64	$128.76	$216.86
99205	Office/outpatient visit, new	$430.00	$172.13	$154.91	$232.37	$206.55	$163.52	$275.40
99211	Office/outpatient visit, est	$53.00	$21.28	$19.15	$28.73	$25.54	$20.22	$34.05
99212	Office/outpatient visit, est	$94.00	$37.71	$33.94	$50.91	$45.25	$35.83	$60.34
99213	Office/outpatient visit, est	$132.00	$52.65	$47.38	$71.07	$63.17	$50.01	$84.23
99214	Office/outpatient visit, est	$205.00	$82.14	$73.93	$110.89	$98.57	$78.04	$131.43
99215	Office/outpatient visit, est	$298.00	$119.11	$107.20	$160.79	$142.93	$113.15	$190.57
99222	Initial hospital care	$275.00	$111.27	$77.89	$150.21	$133.52	$89.01	$178.02
99223	Initial hospital care	$385.00	$154.95	$108.47	$209.18	$185.94	$123.96	$247.92
99231	Subsequent hospital care	$83.00	$33.23	$23.26	$44.86	$39.88	$26.58	$53.17
99232	Subsequent hospital care	$137.00	$54.89	$38.42	$74.10	$65.86	$43.91	$87.82
99233	Subsequent hospital care	$195.00	$78.04	$54.62	$105.35	$93.64	$62.43	$124.86
99235	Observ/hosp same date	$455.00	$181.46	$127.02	$244.97	$217.75	$145.17	$290.34
99239	Hospital discharge day	$238.00	$95.21	$66.65	$128.53	$114.25	$76.17	$152.34
99304	Nursing facility care	$254.00	$97.82	$68.48	$132.06	$117.39	$78.26	$156.52
99305	Nursing facility care	$300.00	$120.97	$84.68	$163.31	$145.17	$96.78	$193.56
99307	Nursing fac care, subseq	$158.00	$63.10	$44.17	$85.19	$75.72	$50.48	$100.96
99308	Nursing fac care, subseq	$215.00	$86.25	$60.37	$116.44	$103.50	$69.00	$138.00
99316	Nursing fac discharge day	$230.00	$91.85	$64.30	$124.00	$110.22	$73.48	$146.96

Note: Sample data.

© 2009 Walker, Woodcock, Larch. Reprinted with permission.

Most states have an unclaimed property law, also known as an "escheats law," that dictates how your medical practice should treat refunds that you cannot return to the patient or payer. For example, you may owe credit balances to a patient who has relocated with no forwarding address or to a payer that is out of business. Or you may be limited in your research on the credit balance because of a practice management system conversion. In many states, if your medical practice cannot locate a creditor after a specified period of time (for example, five years), the money becomes the state's property. Your practice is required to turn the money over to the state, in compliance with the state's escheats law. This is just another good reason why timely research of credit balances is important.

Work all credits daily or weekly and completely research them and return over-payments within 60 days. You can generate daily, weekly, and monthly credit reports from most practice management systems. The payment posters can produce a daily report of credits that are created via the payment posting process and determine whether the credit is accurate or flag it for work. Remember that your credits offset your total accounts receivable. Therefore, if your credits are high, you may be understating the dollar value of your accounts receivable.

Many medical practices continue to have problems with non-governmental payers regarding correspondence about refunds. In some cases, the medical practice identifies a refund due a non-governmental payer and the payer, unable to identify the refund in its system, denies it, returning the funds to the medical practice. In other cases, the non-government payer requests money that is due from the medical practice, but when the practice writes to the payer to say, "Received your request — need more details," the payer does not respond. How the medical practice eventually resolves these issues depends on your medical practice's business risk tolerance, staff resources, and other similar factors. No matter what process you choose, maintain all correspondence on file.

Develop a Streamlined Refund Process

Many medical practices have initiated overly encumbered refund processes that involve multiple individuals and multiple steps. Better-performing practices involve refund staff who investigate and approve the refund request; and all documents are stored and check requests are transmitted electronically. A sample refund request form is presented as Tool 19. Approval levels escalate within the medical practice based on dollar thresholds of the refund amount, but the workflow is streamlined and documentation is electronic and kept to a minimum.

Develop a Streamlined Process for Secondary Claims and Account Follow-up

Medical practices typically assign the actual billing of secondaries to one of three different staff: payment posters, account follow-up staff, or claims staff. We have seen this role performed well by each of these staff, and your work delegation depends on the staffing model you elect.

TOOL 19	Sample Refund Request Form

Patient name: _____

Account number: _____

Date of service: _____

Provider: _____

Refund (circle):   Patient   Guarantor   Insurance

Mailing address:

_____

_____

_____

Refund reason (circle):   Patient overpaid | Patient and ins. paid | Ins. dup. payment |

Other _____

Check 1

Check 2

Check 3

Check 4

Check 5

Total: $

Requested by: _____   Date: _____

Approved by: _____   Date: _____

Check #: _____   Check amount: _____

Ins. = insurance

Dup. = duplicate

© 2009 Walker, Woodcock, Larch. Reprinted with permission.

During the payment posting process, require posters to flag claims that need to be submitted to a secondary carrier. Payment posters should not send a secondary claim that has been automatically crossed over because the payer already has sent it; thus this will create a denial for duplicate submission of claims. For secondary claims that do not automatically cross over, clerical staff should be responsible for duplicating the original EOB or printing a stored image from your document management system. These staff can also attach the EOB to the secondary claim and submit it to the payer. (See Chapter 8: The Claims Management Process for a further discussion of secondary claims processing.)

In summary, payment and denial posting accuracy and completeness are critical to the medical practice's financial performance. Managers need to focus on the quality of posting accuracy, not simply the speed at which this is performed. Determining the correct payment or denial code is part of an account's history and also determines the next action that staff (or your practice management system) need to take. The information the staff post on an account should tell a story of what has happened and what needs to happen next.

By creating codes and posting them accurately in your practice management system, you create information that your medical practice can utilize to improve the performance of your revenue cycle. Every action taken to reduce non-contractual adjustments creates increased collections and reduces rework by the billing staff.

STAFF WORKLOAD RANGES

The staff workload ranges for the payment and denial posting process that we typically expect are provided below. The ability to perform within these ranges may vary due to internal practice-specific factors (such as facility layout, telephone system, and practice management system). The workload ranges are based on a staff member performing these functions approximately seven hours of productive time per day (allowing one hour for breaks, interruptions, and other down time). Note that the workload ranges reflect *quantitative* performance levels. Note that *qualitative* performance — accuracy, completeness, appropriateness, and quality of these functions — should also be measured. When issues of quantity versus quality arise, we strongly recommend that quality be emphasized, even if the performance workload ranges for a particular function need to be relaxed from these levels.

Staff Function	Transactions	
	per day	per hour
Payments and adjustments posted manually	525 to 875	75 to 125
Refunds researched and processed	60 to 80	9 to11

Note: Institute these workload ranges only if accuracy can be assured in this time frame. If not, you may need to increase the time to perform the function in order to avoid mistakes.

© 2009 Walker, Woodcock, Larch. Reprinted with permission.

LEADING PERFORMANCE INDICATORS

Use the following indicators to assess the performance of your payment and denial posting process. We refer to these measures as "leading" performance indicators. If your medical practice is successful in achieving these levels in payment and denial posting processes, you are on the correct path to optimizing your revenue cycle.

Lag time from payment receipt to posting:	Same day or within 24 hours
Identification and return of unidentified or overpayment funds:	Within 60 days
Adjustments due to untimely filing:	0 percent
Credit balances as a percentage of accounts receivable:	< 2 percent

© 2009 Walker, Woodcock, Larch. Reprinted with permission.

THE PAYMENT AND DENIAL POSTING DIAGNOSTIC TOOL

The payment and denial posting diagnostic tool provided below helps you ensure that the process, people, technology, and quality required for effective payment and denial posting processes are in place in your medical practice.

Process:

1. What is your process for posting: (a) time-of-service collections for each site; (b) insurance checks; and (c) patient payments received by mail/in person?
2. When are payments entered with respect to their receipt? When are they deposited at the bank?
3. Are internal controls in place at all points monies are collected?
4. How do you handle overpayments and refunds?
5. What contractual and non-contractual adjustments have been made during the past 12 months — by dollar, by reason, and by month?
6. How do you handle zero payment (denied) EOBs?

People:

1. Are staff trained and monitored for timeliness and accuracy in posting?
2. Are staff trained to use appropriate adjustment codes?
3. Are staff trained to understand how to read and process a denial that is reported on the EOB?

Technology:

1. Are you utilizing EPR and EFT from every payer that offers them?
2. Are you recognizing automatic crossovers and not duplicate billing the secondary payer?
3. Can you track adjustments by reason code?

Quality:

1. Can your practice management system verify that payments from payers received on every claim are appropriate based on your contract?
2. What is the percentage of claims that are denied upon first submission of the claim?
3. What are your five major denials by category (for example, coding and registration) and what action has been taken to resolve the root cause of these denials?
4. Are time-of-service payments being posted to the correct patient and correct date of service?

POLICIES AND PROCEDURES

At the end of each chapter, we provide policies and procedures to assist you in developing a policy and procedure manual for your medical practice. Below are four policies specific to the payment and denial posting process.

Policy 20: Payment Posting

Policy 21: Interest Payments

Policy 22: Credits and Refunds

Policy 23: Account Write-offs and Adjustments

POLICY 20: PAYMENT POSTING

Policy:

It is the policy of the medical practice that payments received by the medical practice will be handled in a timely manner with sensitivity to internal controls.

Procedures:

1. The medical practice will accept payments remitted and transferred electronically from all payers offering electronic payment remittance (EPR) and electronic funds transfer (EFT). Remittances will be accepted when available from the payer, but will not be posted until the medical practice staff confirm the remittance total to the funds transferred.

2. The medical practice will accept all non-electronic payments through a lockbox at a reputable, secure financial institution. This will include all non-electronic payer and patient checks.

3. The financial institution will notify the billing office of the deposits on a daily basis. The bank will transmit scanned copies of all checks on the same or day following receipt and deposit. Payments received will be placed into batches and assigned to the appropriate medical practice staff for manual posting. Medical practice staff are responsible for balancing the batches assigned to them. A summary of all batches posted will be reconciled to the daily deposit and provided to the billing manager or his/her designee.

4. All correspondence with no payments attached, to include rejections, will be flagged manually or electronically. A transaction code will be posted to the charge level on the account to identify the type of rejection. This correspondence will be relayed to medical practice staff assigned to working account follow-up.

5. Medical practice staff posting payments are responsible for accurate posting on a line-item basis.

6. Medical practice staff posting payments are responsible for transferring responsibility for the account balance to secondary or tertiary payers (and manually or electronically marking the primary explanation of benefits, unless the claim was automatically crossed over by the primary payer), or the guarantor.

7. Payment posting will be monitored very closely in order to assure timeliness and accuracy, as well as to identify opportunities for improvement.

POLICY 21: INTEREST PAYMENTS

Policy:

It is the policy of the medical practice to pursue interest due based on contractual or legal obligations by payers in the case of delayed payments to the medical practice.

Procedure:

1. The medical practice executive or his/her designee will monitor contracts and state law regarding prompt payment and interest due to the medical practice for failing to abide by these obligations.

2. The billing office will develop a report to monitor payment time periods by payers. For payers that are contractually or legally obligated to pay interest, requests for payments will be submitted by the medical practice.

3. When interest is earned on claims that have exceeded the allowed amount of time for payment, the interest will be posted to a designated interest account to monitor this revenue.

   If included on the same payment, the payment for the claim will be posted to the patient's account balance. When interest payments are received on multiple patients' claims, the total will be posted as one transaction to the interest account.

4. The billing manager or his/her designee will conduct a reconciliation of the interest account at the end of each month.

POLICY 22: CREDITS AND REFUNDS

Policy:

It is the policy of the medical practice to return all monies that are not due to the medical practice. These may include overpayments from patients or payers. The medical practice is committed to comply with state and federal laws, as well as to minimize the impact that credits have on receivables (credits understate the accounts receivable).

Procedures:

1. Credits will be flagged at payment posting when they are created. The payment poster, or another designated staff member, will work these credits within five business days. This time frame will also include the amount of time necessary to issue a refund check if appropriate. A thorough review of the account will be conducted to determine the cause of the credit. If a posting error caused the credit, a refund will not be made and the account will be corrected. The medical practice will refund overpayments to patients or payers if warranted.

2. In addition to proactively working credits created during the posting process, the billing office is responsible for working outstanding refunds. The accounts must be reviewed thoroughly. Credit invoices should be identified and refunded to the patient, guarantor, or payer within 60 days. Any credits identified that can be transferred to another outstanding invoice should be done within 60 days of creation date. The oldest credits should be worked first.

3. If a credit occurs for a guarantor with multiple patients on the account and a debit balance remains on the total account, the credit will be posted as an open balance payment on the account.

4. Credits of less than $5.00 will not be refunded. They will be maintained on the patient's account and applied to future services, in a time frame that complies with the state's escheats law.

5. Refunds will be posted to the patient's account upon the issuance of the refund check.

6. Requests for refund checks will be submitted to the medical practice executive or his/her designee in writing or via internal e-mail on the manual or electronic Refund Request Form (see Tool 19 for sample form) and will require the designated supervisor's signature prior to debiting to the account.

7. All payer refund procedures will be followed.

POLICY 23: ACCOUNT WRITE-OFFS AND ADJUSTMENTS

Policy:

It is the policy of the medical practice to track and monitor all monies that are written off from the original charge submitted to a payer. Two distinct categories of write-offs will be handled and monitored separately: contractual (amounts considered to be uncollectible as a result of the allowance established by the payer) and non-contractual (amounts considered to be uncollectible as a result of failure to obtain the amount allowed by the payer).

Procedures:

1. In order to track and monitor all write-offs, the medical practice will maintain a dictionary of detailed adjustment codes for contractual and non-contractual write-offs. The non-contractual write-offs may also be attached with transaction message codes, if applicable.

2. The medical practice will maintain current fee schedules, by procedure code, for each payer health plan. As a payment is posted, the medical practice staff is responsible for verifying that the payment allowance matches the expected reimbursement. To assist staff, the medical practice management system will default to the contractual reimbursement for each procedure code posted, based on the agreement with each payer.

3. If the payment allowance matches the expected reimbursement, the residual money (medical practice charge less payment allowance) will be written off with the appropriate contractual adjustment code. If the payment does not match the expected reimbursement, the line item will be flagged manually or electronically for follow-up.

4. From time to time, medical practice staff may work on an account that has a balance outstanding with a payer that cannot be collected. The reasons for the medical practice's inability to collect on the account may include, but not be limited to, a

missed timely filing or appeal deadline or failure to obtain an appropriate authorization or referral. If a write-off as such is identified, medical practice staff must receive approval to write off the account from a supervisor. The medical practice staff working the account in question shall identify his/her efforts to work the account and the recommendation for the write-off. The request will be sent in a standard format via internal e-mail communication or a manual form. (The billing manager may decide that medical practice staff may write off up to a maximum dollar amount without a supervisor's approval.)

CHAPTER 11

Pothole 9
The Insurance Follow-up Process

Insurance follow-up is the process of tracking a claim to ensure that the medical practice receives the payment it expects and deserves. One would think this process would be easy, but unfortunately it is like solving a puzzle; it can be quite complicated. You need to investigate where the claim is, determine its status, then follow a well-defined strategy to ensure that the claim is adjudicated and paid by the payer.

In this chapter, we discuss:

- Open claims follow-up
- Account follow-up structures
- Account follow-up strategies
- Insurance correspondence
- Small balance adjustments

Once claims are sent, one of four events typically occurs:

The claim is paid appropriately: This is obviously the preferred option for the medical practice. The practice submits the claim and receives the expected level of reimbursement in a suitable time frame.

The claim is paid incorrectly: Sometimes the payer adjudicates the claim for payment but the payment is incorrect. The payment may be too much (and thus require a refund to the payer) or it may be too little. If the claim is overpaid, action is required to determine the cause and to process the refund, if applicable. (Overpayments and refunds are discussed in detail in Chapter 10: The Payment and Denial Posting Process.) If the claim is underpaid, action is necessary to understand the cause of the mispayment and to direct the payer to adjudicate it correctly.

The claim is denied: No payment is received for the claim. Whether the denial is due to payer error or practice error, the billing staff must actively pursue the denial, potentially appealing it. We discuss managing claim denials in Chapter 12: The Denial Management Process.

The claim is unpaid and resides in limbo: This is when the claim is sent and no information has been received from the payer. This is often the most frustrating scenario, and it is why we recommend that staff follow accounts on a systematic basis to determine the status of the claim. An "open" claim can occur because the patient provided the medical practice with the incorrect insurance information at registration, staff keyed the patient's information incorrectly, the payer lost the claim, the payer chose to hold the claim for review, or for another reason (often unknown to the medical practice). If these open claims are not pursued, they can lead to write-offs due to untimely filing and delay payments to the medical practice.

If the claim is denied, unpaid, or paid incorrectly, the medical practice should follow up with the payer regarding the account. Working accounts requires diligent, energetic staff and a streamlined process.

To ensure efficient and effective insurance follow-up processes, we present proven strategies to enhance your revenue cycle.

ADVANCED PRACTICES: THE INSURANCE FOLLOW-UP PROCESS
Identify and Classify Outstanding Accounts

Most practice management systems can run an "open" or "outstanding" claims report, which shows all claims that are pending — claims that have been sent but not yet paid or denied. Claims that are outstanding should be separated into two types: (1) those accounts for which you have received no response from the payer and (2) those accounts for which you have a response but more work is indicated.

Prioritize Insurance Account Follow-up Work

Prioritize accounts receivable requiring more work by (a) dollars outstanding and (b) the appeal timelines instituted by the payer. Improve results by focusing staff on high-dollar accounts, as well as those accounts with short appeal time lines. It does not make sense to spend a lot of time putting together an appeal only to realize it is past the appeal filing deadline and the rework was wasted effort. Work insurance and patient correspondence as it arrives; the correspondence may supply the new information you need regarding the account without requiring you to initiate communication with the patient or payer.

To improve the effectiveness of your insurance follow-up, report your outstanding accounts receivable in several different ways. This will help you identify where you need to target insurance follow-up efforts. It is no longer acceptable to work accounts in order of account number or patient name. Most medical practices have limited staff resources. If you initially focus on those accounts with the highest outstanding balances, you will realize a higher return on investment for staff costs.

Tool 20 identifies examples of sorting methods to help target your accounts receivable for follow-up actions. Note that this tool is applicable to accounts that have not been denied. For accounts that have been denied, the prioritization of work should be based on the date of the EOB in which the account was denied.

TOOL 20   **Prioritizing Your Outstanding Accounts Receivable**

- Sort by balance due (highest to lowest)
- Create dollar buckets appropriate for your specialty ($3,000+; $2,000–2,999; $1,000–1,999; $500–999; $100–499; $50–99; $10–49)
- Sort by account type, payer type/plan
- Sort by date claim submitted or date of service
- Sort by age of account
  - Create age buckets (120+ days, 91–120, 61–90, 31–60, current)
- Sort insurance receivables and guarantor receivables separately

© 2009 Walker, Woodcock, Larch. Reprinted with permission.

Ensure Timely Insurance Follow-up by Payer Adjudication Cycle

Every payer transmits payment or correspondence describing its refusal of payment according to a payment cycle. Staff should make note of the average payment/communication cycle by payer, and pull all outstanding accounts from that payer according to its expected response time frame. Medicare, for example, typically responds to claims for payment within 14 to 17 days. Staff should review open Medicare accounts 17 to 20 days after submitting the claim for payment. If staff resources or the practice management system do not allow following each payer's cycle, it is important to review open accounts, at minimum, 45 days after claim submission.

Record All Insurance Follow-up Actions

If the technology is available, use an automated tickler system to develop a queuing strategy that prompts the initial and additional follow-up action on the account. In the account notes on the practice management system, make a record of all actions taken. Include person(s) contacted, telephone number(s) and extension(s) called, and actions taken based on this inquiry.

Define Insurance Follow-up Strategies by Payer

How and when you follow up on an outstanding account varies depending on the payer. Each payer requires specific strategies and techniques. The more you understand the payer, the better prepared you are to define your follow-up strategies. Here are some payer-specific ideas for your follow-up team to consider:

Medicare

Medicare is typically the fastest payer. If you send your claim electronically and it is clean, you receive payment in 14 to 17 days. If a Medicare claim is denied, your appeal will also move quickly unless it involves review of physician documentation or substantiating medical necessity. It is of note that Medicare Advantage plans are administered by commercial payers, which are discussed below.

Medicaid

This payer can also be fast, but Medicaid usually offers your lowest payment per unit of service. Because Medicaid is administered at the state level, the payment process depends entirely on the state(s) in which you practice. Some states have very poorly administered Medicaid programs, and the payer is not only one of the lowest reimbursing payers, but it is also one of the slowest. Even if the Medicaid plan is administered well, experience tells us that handling Medicaid denials is arduous as compared to the initial claims process.

Commercial payers

Also referred to as "private" payers, commercial payers include many different types of companies. Indeed, your medical practice may submit claims to hundreds of commercial payers, for which your medical practice has entered into variable contract arrangements, such as whether or not to accept assignment, required authorizations for services, timeliness of claim and appeal submission, and so forth. This high degree of variability regarding contract terms and medical practice requirements makes commercial payers one of the toughest payer categories in terms of patient financial clearance, pre-adjudication edits, claims submission, payment posting, account follow-up, and denial management. Depending on your market, the reimbursement rate is often good, but the timeliness of those payments can be fast or very slow. Many commercial payers have tight time frames for submitting claims, as well as appeals. Make sure you follow up on denied and open claims promptly; the higher reimbursement from this type of payer makes it a priority.

Health maintenance organizations (HMOs)

Additional administrative requirements such as referrals and authorizations make it more difficult for the medical practice to submit clean claims the first time to HMOs. In general, it also takes HMOs longer to pay or deny your claims. Claim filing limits and appeal filing limits are often the shortest in this payer type.

Workers' compensation

Like Medicaid, workers' compensation is regulated and managed at the state level. Therefore, you may have different experiences with the payment cycle and the reimbursement rates for your workers' compensation claims. In general, there is agreement that this is one of the slowest categories of receivables to collect. Once you know the patient may have been involved in a work-related injury, you need to step up the effort to ensure you capture all of the necessary information. Be prepared for this part of your accounts receivable to take the longest to resolve.

Automobile accidents

The other part of your receivables that rivals workers' compensation is auto accidents and other personal injury claims.

State law is relevant if your medical practice is located in a "no-fault insurance state." In a no-fault insurance state, automobile drivers are required to maintain personal injury protection (PIP), and the state typically offers benefits, including medical coverage, to citizens who suffer personal injury. Most no-fault states have a time limit — typically one year — by which claims can be submitted. To effectively pursue payment, your medical practice must understand your state law and how to submit claims.

If your medical practice is not in a no-fault state, by its very nature the judicial system is slow to assign fiscal responsibility for an injury. However, it's still important to submit the claim for processing in a timely manner. Staff need to understand that some, if not most, of these accounts will result in legal action. It is imperative that staff follow up to identify the responsible party for the claim.

Regardless of state law, time frames for payment are lengthy, often exceeding one year. Accounts receivable balances associated with personal injury claims can be very large in some specialties; thus, these specialties typically have older accounts receivable.

Self-funded plans

Established by the Employee Retirement Income Security Act (ERISA) of 1974, and often referred to as ERISA plans, accounts outstanding to employers with self-funded health plans can pose a significant challenge for medical practices. Because these plans are regulated at the federal level by the United States Department of Labor, they are exempt from any state legislation that addresses payers' prompt payment of clean claims. Although some self-funded plans pay efficiently, it is common for medical practices to dedicate significant resources to follow up on self-funded or ERISA accounts.

See Chapter 12: The Denial Management Process for tips on working claim denials.

Expend Extra Efforts as Required

If a payer is notorious for asserting that it does not receive claims, send claims via certified mail with return receipt required, or drive the claims to the office of the payer and ask for a signed receipt. Some medical practices hire staff simply to contact the payer to determine whether the claim has been received by (a) querying claims status on the payer's Website if the payer provides this functionality and/or (b) calling the payer to determine claim status. For those payers that require a telephone call for follow-up, staff can be given a script to follow up on the claim. A sample of an open claim follow-up script is provided in Figure 11.1.

FIGURE 11.1 ■ Open Claims Follow-up Script

A Simple but Effective Approach

"Have you received the XYZ claim from us?"

If NO, resubmit today.

If YES, ask:

"When was the check cut for the claim?"

"When should we expect to receive payment for the claim?"

If NO CHECK HAS BEEN CUT, ask:

"What information do you need from us to process the payment?"

RECORD your notes.

END call.

© 2009 Walker, Woodcock, Larch. Reprinted with permission.

Although these measures consume valuable employee time and money, some medical practices have found that these steps are the only way they can ensure payment. Importantly, you want to quickly learn if there has been a problem in claims submission so that you can resubmit the claim if the claim batch did not successfully transmit or you can correct claims if appropriate. The adage, "no news is good news" does not apply to professional fee billing. You need to monitor every step in the claim process. Evaluate what percentage of your claims seem to be lost or not paid and calculate the value of collecting on those claims. This will help you decide how best to use your time and resources for insurance claims follow-up.

The Health Insurance Portability and Accountability Act (HIPAA) paved the way for the claims status inquiries with payers to be electronic and automatic. As payers in your market are ready to transmit more standard HIPAA transactions, you should be ready to receive them. Requesting and receiving a claim status transaction electronically will significantly reduce your staff's workload. Ask your payers for transactions 276 and 277 Health Care Claim Status Request and Response. (For additional information on HIPAA, please refer to Chapter 20: Regulations Impacting the Revenue Cycle.)

Do Not Automatically Rebill Accounts

Automatic rebilling is the process by which open claims are systematically resent to the payer on file. Rebilling all outstanding claims can lead to (1) allegations of duplicate billing and (2) denials due to duplicate claims, which require payment posting and staff research time. Regardless of whether or not you have received communication from the payer, do not automatically rebill accounts. Rather, investigate the account and take the action on the claim that is specifically warranted.

Clean Up Your Accounts Receivable

Absent well-formulated reasoning, accounts that are more than one year old should not reside on the accounts receivable. Some exceptions to this rule are claims that are held up due to a legal or appeal issue, or a particular type of claim may take longer than expected, such as a workers' compensation claim or an automobile accident claim. In addition, if your medical practice has been lenient with patients on payment plan agreements, the patient accounts receivable related to these agreements may exceed the one-year period.

If you need to clean up your accounts receivable, develop an action plan, including:

1. Identify number and type of accounts.
2. Determine whether the return on investment is worth the time and resources.
3. If applicable, decide how to allocate resources to work the accounts.
   - Schedule staff to work overtime.
   - Send accounts to an external vendor for follow-up. For a set payment per account or as a percentage of collections, the vendors will assist in following up on the accounts. (Typically this will apply only to higher dollar claims.)
   - Focus a designated number of internal staff on the older receivables, while the other staff focus on the accounts that are more current. In this fashion, all of the account follow-up staff do not get bogged down in the older accounts at the expense of the new.
4. Regularly review the success of the account follow-up efforts and reassess resource deployment as appropriate.

Including these outstanding account levels in your current receivables can mask the actual billing and collection success on current activity. Thus, we recommend that you classify this "exception" accounts receivable separately so that the medical practice can manage and monitor active accounts. Your oldest receivables may include only a few complicated, time-consuming accounts. Consider handling these unusual accounts by identifying and compartmentalizing them to improve the accuracy of your receivables performance measures and analyze your receivables both with and without these accounts. Don't let a few outliers alter your true performance.

Determine Small Balance Adjustment Level

When a patient balance is below an established threshold, suppress the statement to the patient, but maintain the balance on the patient's account. The small balance adjustment level should be based on the cost of producing and mailing the statement. This amount should be collected at the time of service.

If the patient incurs additional charges, it should, of course, be added to the next statement series.

In addition to suppressing statements, the medical practice should decide whether to adjust off small balances after a certain period of time. For example, should a 13-month-old account with $12.00 outstanding be sent to a collection agency? The answer, for most medical practices, is "no." Decide at what level, and at what age, to write off small balances. Typically, practices wait at least six months after the account balance has become self-pay before making the adjustment. Notably, adjusting the balance will write it off of the receivables, but it should be retained on the system. Thus, if the patient returns to the medical practice after the small balance has been adjusted, the adjustment can be reversed and payment collected.

The current industry standard regarding the level of a small balance account is less than $5.00 (set at $4.99 and below) to a maximum of $20.00 (set at $19.99 and below), with the most common level of $10.00 (set at $9.99 and below). The level tends to fluctuate depending on your average account balance (for example, primary care practices typically have lower small balance adjustment levels than surgery practices), and whether you have the resources available to pursue small balances.

Once you decide on the details regarding your small balance adjustment, establish a written policy and procedure regarding these adjustments. Include not only the level and age of the small balance, but also the frequency and process of the adjustment. Importantly, the "value" of using a small balance adjustment is achieved only when this process can be automated as opposed to a manual adjustment to the account. Discuss the procedures to perform scheduled small balance adjustments with your practice management system vendor.

Organize Account Follow-up Staff by Payer

Your staff should be assigned to work a specific payer's accounts unless there is a compelling reason otherwise (which could include a surgeon providing unique services that require in-depth understanding to work the claims, for example). If your medical practice is large, consider organizing staff in work teams by payer and then by specialty. Advantages of a payer-focused strategy include the following:

- Development of relationship with payers;
- Development of local experts in the medical practice to correspond with payers;
- Increased focus on follow-up activity; and
- Assessment of staff performance and productivity on follow-up efforts.

Determine Staffing by Analyzing Payer Complexity

If your medical practice assigns staff members by payer, it is important to recognize that payers require different levels of effort. Assign a score of "1" to Medicare and weight each other payer according to the level of work it requires as compared with Medicare. For example, you may contract with an HMO that has aggressive reimbursement policies and a high denial rate. The weight you assign to account follow-up for this HMO is "3" because those accounts require three times the amount of effort — and staff — as Medicare. Staff your account follow-up according to the volume of claims per payer and the weights. Review volume and weights annually. See Chapter 15: Staffing the Revenue Cycle for a detailed discussion of this and other staffing strategies.

Optimize Electronic Work Files

To facilitate and streamline the account follow-up work, staff should utilize electronic tools in the form of electronic work files that are available in the majority of today's practice management systems. For those medical practices that are still using a manual report, we recommend that priority be given to transitioning to an electronic work file in order to enhance work efficiency. When manual reports are used, we often see staff devoting more time to preparing and prioritizing their work by using multiple colored highlighters than to actually performing account follow-up itself.

The account queuing strategies that determine the electronic work files assigned to the staff should be carefully defined by management, as should the process of account follow-up that the staff is expected to perform. In some medical practices, staff are told to "follow up on accounts," but management often has no idea of what reports or electronic files the staff are working, which report parameters were selected for the work file, the number of outstanding accounts in the work file, the number of accounts that have been worked, and other important information needed to actively manage and oversee this process.

Better-performing medical practices know the following information regarding the monthly account follow-up activity provided by staff:

- Number of outstanding accounts;
- Number of accounts actually worked;
- Number of accounts placed in a tickler file;
- Exact type of account worked (for example, all accounts greater than 90 days for a particular payer); and
- Performance outcomes per staff (for example, percentage of accounts receivable greater than 90 days and the net collection rate for which the staff is responsible).

A systematic assignment and monitoring of this type of work — along with periodic audits — is recommended. The variability in the report parameters used by the staff for account follow-up, the variability in work effort among staff, and the "surprises" that billing managers have when we uncover accounts that have not been followed in a timely fashion support the need for management oversight of this process.

A number of practice management software systems permit staff to automatically "tickle" the account for subsequent follow-up efforts. The staff set a follow-up reminder date based on the next action that needs to be taken on the account. This permits the staff to follow up on an account before it appears in their next electronic work file or on their accounts receivable report. The use of tickler files is valuable to ensuring timely follow-up of the next steps identified for the account. A note of caution however: we have often found the tickler files to be misused; for example, the staff member "touches" the account, but doesn't perform the necessary follow-up tasks needed to get the account adjudicated. Even though the activity wasn't effective, the system records the activity and the account is sent to the end of the queue.

Tickler files can also be problematic if they are too large for an employee to handle. We have seen the tickler files so unreasonably large that the staff are not able to get to their account follow-up report or electronic work file.

In summary, use the tickler files; however, identify the parameters of and processes by which the tickler file should be used, as well as how large they should be.

Educate Staff to Follow a Systematic, Bounded Process

Staff members involved in insurance follow-up activity should be utilizing similar protocols. The process should be systematic and bounded, which means that staff should know the exact steps to take to follow up on the account, rather than invent a process to handle a particular account when the process for follow-up does not yield the expected result. Staff should know when and how to contact a payer, as well as when to escalate issues within the payer's hierarchy and within the medical practice's management team. This will avoid having outstanding accounts that are essentially pended indefinitely because staff are out of options regarding what avenues they have to pursue the account. A process that is systematically followed permits the issue to escalate so that the roadblocks to payment can be managed.

Refer to Tool 21: Payer Collection Checklist to identify successful techniques to collect from payers.

TOOL 21	Payer Collection Checklist

- Develop staff experience by payer.
- Use your practice management system and/or contract management software to identify underpaid or inaccurate remittances.
- Establish insurance follow-up performance measures:
  - Number of claims per day;
  - Dollars collected; and
  - Age of outstanding accounts.
- Follow up on unpaid claims per the payer's payment cycle; at minimum, every 30 to 45 days.
- Automate communication to payers.
- Develop a template for written correspondence to payers.
- Initiate a routine feedback loop to the front-end staff to inform them of denial trends and engage them in correcting claims.
- Escalate issues within the payer's hierarchy to ensure that it knows you will appeal denied claims and pursue accounts due.
- Involve physicians in payer meetings and communications.

Develop Ongoing Communication with the Payer

Establish a method of corresponding with the payer to follow up on accounts. Many medical practices have scheduled monthly telephone conversations or monthly or quarterly face-to-face meetings with provider representatives of the payers with which they participate to follow up on problematic outstanding accounts rather than be limited to a specific number of accounts per telephone call, fax, or electronic inquiry. Developing a relationship with the payer allows misunderstandings and disagreements between the medical practice and the payer to be resolved. Resolution of these challenges enhances cash flow and reduces staff inefficiency.

Use the Internet to Check for Payer Updates

Each month, assign one of your staff to "surf" payers' Websites, record new features, and make changes in your medical practice to respond to new payer rules. Take full advantage of the information and automation that the payer extends on its Website.

Transfer "Non-par" Accounts to Patient Responsibility

If you do not participate with a patient's insurance company but choose to file the claim as a courtesy to the patient, follow up on the claim within 30 to 45 days. Most medical practices will file claims to payers with which they do not participate as a courtesy to their patients, and 30 to 45 days allows the payer ample time to adjudicate the claim. Furthermore, experience has shown that less effort is required to pursue payment from a payer versus a patient. However, if 30 to 45 days have passed without payment, it's appropriate to transfer the balance to patient responsibility.

Work Payer Correspondence

Payers may send letters to your medical practice regarding specific claims. Referred to as "correspondence," this information is valuable to determine how to take action on an outstanding claim. Billing staff, however, will often ignore correspondence received from the payer. Their reasoning is that if they are able to manage their accounts in a timely fashion, they will learn this information through their own account follow-up efforts. While this may work in some circumstances, the correspondence often provides valuable information within a time period that pre-dates the staff member's investigation with the payer. The type of information included in the correspondence from payers may reflect multiple claims. We recommend that all payer correspondence be recorded and worked as it is received to ensure that the medical practice has an early "heads-up" as to problem claims and can intervene in a timely fashion as needed.

Resolve "Information Requested from Patient"

If a payer indicates that payment is being held for information from a patient, contact the patient immediately. Contact can be made by mail (for example, electronically or manually generate a standard letter that requests a response from patients) or by telephone (for example, automatically via a predictive dialer or manually place an outbound telephone call to the current telephone number on record for the guarantor of the account). If staff resources permit, initiate a three-way conference call with the patient, the payer, and your billing staff. Ask the payer to request the information and the patient to respond, then follow this transfer of information with an inquiry as to when to expect payment on your claim.

Regardless of the nature of the contact, if the patient does not supply the information within 30 days, transfer the account to patient responsibility (provided this is consistent with your contract terms).

Develop a Formal Communication Process with Practice Sites

When the insurance follow-up staff research the account with the payer, they often learn that additional information from the physician or practice site is required. Better-performing medical practices have developed electronic tools to request and track this information between the billing office and the practice site, as well as expected turnaround times for which information is provided. Some of these medical practices have instituted a spreadsheet placed on the medical practice's Intranet that tracks the request, the date of the request, the response, the individual responsible for the response, and the date of the response. At a glance, one can see the number of accounts for which additional information has been requested and the status of these requests. This formalizes the process and is more efficient than multiple e-mails or telephone calls that must be tracked. The expected turnaround time for outstanding information required of physicians and/or the practice site should be no longer than one week.

Don't Play the Account Transfer Game

If account follow-up is stymied, don't always resort to automatically transferring the balance to patient responsibility. Some staff believe that the patient is then engaged in the issue and hopefully will intervene to resolve the issue. Unfortunately, automatically transferring balances to patient responsibility lengthens the revenue cycle in the medical practice with no assurance that the account will actually be paid. We strongly recommend that before the account is transferred from insurance to self-pay status, that the bounded account follow-up process be followed. This will avoid the multiple changes of the financially responsible party, from insurance to self-pay to insurance back to self-pay. These transfers are not only confusing to the patient, but also are a waste of time and resources.

Segment Follow-up Work

Some medical practices are working with less-than-optimal resources. If staff volumes are less than optimal for account follow-up functions, consider segmenting tasks throughout the week. For example:

Monday: Account follow-up

Tuesday a.m.: Work payer correspondence; p.m.: Account follow-up

Wednesday a.m.: Work tickler file; p.m.: Work credit balance report

Thursday: Account follow-up

Friday a.m.: Work payer correspondence; p.m.: Account follow-up

In this fashion, prioritization of the work can take place and there is assurance that attention is paid to all assigned tasks.

Identify Financial Rewards from State Prompt Payment Laws

As we discussed in Chapter 10, most states have passed legislation that allows for collection of lost interest or financial penalties on open claims. Understand your state law and pursue deserved remuneration. For information regarding your state's prompt payment law, go to www.elizabethwoodcock.com/resources.html.

As we demonstrate in this chapter, the timeliness and methods by which insurance account follow-up are performed will have a major influence on the success of your revenue cycle. Due diligence in work assignment, prioritization, and oversight of this work is vital to ensuring that the performance of your insurance accounts receivable is at expected levels.

STAFF WORKLOAD RANGES

The staff workload ranges for insurance follow-up that we typically expect are provided on the following page. The ability to perform within these ranges may vary due to internal practice-specific factors (such as facility layout, telephone system, and practice management system). The workload ranges are based on a staff member performing these functions approximately seven hours of productive time per day (allowing one hour for breaks, interruptions, and other down time). Note that the workload ranges reflect quantitative performance levels. Qualitative performance — accuracy, completeness, appropriateness, and quality of these functions — should also be measured. When issues of quantity versus quality arise, we strongly recommend that quality be emphasized, even if the performance workload ranges for a particular function need to be relaxed from these levels.

Given the diverse responsibilities of an insurance follow-up staff member, we have presented the workload expectations for insurance follow-up based on activity. Staffing depends on the volume and level of follow-up needed; if claims are paid without the need for extensive follow-up, staffing levels will be minimal.

(continued on next page)

Staff Function	Accounts per hour	Transaction time per minute
Research correspondence* and resolve by telephone	6–12	5–10
Research correspondence* and resolve by appeal	3–4	15–20
Check status of claim (telephone or online) and rebill	12–60	1–5

* Includes reviewing the correspondence from payer that shows the denial and/or underpayment, identifying the cause of the denial or underpayment, pulling medical documentation, and/or other support and developing a case for reconsideration of payment.

Automation, such as electronic access to payers, medical documentation, and payer reimbursement policies, can increase the performance workload ranges required for account follow-up even further.

Note: Institute these workload ranges only if accuracy can be assured in this time frame. If not, you may need to increase the time to perform the function in order to avoid mistakes.

© 2009 Walker, Woodcock, Larch. Reprinted with permission.

LEADING PERFORMANCE INDICATORS

Use the following indicators to assess the performance of your insurance follow-up process. We refer to these measures as "leading" performance indicators. If your medical practice is successful in achieving these levels in the insurance follow-up process, you are on the correct path to optimizing your revenue cycle.

Follow-up notes documented on the account:	Per payer payment cycles; at minimum every 30–45 days
Accounts receivable greater than 90 days:	15 to 20 percent
Days in accounts receivable:	35 to 40 days
Net collection rate:	97 percent or greater

Note: The aging of your receivables will depend upon the extent of re-aging of your accounts and the report parameters you use to generate aged trial balance reports.

© 2009 Walker, Woodcock, Larch. Reprinted with permission.

See Chapter 19: Measuring and Analyzing the Revenue Cycle for a detailed discussion of performance indicators.

THE INSURANCE FOLLOW-UP DIAGNOSTIC TOOL

The insurance follow-up diagnostic tool below helps you ensure that the process, people, technology, and quality required for effective insurance follow-up are in place in your medical practice.

Process:

1. What is your policy regarding insurance follow-up after the claim is submitted but has not been paid (for example, no response from the payer)?
2. How frequently are open claims reports run?
3. What is the prioritization of accounts for follow-up action (for example, by dollar, payer, or date of service)?
4. Are there efforts to research the account prior to rebilling claims?
5. Is payer correspondence systematically reviewed and worked within an established time period?

People:

1. Who is responsible for working open claims?
2. What staffing deployment model is used for account follow-up? Do you have the right staff? Are they doing the right things?
3. How is the workload between staff balanced to ensure equity? Are weights used to determine the difficulty of the payer and, hence, the level of difficulty in account follow-up?
4. Do staff routinely see the results of their work? For example, do they know how much of their receivables is greater than 90 days, their net collection rate, the number of accounts worked? Are they provided with data and graphs to track their progress over time?
5. How are staff productivity and performance monitored?

Technology:

1. What electronic queuing strategies have been developed? How does a claim get in and out of the queue?
2. What percentage of accounts have been followed in a timely fashion, for example, are notes documented on the account at minimum, every 30 to 45 days?
3. Are electronic tickler systems being used? If so, are staff attending to the tickler files, as well as their electronic work files for account follow-up?

Quality:

1. Are the accounts simply being touched or are they actually worked?
2. Is the entire account worked or only the open line item on the account?
3. Are the account notes made with sufficient information to follow the steps that have been taken to collect on the account? Have common abbreviations or phrases been developed to facilitate account documentation?

POLICIES AND PROCEDURES

At the end of each chapter, we provide policies and procedures to assist you in developing a policy and procedure manual for your medical practice. Below are two policies and procedures specific to the insurance follow-up process.

Policy 24: The Insurance Follow-up Process

Policy 25: Small Balance Adjustments

POLICY 24: THE INSURANCE FOLLOW-UP PROCESS

Policy:

The billing office will be responsible for timely follow-up on monies owed to the medical practice from payers.

Procedures:

Electronic work files will be generated from the practice management system, with staff assigned to work the accounts to ensure timely payment.

For denied or pended claims, the following actions will be taken based on the denial code indicated on the explanation of benefits or remittance:

- If the patient is not eligible for benefits, or if the service is not a covered benefit, the balance will be transferred immediately to self-pay;
- If additional information is required, the claim will be resent with the appropriate information or attachments; or
- If demographic information or policy numbers are incomplete or inaccurate, the patient will be called to obtain valid data. This updated information will be immediately entered into the computer and a rebill will be requested.

The following schedule, which should be amended by payer based on predicted payment cycle, will be followed to assure consistent follow-up:

30 to 60 days after initial claim submission:

1. Confirm receipt of payment.
2. If no payment, contact the payer to determine claim status online or by telephone.
3. If claim was filed as a courtesy to payer with which you have no contract, transfer the financial responsibility to the patient.
4. Determine the reason(s) for denial or claim hold and the actions required for payment to be released.
5. Assemble any documentation requested to adjudicate the claim.
6. Resubmit the corrected claim for payment or initiate the appeal process; copy the patient on the appeal letter.

If payment still has not been received at 90 days after initial claim submission:

1. Confirm receipt of payment.
2. If no payment, contact the payer to determine claim status online or by telephone (particularly in the case of an appeal).
3. Determine the reason(s) for claim hold and the actions required for payment to be released.

4. Assemble any documentation requested to adjudicate the claim.

5. Resubmit the corrected claim for payment or initiate the second level of the appeal process.

6. Contact the patient and request his/her assistance immediately.

7. If possible, conduct a three-way conference call with the patient, payer, and you.

8. Summarize your efforts to follow up on this claim in a letter, and bill patient for balance due, if the contract with the payer in question allows it.

If payment still has not been received at 120 days after initial claim submission:

1. Confirm receipt of payment.

2. If no payment, contact the payer to determine claim status by telephone. Request to speak with a supervisor and/or your provider representative, outlining your efforts to date to follow up on this claim.

3. Determine the reason(s) for claim hold and the actions required for payment to be released.

4. Assemble any documentation requested to adjudicate the claim and rebill if necessary.

5. Resubmit the corrected claim for payment or initiate the final level of the appeal process.

If payment still has not been received at 150 days after initial claim submission:

1. Confirm receipt of payment.

2. If no payment, document your efforts to date. Give the documentation to the billing manager and/or the treating physician with your recommendation(s) regarding follow-up activity.

POLICY 25: SMALL BALANCE ADJUSTMENTS

Policy:

Patient account balances equal to or less than $9.99 will be written off if the account meets certain criteria.

Procedures:

If the account balance meets all of the following criteria, the account will be written off:

1. Less than or equal to $9.99;

2. More than 120 days old from date became self-pay;

3. There are no insurance due balances; and

4. There is no violation of a contractual obligation to continue collection.*

On a monthly basis, a report will be generated to identify accounts that meet these criteria. The account representative will review the list for appropriate criteria and authorize the monthly write-off. The small balance adjustment will be conducted automatically by the practice management system, as initiated by the billing office manager.

Though the small balance adjustment is made to the account, when the patient presents for future services, this amount will be collected from the patient at the time of service, with the adjustment reversed and the payment posted to the patient's account.

*It is of note that the Centers for Medicare & Medicaid Services (CMS) defines a "reasonable" collection effort as follows:

"Presumption of Non-collectibility: If after reasonable and customary attempts to collect a bill, the debt remains unpaid more than 120 days from the date the first bill is mailed to the beneficiary, the debt may be deemed uncollectible."[1]

---

[1] Section 310.2, Provider Reimbursement Manual, Part I, http://www.cms.hhs.gov/Manuals/PBM/ (accessed September 12, 2008).

CHAPTER 12

Pothole 10
The Denial Management Process

In previous chapters, we highlight important strategies to ensure that your claims are received by the payers and do not remain unpaid or in limbo. We also focus on pre-adjudication claim edits to correct the claim before it is submitted to the payer. Now we focus on those claims that the payer has received but has denied. Understanding the cause of claim denials — and actively investigating and appealing them — are critically important if your medical practice is to be appropriately reimbursed for its services.

More often than not, computers, not people, look at the claims, so there's no wiggle room. While every effort should be made to ensure that claims are "clean" so that they won't be denied by payers, given the complexity of the revenue cycle, some claim denials are inevitable. Your medical practice's management of the claim denial process is the key to effectively investigating and appealing denied claims and capturing this revenue for your medical practice.

In this chapter, we discuss:

- Reasons for denied claims
- Denial management strategies
  - Measuring claim denials
  - Denial prevention
  - Deconstructing denials
  - Tools to support denial management
- The appeals process
  - Automated appeal tools
  - Payer guidelines for appeal
  - Escalating appeals with payers
- Payer report cards
- Calculating the cost of rework

COMMON MEDICAL PRACTICE ERRORS THAT CAUSE DENIALS

The most efficient revenue cycle is one in which a high percentage of "clean" claims are paid upon first submission of the claim to the payer. Payers routinely change their claim specifications, and it is up to each medical practice to stay current on payer communications to ensure claims are being submitted consistent with payer requirements. In addition, payers issue specific requirements for reimbursement that need to be met in order to receive payment, such as requiring specific accreditation as a condition of reimbursement.

When claims are denied, it is either due to a medical practice error or to a payer error. Common reasons for denied claims are reported in Figure 12.1.

FIGURE 12.1 ■ Reasons for Denied Claims

- Registration error
- Patient not eligible on date of service
- Charge entry error
- Referrals and pre-authorizations not secured/submitted
- Duplicate billing
- Lack of medical necessity
- Documentation to support the claim is required
- Credentialing or provider enrollment problem
- Coding-related problems (bundling, global periods, modifiers)

© 2009 Walker, Woodcock, Larch. Reprinted with permission.

As demonstrated in this figure, many of the claim denials are preventable and within the medical practice's control if diligent attention is paid to patient financial clearance functions as discussed in Chapter 3: The Patient Financial Clearance Process.

In this chapter, we focus on complex denials that are difficult to understand and even harder to permanently correct. However, there are other preventable denials that no medical practice wants to see. These are simple mistakes that should rarely occur, such as:

- *Patient's subscriber number is incorrect or missing.* This is caused by staff not entering complete registration information into the practice management system. To prevent this denial, set up flags or alerts for required fields and incorrect formats.
- *Patient's name does not match payer's information.* The patient's name on the claim form must match what is on his/her insurance card; otherwise the payer has the right to deny your claim. To prevent this denial, verify information directly from the payer; emphasize keying accuracy to the staff and then monitor performance.

- *Diagnosis not coded to highest level of specificity.* The diagnosis must be coded to the most specific level available. To prevent this denial, train providers and staff on coding; integrate electronic prompts into the charge capture system if and when a more specific code is available for the chosen diagnosis.

- *Claim is illegible.* We have emphasized the need to electronically send claims to improve the efficiency of your revenue cycle process, but there are still payers whose claims must continue to be submitted on paper. To prevent this denial, for those claims that must be printed, make sure that the printer is lined up with the appropriate fields on the claim form and that the printer cartridge is replaced at regular intervals so that paper claims are readable. Most payers that receive paper claims are scanning them; make sure your claims can be read by the scanner.

Common medical practice errors that are a little more complex than those cited above that contribute to denials are outlined in Figure 12.2. The left side of the figure reflects typical descriptions of the reason for the denial as provided on the explanation of benefits (EOB) or via insurance correspondence that is sent to your medical practice. The right side of the figure reflects the action on the part of the medical practice that is likely causing the claim denial to occur.

FIGURE 12.2 ■ Translating Payer Denials

Payer Reason for Denial	Possible Causes
Coverage not in effect at the time of service; Our records indicate patient is enrolled with Payer X. Please bill Payer X first; Patient is covered by another insurance that is primary; or Charges were incurred after patient's cancellation date with plan.	The patient's insurance coverage was not verified prior to service (the patient may have switched jobs, lost coverage or listed the wrong payer, or the medical practice may have collected incorrect information from the patient or failed to obtain all payers). The medical practice failed to note the patient's termination date with his/her health plan; or the practice received verification from the payer but the payer had not updated its records from the employer.
No referral in our system; or Date of service not within referral time period.	The primary care physician did not send the referral to the payer, the specialist failed to obtain the referral, or the valid referral period for the patient's health plan was exceeded.
Charge not covered by subscriber's benefit plan.	The medical practice failed to verify coverage for such services as preventive services or complex services that may not be covered by the plan.

(continued on next page)

FIGURE 12.2 ■ Translating Payer Denials *(continued)*

Payer Reason for Denial	Possible Causes
Claim lacks information needed for adjudication.	Data are missing from a field on the claim form, such as plan identification number, practice number, date of injury, referring physician national provider identification (NPI), and so forth. Pre-adjudication claim edits have not been established to the level of specificity required to ensure correction of these errors prior to claim submission.
Incomplete/invalid patient procedure or diagnosis codes.	The charge ticket is outdated: Deleted codes are still on the ticket, descriptions are not valid, or extra digits are needed for correct diagnosis coding. There is a coding problem involving invalid linkages of procedure and diagnosis data. Your system is allowing invalid codes to be used.
Lack of patient's date of illness/injury; Age conflict with reported diagnosis; Incorrect gender; Capitated services billed in error; Modifiers used incorrectly; or Place of service (location) errors.	There are data entry errors or omissions at charge capture or charge entry.

© 2009 Walker, Woodcock, Larch. Reprinted with permission.

THE PAYER'S POINT OF VIEW

To the payer, adjudicating paper and electronic claims involves many steps and process handoffs. Within seconds, the decision is made to send the claim to medical review, down-code the claim, submit partial payment, pay the claim, or deny it entirely. Anything that a medical practice can do to complete the claim form correctly will help the payer appropriately process its claims the first time. Any omission or error means the claim is not a clean claim and will go into a review status, where it will remain for an indeterminate length of time, as discussed in Chapter 10: The Payment and Denial Posting Process.

When a payer starts denying more and more claims, this can be a signal that it's in financial trouble. While the prompt payment laws in some states may help assure quick payment, the medical practice must monitor the timeliness of payments to avoid lost revenue associated with a payer that has closed its doors (and the potential legal challenges and patient service impact this represents).

To ensure an efficient and effective denial management process, we present proven strategies to enhance your revenue cycle.

ADVANCED PRACTICES: THE DENIAL MANAGEMENT PROCESS

Measure Denial Data and Take Action

Except in extenuating circumstances, less than 7 percent of claims should be denied on first submission. Measure the following denial data for your medical practice on a monthly basis — if not more frequently — and take action to reduce or eliminate the reason for the denial:

- Percentage of claims denied on initial submission;
- Number of denials and dollar value of denials;
- Top 10 reasons claims are denied;
- Denials by payer, location, specialty, and provider;
- Average dollar per denial in major denial reason categories;
- Percentage of denied claims that are reworked;
- Staff time and cost dedicated to denial management;
- Lag time between date of denial received and date the appeal is sent out;
- Percentage and dollars of reworked denied claims that are paid; and
- Percentage and dollars of the denials that are written off.

Prioritize your tasks. First, tackle those areas that are within your medical practice's control and then devote your time to payer errors.

For medical practices that have not yet tracked their claim denial data, Tools 22 and 23 will help you begin to track denial activity and graph your denial trends so you can analyze your preventable claim denials.

For example, using such a tool, a medical practice may discover that it has three major reasons for denial: (1) patient not eligible on date of service; (2) no referral/pre-authorization obtained; and (3) incorrect payer was billed. All of these reasons fall under the control of the medical practice; consequently, the action taken can include resolving the root cause of the problem by improving the completeness and accuracy of the patient financial clearance and registration processes. In this fashion, the claim denial rate can be significantly reduced.

Prevent Claim Denials

Once your medical practice understands the reasons for its claim denials, it can take preventive action so that future claim denials for the same reasons are

TOOL 22	Claim Denial Log

A claim denial log helps track denials. We recommend that you track several payers for a one-week period. This one-week snapshot will identify the top denial opportunities in your medical practice. Immediately take action to determine the originating cause and prevent the denials.

To start: Create this log in a spreadsheet and track one week of EOBs for one payer.

Payer:					Claim Denial Categories									
Physi-cian	Pt#	CPT®	Location	Charge	Not Elig	Incorrect Payer	Ref Auth	Chg Entry	Pt Info	Cred'g	Bun-dled	Not Cov-ered	Dup	Med Nec
TOTALS ($'s and count)														

Pt = patient   Ref = referral   Chg = charge   Cred'g = credentialing
Elig = eligible   Auth = authorization   Info = information   Dup = duplicate   Med Nec = medical necessity

© 2009 Walker, Woodcock, Larch. Reprinted with permission.

minimized (or potentially eliminated). Experts indicate that approximately 90 percent of denials are preventable, and 67 percent of denials are recoverable.[1]

Ask and answer the following question: What is the cause of the denial? If the cause rests with the medical practice, fix the cause of the denial. It sounds easy, but it often requires significant operational change. If the cause is attributed to the payer and it occurs routinely, escalate denials within the payer's structure. Adding billing staff to rework denied claims over and over again is not as good an investment as adding a staff member at the front office to reduce errors that are causing the denials to occur in the first place. Any time you can eliminate a denial cause, the claim will be paid the first time and the cost to rework the denied claim will be eliminated.

The sooner the medical practice can identify and reduce the root cause of the denials, the sooner it will have fewer denials to rework.

---

[1] Health Care Advisory Board Cost & Operations Presentation: *Capturing Lost Revenues*, 2002.

TOOL 23   **Graph of Denial Trends**

A graph of denials can help you initiate your denial analysis. By analyzing the data in graphical form, you can identify causes of denials and track performance over time to determine what action you should take. Trend the denials by payer, originating cause, and location of service.

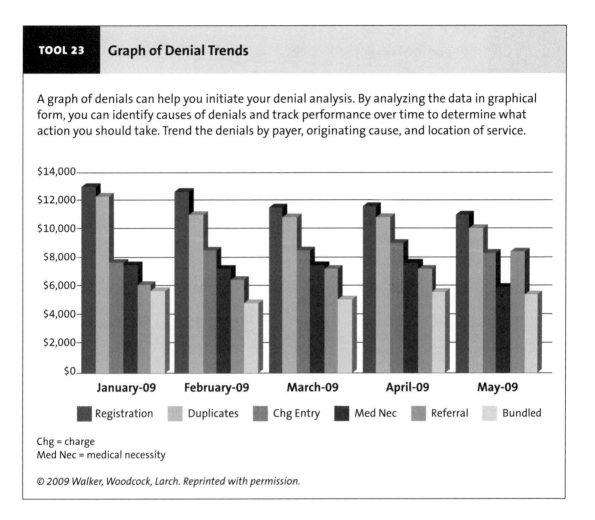

Chg = charge
Med Nec = medical necessity

© 2009 Walker, Woodcock, Larch. Reprinted with permission.

Determine Whether the Claim Has Truly Been Denied

In order to determine what information is missing from the claim, it is necessary to refer to the remark codes that are printed on the EOB. Payers send many EOB remark codes. Many payers continue to send their own proprietary remark codes, even though the Health Insurance Portability and Accountability Act (HIPAA) Transactions and Codes Sets regulations intended to standardize remark and remittance codes. It is important that staff understand what the remark code means. Is it a denied claim? Is it informational only? What has caused this denial? How is it to be researched, resolved, and/or appealed?

For Medicare, these three or four character alphanumeric remark codes can be found on the EOB on the far-right side of the first line of the claim detail on the same line where the patient's name appears. The detailed explanations for the remark codes are found at the end of the EOB under the heading "GLOSSARY," along with the detailed explanation of the denial codes. For other payers, the EOB remark codes are listed below the section that shows payments or on the back of the EOB.

TOOL 24   **Interpreting EOB Remark Codes**

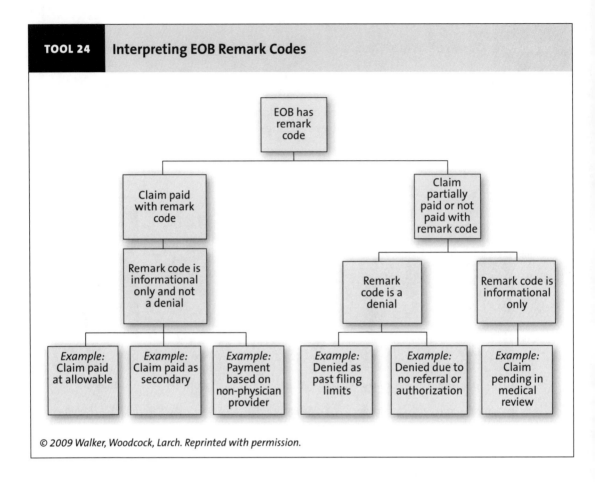

© 2009 Walker, Woodcock, Larch. Reprinted with permission.

Tool 24 provides an example of remark codes submitted by payers. Note that some are informational only, while others indicate the reason for a denied claim. A similar tool can be developed for your staff to help them interpret common EOB remark codes used by your payers.

Once you have determined if the claim has truly been denied, the next step is to determine if the claim is appealable. Tool 25 depicts a flowchart that can be used to facilitate this assessment. It can be customized for your medical practice based on your common denial codes.

Once you have determined if the EOB remark codes are indicating that the claim has been denied, three steps must be taken to work the claim denials.

Step 1:   Does this claim need to be written off?

If yes, write it off ... but use the appropriate adjustment codes.

Step 2:   Does the claim need to be corrected?

If yes, correct it and resubmit it.

Step 3:   Does this claim need to be appealed?

If yes, develop your case and appeal it (per the payer's process).

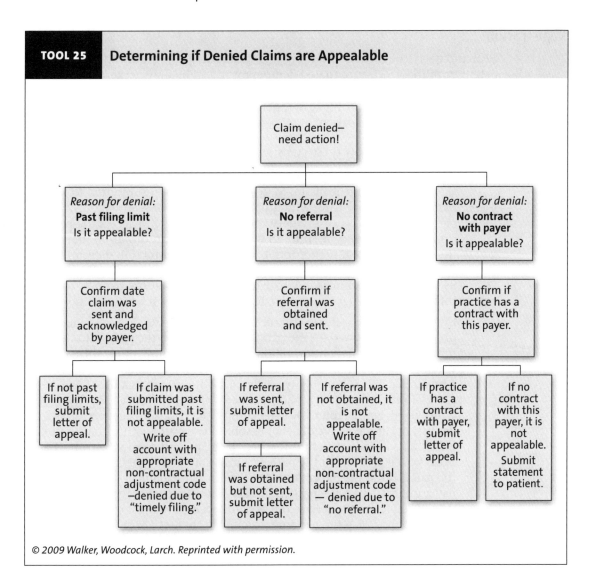

TOOL 25 — Determining if Denied Claims are Appealable

Claim denied—need action!

Reason for denial: **Past filing limit** Is it appealable?

Reason for denial: **No referral** Is it appealable?

Reason for denial: **No contract with payer** Is it appealable?

Confirm date claim was sent and acknowledged by payer.

Confirm if referral was obtained and sent.

Confirm if practice has a contract with this payer.

If not past filing limits, submit letter of appeal.

If claim was submitted past filing limits, it is not appealable. Write off account with appropriate non-contractual adjustment code –denied due to "timely filing."

If referral was sent, submit letter of appeal.

If referral was obtained but not sent, submit letter of appeal.

If referral was not obtained, it is not appealable. Write off account with appropriate non-contractual adjustment code — denied due to "no referral."

If practice has a contract with payer, submit letter of appeal.

If no contract with this payer, it is not appealable. Submit statement to patient.

© 2009 Walker, Woodcock, Larch. Reprinted with permission.

Deconstruct Your Denials

In reality, the actual work of denial management is significantly more complex than this three-step process implies. Deconstructing your denials requires considerable knowledge and persistence on the part of denial management staff. While it is important to engage in action that will prevent denials from occurring, when they do occur, you must apply systematic denial management strategies to work the denial and potentially appeal the denial. Because resources are limited in a medical practice, it is important to consider speed and efficiency when you develop denial follow-up procedures.

The following section provides useful ways to "deconstruct" and resolve denials for frequently observed remark codes. Use these or create your own tools for investigating and determining action that will be taken on your claim denials.

Registration

Far and away the most common type of claim denial, registration-related issues stem from incorrect or outdated demographic and insurance information. Take proactive steps to *prevent* this denial. As discussed in Chapter 4: The Patient Check-in and Check-out Processes, performing insurance and demographic verification before the patient is seen can prevent registration-related denials.

If a denial occurs, follow these steps:

1. Review the patient's account to determine if inaccurate information was submitted on the claim. Match the information submitted to the patient's insurance card, which should be copied or scanned during the patient check-in process. Query the payer's Website to access the patient's information; review carefully to see if the payer's information matches the data submitted. If appropriate, contact the hospital to determine if different registration information exists in its billing system. In summary, use all available sources to locate information about the patient. If the information was keyed incorrectly, correct the claim and resubmit it.

2. Contact the patient if you still haven't been successful. Using the telephone numbers listed on the patient's account, call the patient to determine if more accurate information exists. (For a billing office with a high volume of registration-related denials, this is an excellent activity for a predictive dialer. A predictive dialer electronically dials a list of telephone numbers, linking a staff member with the call once the telephone is answered. See Chapter 13: The Patient Collections Process for further discussion on predictive dialers.) Resubmit the claim with the accurate information, if the patient is reached. If the patient cannot be contacted over the telephone, bill the patient with a statement message informing the patient that the payer denied the claim as ineligible, meaning that the payer indicates that the patient did not have the payer's insurance on the date of service or the service the patient received was not covered pursuant to their policy. Flag the patient's account so that staff answering calls or seeing the patient face-to-face can inquire regarding the registration data.

3. If the patient does not respond to your calls and statements, transfer the account to the collection agency. Collection agencies can perform skip-tracing to attempt to locate the patient to pursue collections.

4. When the account is sent to the collection agency, write off the balance to patient bad debt using a denial code to denote the fact that it was a registration-related problem. Put an alert on the account so that the front-office staff can request payment if the patient returns to your medical practice for care.

Prevention is the key; registration-related denials require significant medical practice resources, and often end up as patient bad debt. Eliminate this rework by doing it right the first time!

Duplicate claims

Many codes are used to denote that a payer is denying a claim as a duplicate, often called "dupes" in industry parlance. When a claim is denied as a duplicate, the payer is indicating that it has received another claim for the same service, and it refuses to pay for the same service twice. The remark on the EOB reads, "duplicate claim" or "previously paid." Payment for this claim/service may have been provided in a previous payment. However, not all "duplicate claim" denials signify that a duplicate claim was, in fact, submitted.

The following scenarios often generate a duplicate claim denial:

- The procedure was performed more than once on the same patient on the same date of service. For example, two chest x-rays were taken and interpreted on the same date of service;

- The procedure was performed more than once by physicians with the same tax identification number on the same patient on the same date of service. For example, two specialists from the same multispecialty group consulted on the same patient in the hospital; and

- The payer system does not read your modifiers as part of their claim adjudication process even though the modifiers were submitted. For example, two of the same CPT® codes may appear for the same patient on the same date of service.

Don't just adjust claims off as duplicates. You must research the claim to determine the facts of the case.

The flowchart depicted in Tool 26 walks through the basic steps of working a denial due to duplicate claim from receipt to resolution.

Claim lacks information needed for adjudication

Payers issue this denial to notify the medical practice that the claim submitted cannot be processed and/or is an invalid claim. The denial, "the claim lacks information needed for adjudication," is usually a signal that a piece of information needed to process the claim is missing from the original claim submission. The missing information could range from an invalid subscriber identification number for the patient to an invalid procedure code.

Once you have determined the information that was missing or invalid and you have made the corrections or additions to the claim that are needed, you should resubmit it to the payer as if it were a new claim.

The reasons why these denials are being received should be communicated to the appropriate staff member or manager to ensure that the information is corrected in the practice management system so that future denials for the same missing information can be avoided.

Overall, the denial, "claim lacks information," is a general denial that covers a wide range of reasons why the payer could not process the claim. By interpreting the remark codes that are provided on the EOB and sending corrected claims electronically to the payer, the claims in question should be paid in short order.

Medical necessity

A denial for medical necessity means that a payer is denying a service provided to a patient because it was not medically necessary. Payers issue definitions of medically necessary services. As an example, one payer's health care definition of medical necessity is provided in Figure 12.3.

TOOL 26	Working a Duplicate Denial Code

The flowchart below walks through the basic steps of working a duplicate denial from receipt to resolution.

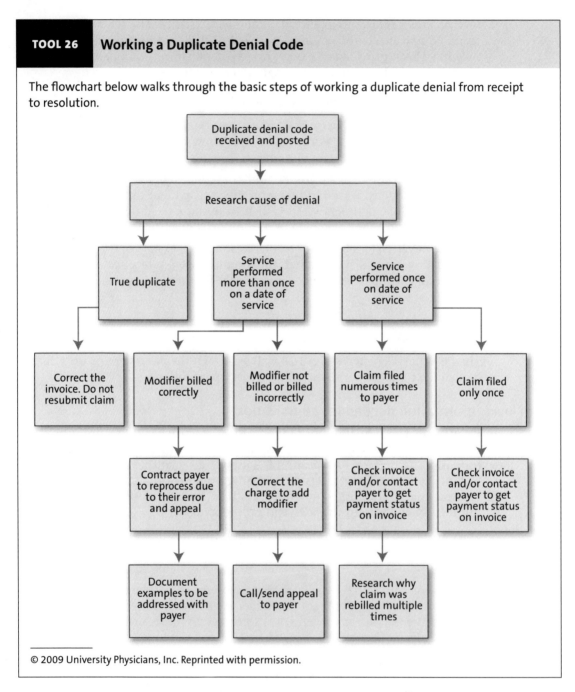

In addition to this sample definition, most payers issue policy statements regarding specific services. For Medicare, its policy statements are called coverage determinations. Medicare publishes National Coverage Determinations (NCD), and each of its carriers publishes Local Coverage Determinations (LCD). Not all procedure codes have established policy statements. These policy statements and coverage determinations document diagnoses that have been determined, by the payer, to support the medical necessity of the procedure for which the medical practice is seeking reimbursement.

FIGURE 12.3 ■ Sample Definition of Medical Necessity

" 'Medically Necessary' or 'Medical Necessity' shall mean health care services that a physician, exercising prudent clinical judgment, would provide to a patient for the purpose of evaluating, diagnosing, or treating an illness, injury, disease, or its symptoms, and that are:

a. in accordance with the generally accepted standards of medical practice;

b. clinically appropriate, in terms of type, frequency, extent, site, and duration, and considered effective for the patient's illness, injury, or disease; and

c. not primarily for the convenience of the patient or physician, or other physician, and not more costly than an alternative service or sequence of services at least as likely to produce equivalent therapeutic or diagnostic results as to the diagnosis or treatment of that patient's illness, injury, or disease.

For these purposes, 'generally accepted standards of medical practice' means:

■ standards that are based on credible scientific evidence published in peer-reviewed medical literature generally recognized by the relevant medical community;

■ Physician specialty society recommendations;

■ the views of physicians practicing in the relevant clinical area; and any other relevant factors.

Preventive care may be Medically Necessary but coverage for Medically Necessary preventive care is governed by terms of the applicable plan documents."

―――――――
Source: Cigna HealthCare.
www.cigna.com/health/provider/medical/procedural/medical_necessity.html (accessed September 15, 2008).

If a policy statement or coverage determination exists for the procedure and if the diagnosis(es) that is submitted is inconsistent with those promulgated, the payer denies the claim with the message saying that the service is not deemed medically necessary.

Four strategies are used to work a claim that has been denied due to medical necessity:

1. Understand all policies and coverage determinations for services rendered at your medical practice. Before the service is rendered, inform the patient that the payer will not provide coverage for the service and that he or she will be financially responsible for the services. For Medicare patients, use the Advance Beneficiary Notice (ABN) and select the appropriate modifier. (The modifier GA indicates that the service is expected to be denied as not medically necessary, the completed ABN signed by the patient is on file, and the patient can be billed; the modifier GZ indicates that the ABN was not signed, and the patient cannot be billed.)

2. Review the medical records. Medical necessity denials are often based on a diagnosis code. That is, payment for a service is denied because the payer disagrees that it should have been performed for the diagnosis cited on the claim. The physician or a coder should be consulted to review the medical record to determine if there is a more specific or appropriate diagnosis documented that illustrates why the procedure was performed. If there is another diagnosis that was documented, but originally overlooked or not submitted on the claim, the claim can be resubmitted with the corrected information.

3. Discuss the denial with your providers. If they disagree with the policy or coverage determination, gather objective information to support your case. This may include medical literature, support from a referring physician, reimbursement policies from other payers, and statements from your specialty society.

4. Write an appeal letter from the physician commencing with the facts of the medical situation. Next, explain why the denial should be overturned, referencing as many objective sources as you have gathered. Finally, attach all supporting documentation to the letter. Mail the appeal and supporting documentation to the payer.

Medical necessity appeals require time and attention, but are frequently successful.

Coding

With thousands of procedure and diagnosis codes, the probability of your medical practice receiving a denial for a claim based on coding issues is high. The coding issue may be the result of a medical necessity denial (for example, the diagnosis does not support the service performed, according to the payer), as discussed above. Other common coding-related issues include global periods, modifiers, bundling, and the level of codes that were selected (for example, CPT® code 99214, in the payer's opinion, should have been a 99213).

To manage these denials, we recommend a two-step process:

1. Review the medical record to determine if the service was correctly coded when it was originally submitted. If it was not coded properly (for example, the documentation supports another procedure and/or diagnosis code), correct the codes and resubmit the claim.

2. If the codes were submitted correctly, decide whether the denial can be appealed. If the service was performed in the global period — for example, an office visit related to the same condition five days after a surgery with a 10-day global period — the denial should not be appealed. But, if the service was a procedure with no global period, the office visit can be appealed with documentation to support the fact that there is no global period. Write the appeal, making use of all coding-related resources. These include, but are not limited to, payer reimbursement policies, such as Medicare's Medical Coverage Determinations; the CPT® Coding Manual and CPT® Coding Assistant by the American Medical Associa-

tion; and the current table of global periods, as published by the Centers for Medicare & Medicaid Services (CMS). File the appeal with supporting documentation.

For more information about coding-related issues, see Chapter 6: The Coding Process.

Coordination of benefits

Some claims are denied because the payer will not pay benefits covered by other policies or coverage will be provided in a specific sequence when more than one policy covers the claims. To prevent coordination of benefits (COB) denials, query the patient about secondary and tertiary coverage at registration. During insurance verification, query the payer to determine whether it is the primary or secondary payer, and whether the patient has other coverage, according to the payer's database.

Many COB issues, unfortunately, percolate despite best efforts during the registration and scheduling process. Here are some rules of thumb to keep in mind about coordination of benefits (though insurance coverage should be verified as special circumstances may exist):

1. *The "birthday rule."* The parent with the earlier birthday in the year, based on a 12-month, January-to-December calendar, covers the dependent child as the primary payer and serves as the primary guarantor for dual-employed spouses with the same family coverage. For example, if both parents of a child are employed and carry health insurance, and the father was born in April, and the mother in January, the mother's insurance is considered the primary payer.

2. *Active employment.* The payer of an active employee is primary over a retired or inactive dependent.

3. *Dependent.* The payer of a guarantor is primary over a family member classified as a dependent.

If a claim is denied for a COB issue, contact the primary payer to determine the status of the claim. Often, you must contact both payers multiple times, as they work out who owes what.

Referrals and authorizations

Although your overall denial rate for referrals and authorizations may not be high, for those payers who require referrals or authorizations, you may have a much higher claim denial rate. You will be denied for no referral/authorization if you did not obtain one, or because you did not follow the payer's process for submitting it.

A medical practice must maintain current information on all policies and procedures related to referrals and authorizations for each payer. Methods used to obtain and submit referrals/authorizations to payers include via telephone, facsimile, Website, paper, or electronic data interchange (EDI) transaction. The methods vary as follows:

- Some payers require a referral or authorization number on the claim;
- Some payers require a referral attached to a paper claim;
- Some payers require a referral be submitted via fax or online prior to the service being provided;
- Some payers require the referral to be signed by the referring physician; and
- Some payers require an authorization to be called in prior to service or within 24 hours if an emergency service.

If a denial occurs due to lack of authorization or referral, follow these steps:

1. Review the account to see if a referral/authorization was obtained and entered into practice management system so the information could be recorded on the claim.
2. If the information is present, resubmit the claim.
3. If the information is not present, contact the referral coordinator to verify whether the referral or authorization was obtained. If it was obtained but not entered, correct the referral/authorization and resubmit the claim.
4. If the referral/authorization was never obtained, the service will not be paid and should be written off to the appropriate non-contractual adjustment code so you can capture the reason in your medical practice's reports. Then take steps to ensure referrals are obtained for all future services.

Credentialing

If you participate with a payer, you are required to submit an application. When the physician has been successfully "credentialed" or "enrolled" by a payer as a provider, your medical practice can then submit claims and be paid. Unfortunately, this application process doesn't happen overnight. Indeed, there is often a lengthy period between when a physician commences to provide services to a payer's beneficiaries and when the payer accepts the physician's application. During this period, claim denials are common.

If a denial related to credentialing occurs, follow these steps:

1. Review the status of the application to the payer. If the application has been submitted, contact the payer to determine its status. If there are missing items, submit them immediately. Follow up with the payer to confirm receipt and glean status of the application.
2. Discern the process of how to bill for a physician during the process of applying for participation status. Processes are payer-specific and include holding the claim until the application is approved and then submitting all claims for payment retroactively, billing under a supervising physician,

or no remuneration allowed until the application is complete (and thus, that physician should not treat that payer's patients until credentialed).

Better-performing medical practices outline the details of payment during the application period in their contracts with all payers, and are fastidious about the application process, as well as documenting receipt of the completion of the application by the payer. If these steps are outlined, take action on the denial as dictated by the contract. Based on the payer's process, follow up for payment or write off the balance to the appropriate adjustment code.

3. Review payer settlements. Several recent legal settlements with payers have related to the payer application process. Evaluate those settlements to determine if they can support your case for an appeal of the claim denied for credentialing issues.

For example, one payer settlement outlined terms regarding physician credentialing as follows:

"New Physician Credentialing: New physician group members will be credentialed within 90 days of the receipt of the application. Physicians also can submit an application prior to their employment."[2]

Credentialing-related denials can turn into a significant source of headaches — and bad debt. By managing your contracts and understanding your rights as a participating provider, you can avoid the problems that commonly lead to denials due to credentialing.

Bill the Patient for Non-participating Plan Denials

Some services are rendered to patients who are beneficiaries of health plans with which the medical practice does not participate. In this case, if your medical practice has elected to submit a claim as a courtesy to the patient and you receive a denial for any reason, the patient should be billed immediately.

Be Proactive and Anticipate the Denial

Knowing the payer's reimbursement policy will help you know when a denial is likely and what kind of information you can provide to get the claim paid. If a denial is inevitable, print the initial claim to paper and attach a letter of support for your claim. Examples include, but are not limited to, unlisted procedure codes, unspecified diagnosis codes, multiple procedures, complex surgeries, and other extenuating circumstances. Some claims scrubbing software modules allow custom edits for this purpose.

Deploy Tools to Support Denial Management

There are companies that sell denial modules as stand-alone tools or modules that can be integrated into your practice management system. There are companies that sell books of recommended appeal letters and software to help

---

[2] *How the Aetna Settlement Agreement Helps the Physician Practice*, American Medical Association, December 2006, http://www.ama-assn.org/ama1/pub/upload/mm/368/new_aetna_stt_b_0705.pdf (accessed November 27, 2008).

manage the appeal process. Before purchasing new products, contact your practice management system vendor to determine what it can offer you within your current investment and/or what other vendors it is partnering with in this arena.

Maintain Records of Inappropriate Denials

Keep a file for each of your top payers. Place copies of inappropriate denials in the file. Use the information as an agenda item in your routine meeting with your payer representative. This does not replace the claim appeals process that should be followed as usual — it is an extra step to focus the payer on key recurring issues. Use actual examples, instead of spoken anecdotes or general complaints, to focus the payer on your concerns.

Compare Your Denial Rates by Payer

Compare your denial rates by payer. This helps identify those payers that deny your claims at a higher rate than other payers of similar types. In general, we expect a relatively similar denial rate by each of your payers; your staff typically conducts their work processes in a similar fashion regardless of payer. So, higher claim denials from a particular payer is an indication that the payer either (a) requires additional hurdles to get paid (for example, prior authorization for services), and/or (b) creates obstacles to payment at a level greater than other payers. Tool 27 will help you monitor payer denial activity.

TOOL 27   Use Denial Data to Compare Payers

This tool provides a succinct way of seeing payer-specific denial data. In this example, the medical practice experiences the lowest denial rate from Payer 2 and the highest from Payer 4.

Specialty	Payer 1	Payer 2	Payer 3	Payer 4	Payer 5	Payer 6
Dermatology	27	4	16	12	22	21
Medicine	220	64	187	49	65	65
Pediatrics	1,609	563	1,038	44	106	133
Radiology	547	182	173	204	446	498
Surgery	55	8	27	12	27	87
Total denials	2,458	821	1,441	321	666	804
Total encounters	8,475	13,683	6,004	1,003	3,171	4,020
Denials as a % of encounters	29%	6%	24%	32%	21%	20%

© 2009 Walker, Woodcock, Larch. Reprinted with permission.

Calculate your claim rejections as a percentage of total claims submitted or total encounters for each payer. Monitoring and comparing the frequency of payer denials provide a statistical measure that you can share with payers at the time of contract negotiation or in regular meetings with the payer to improve practice-payer interactions and practice revenue.

Assign Staff to Denial Follow-up Activity

Medical practices need to post claim denials in their practice management systems on the service-specific line item in the patient's account using information reported on the payer's EOB or payer correspondence. The denials can be automatically posted from your electronic remittance or they can be manually posted from your EOB as we discussed in Chapter 10: The Payment and Denial Posting Process.

Make sure your denied payments are not being written off by the payment poster. In many practice management systems, electronic work files are available so staff can work in a paperless environment. Staff working denials greatly benefit from electronic work files so they can track and prioritize denials and store the documents necessary for a successful appeal.

Assign different types of claim denials to specific staff so they can develop an expertise in that area or with that payer. For example, if a claim is denied as a result of a coding issue, forward the list of claims denied for that reason to your coder. The coder will need to review the codes submitted, access the medical record, and review the chart documentation to determine if a corrected claim can be submitted. As another example, claim denials due to front-end billing should be reported to the front office so that errors are not repeated. In some medical practices, staff at the practice site play a major role in researching and obtaining the information needed to investigate and/or appeal the denial. As we discuss in Chapter 15: Staffing the Revenue Cycle, another staffing strategy for claim denial management is to link the payment posting and account follow-up process, residing the work of denial management with that staff member who possesses payer-specific knowledge and expertise.

Rework Appealable Claims

Track all denials and promptly rework claims that are appealable. Review the top 10 denials for your major payers, identify which denials are appealable, and define the actions necessary for successful appeal. When possible, develop automatic adjustments via your practice management system for denials that you can't appeal.

Automate Your Appeal Strategy

The success of an appeal depends on locating, retrieving, and submitting additional information that was not included in the initial claim submission. Most denial management efforts are labor intensive. Staff spend days finding and copying documents, creating further delays for the medical practice's cash flow. You need to identify ways to automate the work effort. Here are some ideas to consider:

- Develop appeal letter templates for the most common denial reasons. We have provided sample appeal letters for you to customize for your use in Tool 28. These letters outline the specifics of the matter under appeal and provide an opportunity for your medical practice to state its case succinctly and clearly. Where possible, use the specific wording from the payer's written or electronic publications.

- Use an electronic health record or scan operative reports, office visits, and other documentation to access this information easily; attach these documents to the appeal letter.

- Obtain access to the hospital's information system so you can easily pull supporting documentation, such as discharge summaries and operative reports.

- Use medical literature and your specialty society's Website to obtain information about treatment protocols, clinical practice guidelines, and policy statements to supplement appeals regarding denials for medical necessity.

- Track your appeals through the practice management system. Institute an automated calendar function or scan a copy of the appeal and file it in a tickler file in date order so you can review it for action and resolution in 30 days.

Adopt Appeal Follow-up Techniques

The following techniques for appealing claim denials with payers improve the efficiency and focus of your staff on the appeal process.

Create a list of the payer's appeal deadlines

The deadlines typically vary from 45 days from the date of denial to 12 months. During the contract negotiation process, negotiate longer deadlines to allow more time to appeal.

Prioritize by payer with the shortest deadline, then dollar amount

Your priority is the denied claims with the shortest time to appeal and the highest dollar value. Remember, if you wait too long, the claim will be worth zero if it is past the appeal deadlines.

Develop a dedicated appeals team

Some medical practices have identified staff members to handle all appeals, while other staff focus on accounts in limbo. This ensures that a team is focused on appeals and meeting appeal filing deadlines.

Establish a written protocol for appeals

Outline specific steps that billing staff should take to work denied claims, including sample letters to use in the appeal process.

TOOL 28   **Sample Appeal Letters**

To Whom It May Concern:

Thank you for the opportunity to submit this denied claim for reconsideration of payment. We are contacting you about the services rendered to [details about the patient's name, date of service, and services rendered].

Scenario #1: Medical necessity

Your company defines "medical necessity" to your beneficiaries as "a course of treatment seen as the most helpful for the specific health symptoms you are experiencing. The course of treatment is determined jointly by you, your health professional, and XYZ HealthCare. This course of treatment strives to provide you with the best care in the most appropriate setting."

The services rendered were medically necessary for this patient. The medical literature (which is attached) supports the rendering of this service in the setting in which it was rendered. Indeed, the services provided were the "course of treatment which was the most helpful for [patient's name] health symptoms" in the "most appropriate setting."

In addition to Dr. [name of treating physician], the physician who referred the patient to our practice supported our treatment decision. His/her letter of support is attached.

We feel that the service did meet your criteria for medical necessity, and is supported by other professionals in the field, as well as the patient's primary care physician.

Scenario #2: Retroactive denial of benefits

Your company retroactively denied the services rendered to this patient in your correspondence of [date of denial].

The services were authorized by [contact name and extension number] on [date and time]. Our record of the discussion is attached.

Dr. [name of treating physician] relied on your authorization to provide the services to [patient's name] on [date of service]. Under the doctrine of Promissory Estoppel, which allows recovery on a promise made when the reliance on the promise was reasonable and the promisee [the treating physician] relied on it to his or her detriment, we request payment for these services. We relied on your authorization to our detriment.

Scenario #3: Coding/modifier

Your company denied the procedure as bundled into the primary procedure. According to the source of authority for procedure codes, the American Medical Association, the [quote directly from the AMA]. The copy of the AMA's statement regarding this service is attached. This service is not bundled into the primary service, and payment in full is expected.

(continued on next page)

TOOL 28
(continued)   **Sample Appeal Letters**

Scenario #4: State prompt payment/open claim

Note: Sample provided for Georgia; contact your state medical society for information regarding your state's prompt payment law.

We request immediate payment of the above-referenced claim. According to our records, this claim was filed on [date of filing]; however, payment has not yet been received.

We believe that failure to release payment may be a violation of Georgia Code 33.

According to Georgia Code 33-24-59.5.(b)(1):

All benefits under a health benefit plan will be payable by the insurer which is obligated to finance or deliver health care services under that plan upon such insurer's receipt of written proof of loss or claim for payment for health care goods or services provided. The insurer shall within 15 working days after such receipt mail to the insured or other person claiming payments under the plan payment for such benefits or a letter or notice which states the reasons the insurer may have for failing to pay the claim, either in whole or in part, and which also gives the person so notified a written itemization of any documents or other information needed to process the claim or any portions thereof which are not being paid. Where the insurer disputes a portion of the claim, any undisputed portion of the claim shall be paid by the insurer in accordance with this chapter. When all of the listed documents or other information needed to process the claim have been received by the insurer, the insurer shall then have 15 working days within which to process and either mail payment for the claim or a letter or notice denying it, in whole or in part, giving the insured or other person claiming payments under the plan the insurer's reasons for such denial.

Based on this state mandate and the fact that this is a "clean claim," we ask that this claim be adjudicated immediately.

Thank you for your reconsideration.

———————

Note: The sample appeal letters do not guarantee payment, and are offered as exhibits only.

© 2009 Woodcock. Reprinted with permission.

Investigate appeals software tools as an option

Appeals software can assist staff in working denials. Key functions to look for include integration with your existing practice management system and minimal disruption to day-to-day operations.

Follow Payer Guidelines to Appeal

Different payers have different processes for appeals. For example, Medicare provides specific details regarding the method by which redetermination requests should be submitted.[3] In order to be effective, compile the payer appeal process requirements and determine the best method to appeal the denial. These include:

- Resubmit the corrected claim; don't spend time on an elaborate appeal when the claim just needs to be corrected and resubmitted;
- Appeal via Website;
- Appeal via telephone call;
- Appeal via facsimile; or
- Appeal via letter.

Understand Payers' Appeal Processes

Absent a clearly understood reason for a denial, or a lack of ability to support your original claim (for example, no documentation exists for the service), appeal your denials. If your claim appeal efforts do not succeed, move to a formal appeals process. A formal appeals process is structured by each payer. Providers and patients can submit appeals for treatment authorization or reimbursement decisions. There are usually several levels of appeal:

Urgent review

If the payer denies authorization for treatment or post-treatment, a medical practice needs to request an immediate telephone consultation.

Level 1 appeal

The first appeal goes to the reviewer or clerk who initially denied the claim. He/she looks at any additional records submitted and claims submitted.

Level 2 appeal

This usually involves a physician or medical director at the payer organization and may include a telephone conversation with the provider.

Level 3 appeal

This level of review involves an appeals committee or board. Board members review the documents and actions in the appeal process thus far. This may be the last stop, unless your contract includes an arbitration clause or an additional level of appeal.

There may be different contacts and/or addresses for each level of appeal. Be sure to check with the payer to determine the correct channels of communication for the appeal process.

Escalate Appeals When Necessary

If the payer's formal appeals process is not effective, there are other ways to escalate denials in the payer's structure. Start with the claims office of the payer with which you contracted, then systematically move to provider relations,

---

[3] For Medicare's specific procedures related to redetermination requests, see http://www.cms.hhs.gov/cmsforms/downloads/cms20027.pdf (accessed November 27, 2008).

contracts office, nurse manager, medical director, and, if necessary, the executive office (chief operating officer and chief executive officer). Other external resources that may be of assistance to a medical practice in getting the payer's attention include:

- State insurance commissioner;
- State attorney general and legislators;
- State MGMA-affiliated organizations; and/or
- County and state medical societies.

Escalate from calls to letters to in-person meetings. A medical practice can ask its legal counsel to get involved. The patient should be copied on all correspondence, as the patient may be able to provide additional leverage with the payer. One medical practice determined that it could not afford the $850.00 round-trip ticket to fly a physician to the main office of the payer, yet it had $40,000 in outstanding claims with this payer! Clearly a trip may be worth the effort and expense — you typically do not have to make these trips more than once.

Develop a Payer Report Card

We recommend that medical practices develop a payer report card. The report card should contain key information that permits the medical practice to compare and contrast key components of its relationships with its payers. These include timeliness and accuracy of payments, denial rates based on key denial categories, administrative costs associated with the payer, and other key data to help the medical practice assess the relationship and performance it has with its payers. This information is also invaluable in contract negotiations.

Tool 29 helps you develop a Payer Report Card for your medical practice.

The National Health Insurer Report Card (NHIRC), published by the American Medical Association (AMA),[4] compares payer performance in key areas that impact the revenue cycle. This national report card evaluates key payers on payment timeliness, accuracy, transparency of contracted fees and payment policies on payer Websites, compliance with generally accepted pricing rules, and claim denials. It is useful to compare your payer report card to the national report card to gain understanding of payer performance.

Calculate Your Cost of Rework

You can easily compute the total cost of claim rework for your medical practice. For example, let's assume that a medical practice files 12,000 claims per year, or 1,000 claims each month. In an average month, 200 claims are denied for the following reasons:

- 100 are denied due to registration and insurance verification errors;
- 40 are denied due to the lack of a required authorization or referral;
- 10 are denied due to credentialing problems; and
- 50 are denied due to coding-related errors.

---

[4] The AMA National Health Insurer Report Card is available at the following Website: http://www.ama-assn.org/go/cureforclaims (accessed November 27, 2008).

TOOL 29	Sample Payer Report Card

Performance Measures	Payer A	Payer B	Payer C
Collections:			
Net collection rate	_____	_____	_____
Percentage of accounts receivable greater than 90 days	_____	_____	_____
Days revenue outstanding	_____	_____	_____
Average days to initial payment	_____	_____	_____
Payments vs. contract rate variance	_____	_____	_____
Success in collecting patient portion of payment	_____	_____	_____
Denials:			
Denials as a percentage of claims	_____	_____	_____
Denial reason #1 _____	_____	_____	_____
Denial reason #2 _____	_____	_____	_____
Denial reason #3 _____	_____	_____	_____
Denial reason #4 _____	_____	_____	_____
Denial reason #5 _____	_____	_____	_____
Administrative Costs:			
E-claims availability	_____	_____	_____
Electronic payment remittance	_____	_____	_____
Electronic funds transfer	_____	_____	_____
Contact failure rate (busy/no answer)	_____	_____	_____
Online claim status access	_____	_____	_____
Online insurance verification and eligibility	_____	_____	_____
Provider enrollment	_____	_____	_____
Productivity (Annual):			
Gross charges	_____	_____	_____
Net collections	_____	_____	_____
Admissions	_____	_____	_____
Surgeries/procedures	_____	_____	_____
Office/outpatient visits	_____	_____	_____
Claims	_____	_____	_____
New patients	_____	_____	_____
Established patients	_____	_____	_____

© 2009 Walker, Woodcock, Larch. Reprinted with permission.

Before we go any further on the calculation, let's take a look at the example above. The medical practice has already identified that it has a 20 percent denial rate (200 of the 1,000 claims submitted were denied) and 50 percent of its denials (100 of the 200 denied claims) are due to registration and insurance verification. Before spending more time on tracking denials, we would recommend that the medical practice spend time investigating the reason for these registration and insurance verification denials. The individual EOB remark codes must be analyzed. Are there any discernable patterns, such as a high volume of denials specific to place of service or payer?

Two examples illustrate the ability to carefully hone in on the data and take appropriate action to resolve the denials. For example, let's assume that there is a high volume of claim denials due to registration-related errors for those patients who were admitted to the hospital through the emergency department (ED). Where indicated, new procedures need to be put in place. For the ED admissions, for example, the insurance and demographic information received on the face sheets could be run through a verification process directly with the payer before being submitted.

As another example, if it looks like staff errors or omissions are causing a high volume of claim denials, then staff training and performance monitoring are indicated. Automated insurance verification should also be considered.

The sooner the medical practice can identify and reduce the root cause of the denials, the sooner it will have fewer denials to work!

Returning to our example, if the medical practice has $100.00 in revenue per claim, 200 denied claims translates into $20,000 per month in denials. Each denial, we estimate, costs $15 to work. (See Chapter 2: The Revenue Cycle: An Overview for more detailed analysis; the cost of the denial may be more or less based on the nature of the denial.) This rework cost includes staff time, supplies, lost interest, and overhead. In the most optimistic of cases, all $20,000 would eventually be recovered each month; however, recovering all monies is unusual. Typically, medical practices are able to recover 75 percent of denied claims. For this medical practice, using these assumptions, $96,000 is spent or lost per year on denials, as demonstrated by Figure 12.4.

FIGURE 12.4 ■ Cost of Rework

Cost Type	Financial Impact	Calculation
Loss due to denial management	$36,000	$15.00 to work each denial. ($15.00 x 200 claims per month x 12 months per year)
Loss due to non-recovery of denials	$60,000	25 percent of denials are never recovered ($20,000 per month x 25 percent x 12 months per year)
Total cost of denials	$96,000	

© 2009 Walker, Woodcock, Larch. Reprinted with permission.

Determine the cost to rework a claim for your medical practice, and then calculate your total cost of rework by multiplying it by the volume of the denied claims. You cannot reduce the volume of claim denials and the cost of rework until you know and act on the originating cause of the denial. In most cases, the cost of rework exceeds the cost to improve the process and eliminate the cause of the denial in the first place. This data alone support change needed to improve the process. Don't just keep reworking claims; fix the root cause!

In today's complex reimbursement environment, some claim denials are inevitable. An efficient and effective denial strategy is critical. There is a right way and a wrong way to submit an appeal. The wrong way is to resubmit a claim without explaining why it should be reconsidered for payment. The right way is to follow a timely, systematic process consistent with payer guidelines.

Combine denial prevention and management techniques to ensure optimal revenue cycle performance. Many of the denials represent outstanding revenue that is due your medical practice.

STAFF WORKLOAD RANGES

The staff workload ranges provided in Chapter 11: The Insurance Follow-up Process also apply to denial management.

LEADING PERFORMANCE INDICATORS

Use the following indicators to assess the performance of your denial management process. We refer to these measures as "leading" performance indicators. If your medical practice is successful in achieving these levels in the denial management process, you are on the correct path to optimizing your revenue cycle.

Claim denial rates:	Less than 7 percent
Appeals:	Filed within 5 days of payment posting
Payment after first appeal:	75 percent rate of success

THE DENIAL MANAGEMENT DIAGNOSTIC TOOL

The denial management diagnostic tool provided below helps you ensure that the process, people, technology, and quality required for effective charge capture are in place in your medical practice.

Process:

1. How do you manage denials? When are they received? How are they communicated? How are they tracked? What is the follow-up procedure used by type of denial?
2. Do you have a process in place to appeal claims in a timely manner?
3. Do you appeal denials? By telephone? In writing? What is the process and what tools are used?
4. What are your top reasons for denials? How are they tracked?
5. Are the root causes of denials identified and fixed?

People:

1. Who is responsible for working denials, and submitting and tracking appeals?
2. Are your staff trained in denial management?
3. Do they understand the appeal process by payer?
4. Do you have sufficient staff devoted to the denial management process?
5. Are the staff focused on preventing claims or reworking claims?

Technology:

1. Do you utilize any denial software to automate the appeal letters process?
2. How do you distribute denial trends to all practice locations?
3. Have you developed automated work files to monitor all denial management activities?
4. Do you trend your denials by payer? By practice site? By service type?

Quality:

1. Do you audit your claim appeals to identify improved appeal processes?
2. What percentage of appeals are successful?
3. Have you taken the appropriate action to prevent claim denials from occurring in the first place or are you focused on rework alone?

POLICIES AND PROCEDURES

At the end of each chapter, we provide policies and procedures to assist you in developing a policy and procedure manual for your medical practice. Below is a policy specific to the denial management process.

POLICY 26: CLAIM DENIALS

Policy:

It is the policy of the medical practice to identify, monitor, and take action on all claims submitted by the medical practice that are denied by payers.

Procedures:

1. Medical practice staff will be assigned responsibility for reviewing and taking action on all claim denials. All denials will be reviewed and acted upon within 48 hours of receipt.

2. Medical practice staff will utilize all available resources to research and correct the claim, including the documentation of the service, medical literature, pre-certifications and authorizations, procedure and diagnosis coding manuals and reference materials, specialty society policy statements, payers' payment policies, and state and federal government coverage policies. Depending on the nature of the rejection, a claim will be corrected and resubmitted or an appeal will be communicated over the telephone, via the Website, or in writing to the payer.

3. Denied claims will not be resubmitted without ensuring that the service has been documented in the medical record. Any claims that have missing documentation must be brought to the attention of the medical practice compliance officer immediately.

4. Denied claims will not be resubmitted until corrections are made to the claim. Resubmitting claims without correction is grounds for disciplinary action for medical practice staff assigned responsibility of working denied claims.

5. The billing office will monitor and research claims denied by payers to determine the causes of the denials. The claims denial report will be analyzed to determine the specific claims that have been denied and the causes for denial. The analysis will be used to train providers and staff regarding steps that can be taken to reduce claim denials received by the medical practice.

CHAPTER 13

Pothole 11
The Patient Collections Process

An important pothole in the road to getting paid is the process of securing payments due from patients, particularly due to new health plan products in which patients have large deductibles and out-of-pocket obligations. It is important that you perform patient account follow-up in a timely fashion, communicating clearly to the patient, as the longer these balances stay in the accounts receivable the harder it will be to collect. In Chapters 3 and 4, we cover patient collections when the patient is physically present in your office; in Chapter 9, we outline the patient statement process. In this chapter, we focus on patient collections that remain outstanding after you've asked for the money due in person and via statements.

In this chapter, we discuss the following key components of the patient collections process:

- Collections cycle
- Patient account follow-up policies
- Medical billing advocates
- Patient correspondence
- Non-sufficient funds
- Payment plans
- Collection agencies
- Small claims court
- Discounts and uninsured patients
- Predictive dialers
- Patient dismissal

The patient collections process involves asking patients for payment at the time of service and submitting statements to patients to collect the balance they owe on the bill — and then taking appropriate steps to ensure that payment has been received. Once the account transfers to patient responsibility, staff need to exert systematic and diligent efforts to follow up with the patient, or "patient pay" can quickly degenerate to "zero pay."

It is notable that we refer to patient collections, however the party who is financially responsible is typically called the "guarantor" of the account.

To ensure efficient and effective patient collection processes, we present proven patient collections strategies to enhance your revenue cycle.

ADVANCED PRACTICES: THE PATIENT COLLECTIONS PROCESS

Establish a Collections Cycle That Works for You and Your Patients

Determine how aggressively you will pursue patient balances. Given the small profit margin available in most medical practices, collecting every dollar may be critical to the survival of your medical practice.

Tool 30 outlines four examples of a patient collection cycle. This is often referred to as "pre-collections," which consists of the steps taken by the medical practice to collect patient payments before the account is sent to an external collection agency. Collection Policy A incurs significant staff resources and time delays, while Collection Policy D represents the least resources required and the shortest time to send the account to the collection agency. Define your patient collection cycle — not necessarily policy A, B, C, or D — but be sure you establish one for your medical practice in writing and apply it consistently.

As discussed below, your collections cycle may include a different protocol for managing outstanding accounts that your medical practice considers to be large. A "large" balance is determined by the average amount outstanding on accounts for your medical practice. This may range from $500 in a primary care practice to more than $5,000 in a surgery practice. Accounting for the average balance and the resources available within your medical practice to pursue patient balances, outline your protocol for collecting on balances over a certain dollar amount as a part of your collections cycle.

Establish Protocols for Patient Follow-up

Prioritize the accounts to be followed based on the date of service and the dollar balance. Work higher-dollar accounts first. Deploy queuing strategies that alert staff to these levels. Your practice management system should have a reminder flag or a tickler system your staff can use. Software-based calendars also feature automated reminder systems. Do not simply follow up on accounts in alphabetical order by patient last name; instead, prioritize your account follow-up efforts. If patients have seen more than one provider in your practice or have multiple invoices due, prioritize based on the total account balance — you want to work the whole account at one time.

TOOL 30	Sample Collection Policies

COLLECTION POLICY A

Three statements sent at 0, 30, and 60 days after the date the account becomes due from the patient.

Next 14 days: Letter #1 is sent

Next 14 days: Telephone contact #1 is attempted

Next 14 days: Letter #2 is sent

Next 14 days: Request for approval for outside collections is sent to physician

Next 14 days: Account sent to collection agency

Total lapsed time: 130 days

COLLECTION POLICY B

Two statements sent at 0 and 30 days after the date the account becomes due from the patient.

Next 14 days: Telephone contact #1 is attempted

Next 14 days: Statement #3 is sent to patient, telephone contact #2 attempted, collection letter #1 sent, pre-approval from physician to send account to collections

Next 15 days: Collection letter #2 sent; certified letter with 10 days to respond (*Note:* Time reflects an estimated five days for letter to reach patient.)

Next 10 days: Account sent to collection agency

Total lapsed time: 83 days

COLLECTION POLICY C

Two statements sent at 0 and 30 days after the date the account becomes due from the patient.

Next 5 days: Three attempts to reach patient by telephone over a five-day period

Next 15 days: Certified collection letter with 10 days to respond (*Note:* Time reflects an estimated five days for letter to reach patient.)

Next 10 days: Account sent to collection agency

Total lapsed time: 60 days

COLLECTION POLICY D

Two statements sent at 0 and 30 days after the date the account becomes due from the patient.

Next 15 days: Certified collection letter with 10 days to respond (*Note:* Time reflects an estimated five days for letter to reach patient.)

Next 10 days: Account sent to collection agency

Total lapsed time: 55 days

Develop Collection Letters

In many patient collections cycles, following the issuance of a set number of patient statements, a formal letter is sent to the patient. Design your collection letter for maximum effectiveness. Consider addressing the letter from the physician so that the patient knows of the physician's interest in account collection.

Tool 31 provides an example of such a letter, which can be customized for your medical practice.

TOOL 31	Sample Collection Letter

[Medical practice name and logo]

Dear [patient name]:

Your account with our practice has been unpaid for several months, and we have exhausted all routine attempts to aid you in settling your debt, to no avail.

Because of rising business costs and in fairness to our patients who have paid their bills, our accountant will not allow us to carry your unpaid balance any longer.

Therefore, please be advised that if this balance is not paid within 10 days, it will be given to [collection agency or attorney] for collection processing. As of that date, we will allow 30 days of emergency care while you are seeking another health care provider; however, after that time you will be discharged as a patient of our medical practice.

We sincerely hope that you will contact us to clear your unpaid bill so that you can maintain good standing with our medical practice and your credit rating.

Sincerely,

[PHYSICIAN NAME]

© 2009 Walker, Woodcock, Larch. Reprinted with permission.

Provide Telephone Scripts to Staff

It is important to identify the most effective staff members to make collection calls and to have telephone scripts they can follow. The Fair Debt Collections Practices Act (FDCPA), as well as other federal and state laws, have been designed to protect consumers from inappropriate or devious debt collection activities, and your medical practice should consult these sources to ensure that your collection process is legal. Although the FDCPA applies to third-party collection companies (for example, collection agencies), the act outlines fair and reasonable processes for collection activities.

Develop a Collection Code of Ethics

To ensure that your collection style and your patient satisfaction goals are in sync, create a collection code of ethics for the staff to follow. A sample code of ethics is provided in Figure 13.1.

FIGURE 13.1 ■ Collection Code of Ethics

- Medical practices should fully explain the terms of any collection transaction to their patients.

- Statements should be sent as soon as possible after the account becomes due.

- Telephone calls or correspondence from a patient claiming a billing error should be acknowledged promptly.

- Collection practices should be based on the presumption that every patient/ guarantor intends to pay and would pay if able.

- Patient complaints concerning collection practices should be investigated immediately.

- Patients who show a sincere desire to pay their debts should be offered, if necessary, extended payment schedules, financing arrangements, or similar methods that would help re-establish solvency.

- If the patient does not respond to an offer to help make alternative arrangements, the collector should explain the seriousness of the continuing delinquency and advise the patient regarding courses of action.

- Telephone calls must be placed between hours of 8 a.m. and 9 p.m. in the patient's time zone.

- Outside collection agencies, attorneys, and other agents employed to collect delinquent accounts should be furnished with written instructions on how patients are to be approached and which collection practices are and are not sanctioned.

Source: *Financial Management for Medical Groups* by Ernest J. Pavlock, PhD, CPA. Adapted with permission from the MGMA Center for Research, 104 Inverness Terrace East, Englewood, Colorado 80112-5306; 303.799.1111. mgma.com. © 2000.

Establish Protocols for Payment Plans

Outline in your financial policy your willingness to negotiate patient payment plans. Your medical practice needs a policy that includes acceptable payment thresholds. For example, if the account balance ranges from $10.00 to $499.00, 50 percent could be paid in the first month, with 25 percent in the second month and the remaining 25 percent in the third month. Your goal should be to collect all balances in six months or less. Monthly payment amounts should never be less than your cost of billing.

We have provided examples of both a payment plan agreement (Tool 32) and a payment plan structure (Tool 33) as tools for patient account follow-up. A payment plan agreement is a contract between the medical practice and the patient regarding an alternate payment arrangement. Patients who are unable to pay their account balance in full at the time of service as a result of limited or no insurance coverage may be offered the opportunity to pay the balance in full within specified time periods. A payment plan is not applicable to copayments, which must be collected at the time of service.

A payment plan structure, also referred to as a "budget plan," outlines the specified time periods and amounts that are to be paid by patients on payment plan agreements based on dollar thresholds of amounts owed to the medical practice.

Once a patient enters into a payment plan agreement, your medical practice should immediately contact the patient in the event that he/she does not make timely payments consistent with the terms of the agreement. In fact, in many medical practices, this function is centralized with one individual charged with

TOOL 32 Payment Plan Agreement

Patients who are set up on a payment plan are asked to sign a payment plan agreement that indicates their understanding of the terms of the payment plan. Below is an example of a payment plan agreement form that can be customized for your medical practice.

I have reviewed all charges for services rendered. My balance of $_____ is, to my knowledge, correct. Although I have been encouraged to pay the entire balance in full, I have elected to make monthly payments as outlined below.

Beginning balance: $_____   Date of service: _____

Number of monthly payments: _____   Amount of each payment: $_____

Today's payment: $_____   Today's date: _____

Next payment date: _____

I understand that my account will be considered delinquent if my scheduled payment is more than four days late. I understand that I may be legally responsible for all collection costs involved with the collection of this account including all court costs, reasonable attorney fees, and all other expenses incurred with collection if I default on this agreement. I further understand that failure to meet the prescribed payment schedule can result in the listing of this debt with national credit reporting agencies and it may have a negative effect on the granting of future credit.

I have read the above description of the arrangement and agree to its terms.

Patient name: _____ Account number:_____

Patient signature: _____ Date: _____

Authorized signature and title for the practice: _____

Date: _____

© 2009 Walker, Woodcock, Larch. Reprinted with permission.

reviewing the timeliness of payments made by patients on payment plan agreements so that immediate action is taken if patients are delinquent.

Create a payment plan agreement and payment plan structure that staff have the authority to implement. The practice executive or physician should not have to approve each payment plan that is negotiated; instead, a formal structure and policy should be implemented.

TOOL 33	Payment Plan Structure						
Total Payment Due	Time Period of Plan	Payment Plan Monthly Payments Due					
		Month 1	Month 2	Month 3	Month 4	Month 5	Month 6
<$200	3 month	due at the time of service					
$200	3 month	$ 66.67	$ 66.67	$ 66.67			
	6 month	not available					
$300	3 month	$ 100.00	$ 100.00	$ 100.00			
	6 month	not available					
$400	3 month	$ 133.33	$ 133.33	$ 133.33			
	6 month	not available					
$500	3 month	$ 166.67	$ 166.67	$ 166.67			
	6 month	$ 83.33	$ 83.33	$ 83.33	$ 83.33	$ 83.33	$ 83.33
$600	3 month	$ 200.00	$ 200.00	$ 200.00			
	6 month	$ 100.00	$ 100.00	$ 100.00	$ 100.00	$ 100.00	$ 100.00
$700	3 month	$ 233.33	$ 233.33	$ 233.33			
	6 month	$ 116.67	$ 116.67	$ 116.67	$ 116.67	$ 116.67	$ 116.67
$800	3 month	$ 266.67	$ 266.67	$ 266.67			
	6 month	$ 133.33	$ 133.33	$ 133.33	$ 133.33	$ 133.33	$ 133.33
$900	3 month	$ 300.00	$ 300.00	$ 300.00			
	6 month	$ 150.00	$ 150.00	$ 150.00	$ 150.00	$ 150.00	$ 150.00
$1,000	3 month	$ 333.33	$ 333.33	$ 333.33			
	6 month	$ 166.67	$ 166.67	$ 166.67	$ 166.67	$ 166.67	$ 166.67
>$1,000	Please see billing manager.						

Involve Schedulers in Collecting Patient Responsibility Balances

In better-performing medical practices, when the patient calls to schedule an appointment, the scheduler is able to see the patient responsibility balance and accept payment over the telephone via credit card or transfer the patient to a billing office staff member to collect the payment. In this fashion, the outstanding patient payment is collected prior to the patient presenting for further care.

Review Appointment Schedule and Contact the Patient Prior to Appointment

Many better-performing medical practices review their patient schedules one or two days before the patient visit to determine the outstanding amounts that are owed by patients. These medical practices then either contact patients by telephone to attempt to collect the outstanding payment via credit card prior to patients presenting for care, or are prepared to collect the outstanding payment at the time patients present for their visits.

Collect When the Patient is in the Office

In order to ensure timely reimbursement and reduce the cost of billing, your medical practice should collect prior patient balances including co-insurance and unmet deductibles, in addition to copayments, when the patient is physically present in the office. (See Chapter 4: The Payment Check-in and Check-out Processes for more ideas on time-of-service payments.)

Get the Patient Involved to Help You

If the claim is clean and the payer has not paid within a timely manner (as dictated by your state's prompt payment law and/or reasonable period of time), send the patient a letter indicating that his/her insurance company has not paid. Ask your patient to contact the insurance company regarding the delay, or to contact you if your medical practice billed the incorrect insurance company. If your medical practice does not participate with the patient's insurance, transfer the balance to the patient and send the patient a statement. For payers with which your medical practice participates, negotiate circumstances in your contract under which the account of an insured patient may be transferred to patient financial responsibility. For example, rather than tolerate a significant delay after the payer requests that the patient provide additional information in order for the claim to be adjudicated, request that patients be given 30 days to respond to such notices, or the account balance will be transferred to patient responsibility. (This issue, as well as other contracting tips, is discussed in Chapter 14: The Contract and Reimbursement Management Process.)

Collect Cellular Telephone Numbers from Patients

As cellular telephones replace home and even work telephones, cellular telephone numbers can be vital to your medical practice during the collections process. Collect cellular telephone numbers from patients during registration to give your medical practice a more effective means of communicating with the patient during the collections process.

Research Coverage for Self-pay Patients

Always utilize all information available on uninsured patients. If collection efforts are failing and the registration process was compromised (for example, a trauma patient presented through the emergency department and registration was not formally performed prior to medical services), repeatedly query the Medicaid eligibility database, as well as the hospital's registration system, for said patients. The patient may have become Medicaid eligible since your initial query. If you determine he/she is covered, submit the claim immediately. For patients who have received complex, high-dollar services, such as trauma care, transplants, or oncology services, the actual time required to obtain Medicaid coverage may be longer than expected, thus necessitating the frequent query of the database over a defined time period.

Determine Financial Aids for Patients Without Insurance

Determine the role you want your medical practice to play in assisting patients who do not have insurance and/or who are not able to pay their out-of-pocket obligation. Some medical practices refer patients to a financing program, arrange for a Medicaid application, identify a list of grants, and/or provide contact information for social agencies in the community that can assist patients. Each medical practice should determine the role it wants to play in providing this type of patient assistance.[1]

Be Aware of Patient Billing Advocates

Companies and independent contractors are filling a growing need to help patients with their bills. Organizations and individuals serving as "patient billing advocates" started as an entrepreneurial response to patients being confused with the amount of medical bills for which they were responsible. Initially, patient billing advocates helped people organize their medical bills and statements, monitored all claim and statement activity, and let the patient know when he/she should or should not pay a bill. In addition to these basic services, billing advocates are trained to evaluate insurance policies, audit claims, identify payment errors, and appeal denials and underpayments. In addition, some advocates have evolved to include a division that works with providers to intervene with payers — in order to avoid the patient ultimately getting the bill when the payer refuses payment. Determine your medical practice's role with patient billing advocates. While they are traditionally viewed as patient advocates, they could also potentially be of help to your medical practice when payers are not forthcoming with reimbursement.

---

[1] For more information on this type of program, see the Robert Wood Johnson Foundation initiative, http://covertheuninsured.org (accessed December 3, 2008).

Develop and Use a Financial Hardship Policy

Develop a financial hardship or charity care policy. For patients experiencing financial hardship, offer a discount and/or assist the guarantor in locating coverage. If you offer a discount, it may be a fixed percentage of your charge up to 100 percent of the patient's financial responsibility. In addition to addressing the nature of the discount, the policy should define the financial need that meets your criteria of charity, as well as the document(s) that you will collect to prove it.

The Centers for Medicare & Medicaid Services (CMS) addresses the issue of substantiating financial hardship as follows:

> In some cases, the provider may have established before discharge, or within a reasonable time before the current admission, that the beneficiary is either indigent or medically indigent. Providers can deem Medicare beneficiaries indigent or medically indigent when such individuals have also been determined eligible for Medicaid as either categorically needy individuals or medically needy individuals, respectively. Otherwise, the provider should apply its customary methods for determining the indigence of patients to the case of the Medicare beneficiary under the following guidelines:
>
> A. The patient's indigence must be determined by the provider, not by the patient; that is, a patient's signed declaration of his inability to pay his medical bills cannot be considered proof of indigence;
>
> B. The provider should take into account a patient's total resources which would include, but are not limited to, an analysis of assets (only those convertible to cash and unnecessary for the patient's daily living), liabilities, and income and expenses. In making this analysis the provider should take into account any extenuating circumstances that would affect the determination of the patient's indigence;
>
> C. The provider must determine that no source other than the patient would be legally responsible for the patient's medical bill; for example, title XIX [Medicaid], local welfare agency and guardian; and
>
> D. The patient's file should contain documentation of the method by which indigence was determined in addition to all backup information to substantiate the determination.
>
> Once indigence is determined and the provider concludes that there had been no improvement in the beneficiary's financial condition, the debt may be deemed uncollectible without applying the §310 procedures.[2]

Your financial hardship policy must be consistently applied. For a sample policy, please see the financial hardship policy at the end of this chapter.

---

[2] http://www.cms.hhs.gov/Manuals/PBM/. Publication 15.1: *Provider Reimbursement Manual*, Part I. Section 312: Indigent or Medically Indigent Patients (accessed September 15, 2008).

Denote Financial Hardship

If an account is adjusted off the accounts receivable as uncollectible for financial hardship or charity care, use an appropriate adjustment code to designate it as such. Do not write off the money to a generic bad debt adjustment code.

Unfortunately, physicians cannot utilize financial hardship write-offs for tax purposes because they provide their time as a service. (Consider, for example, that you cannot declare your volunteer time at the local homeless shelter as a tax benefit.) If your medical practice is assessed taxes based on a percentage of revenues pursuant to local and/or state laws, your charity care may be exempt from this assessment and you should verify this with your accountant. Furthermore, the information can be used collectively to report your medical practice's community benefit to legislators and other stakeholders who are making decisions about professional fee reimbursement rates.

Request Payment on Bad Debt Accounts

When an account is deemed uncollectible by a medical practice, it is adjusted off the accounts receivable. Many medical practices also then initiate the process of discharging the patient from the practice. However, if the patient is not discharged from the medical practice, most practice management systems allow the debt to be adjusted off but to remain visible on patients' accounts. Patients who are in bad-debt status who contact the medical practice for an appointment are informed of their outstanding balance, with payment requested in full and paid via credit card at the time of appointment scheduling or collected prior to or at the time the patient presents for his/her visit.

Avoid Routine Waiver of Patient Financial Responsibility

If resources are constrained or the medical practice is frustrated with patient collections, some medical practices might consider waiving the patient's financial responsibility and pursuing the insurance portion only. This practice, once commonplace, is often referred to as "insurance only." We strongly discourage you from considering this option, which would conflict with your payer contracts and often state law. With the exception of patients who qualify for your financial hardship policy, which is discussed above, the patient's financial responsibility should not be waived.

The American Medical Association (AMA) offers the following recommendations in this area:

> "In some cases, financial hardship may deter patients from seeking necessary care if they would be responsible for a copayment for the care. Physicians commonly forgive or waive copayments to facilitate patient access to needed medical care. When a copayment is a barrier to needed care because of financial hardship, physicians should forgive or waive the copayment. ... Physicians should be aware that waiver of copayments may violate the policies of some insurers, both public and private; other insurers may permit forgiveness or

waiver if they are aware of the reasons for the forgiveness or waiver. Routine forgiveness or waiver of copayments may constitute fraud under state and federal law. Physicians should ensure that their policies on copayments are consistent with applicable law and with the requirements of their agreements with insurers."[3]

Further, the Office of the Inspector General advises, "One important exception to the prohibition against waiving copayments and deductibles is that providers, practitioners or suppliers may forgive the copayment in consideration of a particular patient's financial hardship. This hardship exception, however, must not be used routinely; it should be used occasionally to address the special financial needs of a particular patient. Except in such special cases, a good faith effort to collect deductibles and copayments must be made."[4]

Define Protocols Related to Professional Courtesy

Once commonplace for colleagues and friends, extending professional courtesy must be performed thoughtfully. Professional courtesy is writing off the entire account — both the patient and insurance balance. If performed, monies written off to professional courtesy should be denoted under an adjustment code specific to that reason.

Professional courtesy write-offs have come under scrutiny because linkages to the referral of business have been evaluated. If, for example, a radiologist performs a free imaging study for the wife of a pulmonologist, and the pulmonologist refers patients to the radiologist, the intent of the professional courtesy can be questioned. In sum, providing free services can be construed as an inducement for referrals. Even if there is no intent to garner business, professional courtesy can be considered problematic by the regulating authorities.

Professional courtesy is defined in the Stark II law as "the provision of free or discounted health care items or services to a physician or his or her immediate family members or office staff." According to Stark II, professional courtesy:[5]

- Must be offered without regard to volume or value of referrals;
- May include only those services regularly offered by the practice;
- Must be in a written policy;
- Cannot be offered for copayment waivers unless the insurance company paying the bill is informed in writing; and
- Must not violate anti-kickback laws or claims submission rules and regulations.

---

[3] Policy E-6.12. Forgiveness or Waiver of Insurance Copayments. Chicago: American Medical Association; issued June 1993. Available from: www.ama-assn.org.

[4] Special Fraud Alert: Routine Waiver of Copayments or Deductibles under Medicare Part B. Washington: United States Department of Health and Human Services, Office of Inspector General; issued May 1991; published in the Federal Register, December 19, 1994. http://oig.hhs.gov/fraud/fraudalerts.html (accessed September 15, 2008).

[5] See the March 26, 2004, *Federal Register* at http://www.cms.hhs.gov/ PhysicianSelfReferral/Downloads/69FR16054.pdf (accessed September 15, 2008).

From a financial perspective, professional courtesy means rendering a service with no payment, often for patients who are covered by insurance and/or can afford to pay.

There is one exception as to when professional courtesy is, in essence, required. Although charges can be billed, the CMS will not pay for services rendered by a physician to his or her immediate relatives. According to the Medicare Benefit Policy Manual:

> Medicare regulations do not provide payment under Part A or Part B of Medicare for expenses that constitute charges by immediate relatives of the beneficiary or by members of his/her household. The intent of this exclusion is to bar Medicare payment for items and services that would ordinarily be furnished gratuitously because of the relationship of the beneficiary to the person imposing the charge. This exclusion applies to items and services rendered by providers to immediate relatives of the owner(s) of the provider. It also applies to services rendered by physicians to their immediate relatives and items furnished by suppliers to immediate relatives of the owner(s) of the supplier. The following degrees of relationship are included within the definition of immediate relative.
>
> - Husband and wife;
> - Natural or adoptive parent, child, and sibling;
> - Stepparent, stepchild, stepbrother, and stepsister;
> - Father-in-law, mother-in-law, son-in-law, daughter-in-law, brother-in-law, and sister-in-law;
> - Grandparent and grandchild; and
> - Spouse of grandparent and grandchild.
>
> This exclusion applies to physician services, including services of a physician who belongs to a professional corporation, and services furnished incident to those services (for example, by the physician's nurse or technician) if the physician who furnished the services or who ordered or supervised services incident to their services has an excluded relationship to the beneficiary.[6]

Taking these factors into consideration, exercise due diligence in developing a professional courtesy policy for your medical practice. In some medical practices, the policy may be to not extend professional courtesy, due to the potential business risk this presents.

Report Bad Debt to the Credit Bureau(s)

Some patients may default on their accounts. In this case, one consequence of their actions can be to report the patient's debt to a credit bureau. You

---

[6] Charges Imposed by Immediate Relatives of the Patient or Members of the Patient's Household (Rev. 1, 10-01-03) A3-3161, HO-260.12, B3-2332 p. 130. http://www.cms. hhs.gov/manuals/downloads/bp102c16.pdf (accessed September 15, 2008).

can explore direct reporting to the credit bureau (for example, Equifax, Transunion, or Experian); alternatively, you can direct your collection agency to report the debt (see below for further detail about working with a collection agency). When a debt is reported, it will reside on the patient's credit report. Communicating your ability to report bad debt to a credit bureau can be a useful collections tool in your final collections letter to the patient. Often, patients' concern about credit bureau reporting prompts them to contact you to make payment.

Use a Collection Agency

Include in your financial policy a decision about whether and when you will send patient accounts to an external collection agency. Although medical practices have traditionally used collection agencies after exhausting all internal collection efforts, many medical practices establish relationships that encompass other functions. The role of a collection agency typically falls into one of the following three categories.

1. *All patient collections*: When an account becomes the responsibility of a patient, the medical practice transfers the balance to the agency to collect.

2. *Pre-collect process (often referred to as an "early out" process)*: After a medical practice has sent an account through the practice's collection cycle (for example, three statements have been sent to the patient), it transfers the account to the agency to send out one final correspondence before the collection agency takes over all collection efforts on the account.

3. *Bad debt*: After a medical practice has exhausted all internal collection efforts, the medical practice writes the account balance off the accounts receivable as bad debt, and transfers all responsibility for collections to the agency.

Collection recovery percentages fall dramatically as time increases before the collection agency takes over. The industry standard for the recovery of medical accounts from collection agencies is 5 to 20 percent; however, your results may vary based on your market and the age of the accounts at the time you place them with the collection agency.

Collecting outstanding payments from patients requires significant resources. Medical practices with limited staff are also reaching out to collection agencies for assistance with payment plan monitoring, pre-visit identification verification, returned mail, and so forth.

Regardless of how you use a collection agency, streamline the process of sending and receiving accounts. The manual labor used by medical practices in this process often exceeds the financial recoveries made by the agencies. Don't let this be the case for your medical practice; establish a standard, automated process in your practice management system to pull qualifying accounts, send account details to the agency through a secure, electronic connection, and receive information about account activities, including payments.

Streamline Physician Approval for Collection Agency Accounts

If physicians elect to review and approve patient accounts before staff send them to a collection agency, provide the list to them as you start your final in-house collections effort. This way, the physician approval does not delay the time before the account is sent to collections. Not all medical practices require physician approval. Those that do typically state that if the physician has not responded within a defined time period (for example, 10 days), the account will be automatically forwarded to the collection agency. (Note: physician approval is typically a malpractice issue. Some experts advise a physician to review all delinquent accounts such that an adverse situation doesn't develop from sending a patient who has experienced poor quality care [or otherwise made a complaint about his/her care] to the collection agency. Discuss this issue with your malpractice carrier to determine if this should be a consideration in your collections protocol.)

Tool 34 is an example of a physician approval form for accounts to be sent to the collection agency. In this fashion, the request to the physician is formalized, with information provided to the physician regarding attempts that have been made to collect the outstanding account balance.

TOOL 34   **Physician Approval Form — Accounts to Collection Agency**

Date:_____Patient name: _____

City, State, Zip Code:_____

Home telephone number:_____Work telephone number: _____

Cellular telephone number: _____

Patient account number: _____

Insurance coverage: _____

Account balance: _____

Efforts made to collect: _____

This patient's account balance has been taken through the standard collection procedure process of the medical practice. The patient has not responded to three notices of payment due, and therefore it is recommended that this account be turned over to collection agency for further collection.

Please indicate your approval for disposition of this patient account balance through the collection agency process. If the billing manager does not receive a response to this correspondence within 10 days, it will be assumed that it is appropriate to send the account to collection and the process will be initiated.

Physician name:_____Date: _____

Establish Contracts with Two Collection Agencies

If you set up contracts with two collection agencies, you can compare performance levels. This will place your medical practice in a stronger contract negotiating position with both agencies. Measure and monitor recovery rates and patient service complaints between the two agencies and watch performance over time. Formally review your collection agency arrangements at least annually.

Establish Appropriate Internal Controls for Collection Agency Funds

For payments on charges that have been adjusted off the accounts receivable, you can choose to either post the payments net of the collection fee (if applicable) or post the payments received in full and record any collection fees as an expense. We generally recommend that payments collected by the collection agency be posted in full, with the fees assessed by the collection agency recorded as an expense to the medical practice. In this manner, the amount the patient actually paid is reflected on the practice management system, as opposed to a payment net of the collection agency fees. However, you should obtain your accountant's advice about handling the revenue and expense associated with these funds. Regardless of how you choose to post the monies recovered by the collection agency, be careful to separate duties and maintain internal controls. Since these accounts are essentially adjusted off the accounts receivable, no one is actively "looking for" the funds, necessitating careful management and oversight of this process.

Charge Billing Fees to Patients Who Fail to Pay in a Timely Manner

Many medical practices have implemented financial penalties to patients who don't pay their bills on time. In order to comply with the Truth in Lending Law (also known as Regulation Z), you may charge patients these fees only if you previously informed them of this fact. You can include it in the financial policy you provide to each patient.

Pass the collection agency fee onto the patient. That is, charge the patient the collection agency fee that the medical practice must pay the agency. Alternatively, pursue additional charges, including (1) finance charges, (2) rebilling fees, and (3) fees for failure to pay at the time of service.

The fees should represent a cost that can be justified as reasonable and appropriate. But before you implement these fees, evaluate the downside to charging these types of fees and perform a cost/benefit analysis. Determine whether the fees can be added automatically to the patient's account. Further, note that these fees may hurt patient relations or create perceptions of an aggressive financial focus by the medical practice — without any positive impact.

The AMA has published the following position on this issue: "Although harsh or commercial collection practices are discouraged in the practice of medicine, a physician who has experienced problems with delinquent accounts may properly choose to request that payment be made at the time of treatment or add interest or other reasonable charges to the delinquent account. The patient must be notified in advance of the interest or other reasonable finance or service charges by such means as the posting of a notice in the physician's waiting room, the distribution of leaflets describing the office billing practices, and appropriate notations on the billing statement. The physician must comply with state and federal laws and regulations applicable to the imposition of such charges. Physicians are encouraged to review their accounting/collection policies to ensure that no patient's account is sent to collection without the physician's knowledge. Physicians who choose to add an interest or finance charge to accounts not paid within a reasonable time are encouraged to use compassion and discretion in hardship cases."[7]

Develop Policies and Procedures Regarding Patient Dismissal

If the account of a patient is deemed uncollectible and is sent to a collection agency, many medical practices follow formal policies and procedures to initiate efforts to discharge the patient from the medical practice, provided certain conditions are met. In the case of non-payment, the patient should be informed of the dismissal in writing. The letter should clearly state that the patient is dismissed from the medical practice as of a specific date. The letter should be sent to the patient via regular mail and certified mail and return receipt, with a copy of the letter and the receipt filed at the medical practice. It is common practice to allow the patient 30 days to find alternative care, while in the meantime providing acute care services only with full payment required at the time of service. To facilitate the transfer of care to another physician, the letter should include contact information for a physician referral service or the local hospital. Finally, enclose in the letter your medical records release form and instructions.

Consult with your malpractice carrier about your dismissal process, as well as any extenuating circumstances that may be presented by a particular patient's dismissal.

Consider Small Claims Court to Pursue Collections

The United States judicial system allows creditors to pursue debtors in court. Most delinquent patient accounts fall under what the judicial system considers to be a "small" claim. There is a process by which small claims can be pursued in all 50 states; most states consider small claims to be $5,000 and less. Although most states use the term "small claims court," there may be alternate names, such as "magistrate court." Regardless, this is the court system by which you can submit an application and documentation regarding a debt owed to you by a patient.

Each court has rules regarding submitting the claim, how it is processed, and what the outcome will be. The application process typically costs $50.00 to $100.00 per claim. Contact the court for the application, and determine what

---

[7] Policy E-6.08. Interest Charges and Finance Charges. Chicago: American Medical Association; issued June 1994. Available from: www.ama-assn.org.

documentation the court requires to accompany your request. Most courts have posted the application paperwork and accompanying instructions on their Websites. Some courts may require you to be present at the trial; others may require an attorney to represent you.

In most cases, you likely will be awarded the judgment. The court will then indicate how you can pursue the debt. Common methods include wage garnishments, property liens, and the repossession of assets (for example, an automobile). After awarding the judgment, the court will provide direction on how the debt can be pursued, but it will not collect the debt for you.

Small claims court is certainly an option to pursue delinquent accounts. Before pursuing, understand all of the rules and regulations of the small claims court that has jurisdiction over your county or city. Further, decide whether the application fee and staff time is worth the outcome. Finally, consider whether your medical practice is willing to pursue the aggressive collection efforts granted by the court to collect these funds.

Pay Careful Attention to Bankruptcies and Estates

Outstanding monies may be owed by a patient who has declared bankruptcy or who is deceased. In the event of a bankruptcy or a declaration or death, collection efforts must be carefully considered. In order to perform appropriate collections efforts, your medical practice should have a protocol in place for receiving and processing notification about patients who declare bankruptcy or are deceased. Creditors must make a claim for any amounts owed within a fixed period of time, which is determined by local or state law.

If a patient files for bankruptcy, suspend all collection efforts immediately upon notification of the declaration. File a "proof of claim" with the local bankruptcy court if the patient owes money. The "proof of claim" is a document that puts you in line as a creditor after the bankruptcy has been filed. Your medical practice may receive monies dispersed by the trustee of the bankruptcy, typically dispersed over a one- to five-year period, but it is unusual that all monies owed are paid. In fact, medical practices generally receive little, if any, payment after a patient files bankruptcy.

In the event of a deceased patient, the debt will be considered by the patient's estate. Information about the estate can be gleaned from the county clerk's office where the patient resided, or the death certificate or funeral home. According to law, a debt may be filed with the probate court or directly with the executor of the estate. "Probate" is the legal proceeding to determine the deceased's assets, their value, and how they will be distributed to creditors and heirs. The probate court judge supervises the work of the executor of the estate. By filing the patient's outstanding debt, your medical practice will be considered when the estate is probated. Unfortunately, in many instances, the estate does not contain enough assets for the medical practice to receive all monies due.

In the event that an account needs to be adjusted off the accounts receivable for a bankruptcy or deceased patient, establish and use specific adjustment codes for these purposes.

Implement a Predictive Dialing Campaign

Placing outbound collection calls requires considerable staff time. Although dozens of calls are often placed, it is common for staff to connect with one patient out of every 10 or more calls. Thus, it may take 30 minutes just to get one patient on the line. Depending on the amount of the outstanding account and the patient population, outbound telephone calls may not exhibit a positive return on investment. That is, you may spend more on staff placing the telephone calls than you do on collecting payments on the outstanding accounts.

A predictive dialer can enhance your telephone-based collection efforts. This telephony product places calls automatically to a list of accounts that you designate. (The most effective use of a dialer is to interface it with your practice management system or upload data from your practice management system to a predictive dialer system.) The dialer automatically places outbound calls to the designated accounts. When a live voice is detected (versus an answering machine or voice mail), the system simultaneously connects the call to a staff member and displays the patient's account on the staff's computer screen. Using a predictive dialer, staff effort migrates from placing calls to pursuing collections, thus improving productivity. Based on how many accounts need to be contacted and the number of staff available, predictive dialers can place dozens, even hundreds, of calls every minute.

In addition to assisting staff with outbound calling campaigns, predictive dialers can be programmed to perform small balance collections, providing a friendly message to patients and providing automated inbound payment options 24 hours a day, seven days a week, with an option to connect to a staff member during business hours. In many medical practices, strategies have been designed specifically around this predictive dialer feature. One such strategy is to use a predictive dialer to contact patients who have a small balance on their account (for example, a range of $250.00 to $500.00, a level that typically could be paid by credit card over the telephone). This saves considerable staff time collecting from patients and at the same time, the resources are leveraged toward those accounts that have a higher probability of being paid via this method.

Make It Easy for Patients to Pay You

When patients are on a payment plan, many medical practices continue to send statements to the patient, incurring statement preparation and mailing costs. Better-performing medical practices establish secure, electronic correspondence (directly, via a Web portal or an online billing system) between the patient and the medical practice so the practice can submit payment reminders in electronic format. If your medical practice does not employ this technology, provide coupon books to patients to facilitate receipt of these funds and to reduce billing costs.

Maintain a Record of Patient Inquiries and Dispositions

Many medical practices use an inquiry tracking system integrated within their practice management system, or a database or spreadsheet to document and track patient inquiries and their resolution and disposition. They review this record periodically to discuss trends, identify opportunities for process improvement, and ensure equitable treatment. If patients keep calling with a particular question, you can fix your process and avoid the repeated calls. A sample call log is presented in Tool 35. Communication from patients, particularly billing calls, exhausts staff members. We have overheard one too many conversations in which the patient states in frustration, "This isn't the right insurance! I handed my new card to the front office. Why didn't they get it right?" A better-performing billing office has a negligible amount of billing inquiries from patients because (1) the registration process is timely and accurate; (2) many patient payments are collected at the time of service (thereby reducing inbound telephone demand); (3) patients understand their statements; and (4) the statements are accurate. In other words, there is no reason for the patient to call.

TOOL 35   Billing Inquiry Call Log

This tool provides an easy way to record billing inquiry calls. Evaluate calls each week, looking for opportunities to reduce inbound telephone demand from patients. For example, if a trend shows that patients are calling to ask if their secondary insurance paid on the claim before submitting a patient payment for the account balance, you may want to restructure the patient statements to record primary and secondary billing status. This tool may also be used to track online patient inquiries regarding their bills.

Date: _____ Operator's name: _____

	Name/Account	Nature of call (brief description)	Resolution
1			
2			
3			
4			
5			
6			
7			

Action:
1. Evaluate the log each week.
2. Determine root causes and trends that can be fixed.
3. Establish an action plan and implement a solution to the problems — to avoid future calls.

© 2009 Walker, Woodcock, Larch. Reprinted with permission.

Identify Focused Staff for Patient Inbound Billing Calls

Designate a small number of employees who are responsible for managing inbound patient billing calls, rather than distributing this function among all billing staff. Patient inquiries often take precedence over other critical billing functions, such as account follow-up activity. (A ringing telephone is hard to ignore.) In smaller practices where billing staff are more multitasked, assign telephone responsibility in two-hour or half-day segments to staff, rotating this function among employees throughout the day. But be sure to focus on the root cause of the calls — and attempt to prevent them from occurring in the first place — instead of simply allocating more staff to the problem.

Require Insured Patients to Pay Their Out-of-Pocket Obligations

Your payer expects you to collect a portion of the total allowable from the patient (pursuant to your contract with the payer). Patients' participation in their insurance plan defines what they are required to pay. Yet, insured patients do not pay their portion of the allowable all the time. For those patients with insurance, track payments made by patients by type of payer to learn the success rate of your patient collections for a particular payer.

Tool 36 is an example of that tracking and can be a useful tool when renegotiating your contract with a payer. The question to be posed to the payer is, "What are you doing to educate your patients that they need to pay their portion of the bill?" Your position (if applicable) is to let the payer know that you cannot continue to discount your rates to the payer at the current level when the payer's patients are paying at a much lower rate than others.

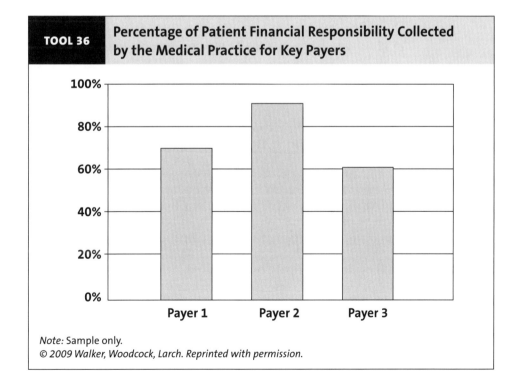

TOOL 36 — **Percentage of Patient Financial Responsibility Collected by the Medical Practice for Key Payers**

Note: Sample only.
© 2009 Walker, Woodcock, Larch. Reprinted with permission.

Segment Patients Based on Credit Worthiness

It is common practice for collections in the banking, real estate, automotive, and other industries to analyze customers' credit worthiness before extending financial assistance or to define the terms of said assistance. Medical practices cannot apply these same protocols to their collections practices, as the nature of health care varies from commodity purchases. However, data can be gathered about the patient to predict the probability of collecting payment on the account, as well as the best means to pursue collections. A credit segmentation strategy is using a predictive risk model to allow a medical practice the ability to forecast the probability of collections and thus adopt subsequent actions.

Your medical practice can begin to group patients into risk categories or segments for both pre-payment and account follow-up actions. As we discussed in Chapter 3: The Patient Financial Clearance Process, credit segmentation can be performed prior to the service to predict collections and, accordingly, pursue the best strategy to collect patient payments upfront. Alternatively, medical practices utilize credit segmentation to pursue unpaid accounts after services are rendered.

The data (which is already captured by the registration and practice management system) used to analyze patients' credit worthiness includes, but is not limited to:

- Correct identity (for example, valid street address and telephone number);
- Nature of admission (for example, emergency admit);
- Dollars outstanding;
- Insurance coverage;
- Account balance;
- History of payments to the medical practice; and
- History of employment.

Technology vendors offer automated solutions that produce "health care credit scores" for patients based on the data. Like Fair Isaac Corporation (FICO) scores, these "health care credit scores" segment your patient population into "likely to pay" or "unlikely to pay" subsets.

Better-performing medical practices use the data to direct their patient collections efforts, based on an internally maintained algorithm or sophisticated software that is interfaced with the practice management system. For example, a medical practice may discover that an account with $100.00 outstanding is always paid by insured and employed patients who have historically paid their bills. Alternatively, for accounts over $500.00, the medical practice may realize that these are never paid by uninsured and unemployed patients. Unlike other industries in which credit for the service or product the customer wishes to purchase may not be extended at all, medical practices typically use the information to determine how and when to pursue collections. For example, in the former case, the $100.00 can be collected at the time of service; in the latter, the patient can be presented with a financial hardship or Medicaid application at the time of service.

An example of a basic credit segmentation strategy (pre-visit and post-visit) is presented in Tool 37. The example can serve as a template in developing a segmentation policy specific to your medical practice.

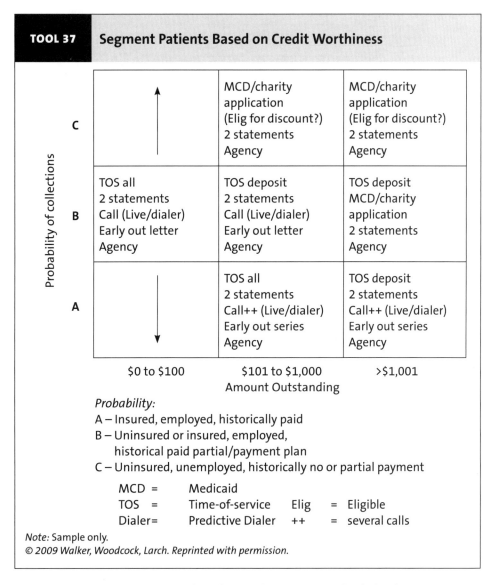

| TOOL 37 | **Segment Patients Based on Credit Worthiness** |

	$0 to $100	$101 to $1,000	>$1,001
C		MCD/charity application (Elig for discount?) 2 statements Agency	MCD/charity application (Elig for discount?) 2 statements Agency
B	TOS all 2 statements Call (Live/dialer) Early out letter Agency	TOS deposit 2 statements Call (Live/dialer) Early out letter Agency	TOS deposit MCD/charity application 2 statements Agency
A		TOS all 2 statements Call++ (Live/dialer) Early out series Agency	TOS deposit 2 statements Call++ (Live/dialer) Early out series Agency

(vertical axis: Probability of collections)
(horizontal axis: Amount Outstanding)

Probability:
A – Insured, employed, historically paid
B – Uninsured or insured, employed,
   historical paid partial/payment plan
C – Uninsured, unemployed, historically no or partial payment

MCD =   Medicaid
TOS =   Time-of-service   Elig   = Eligible
Dialer=   Predictive Dialer ++   = several calls

Note: Sample only.
© 2009 Walker, Woodcock, Larch. Reprinted with permission.

You can also segment patients' credit worthiness using the federal poverty guidelines. Many medical practices already utilize federal or state poverty guidelines as a framework for a sliding scale to determine financial discounts based on household income and size of family. Look at Tool 38: Using Federal Poverty Levels to Determine Credit Worthiness for such a segmentation strategy. It shows one practice's patients arrayed by poverty guidelines.

As you define the segments, your medical practice can determine the different techniques you may need to be successful in patient collections. Where applicable, these segments should then tie to your overall financial policy and to your financial hardship policies.

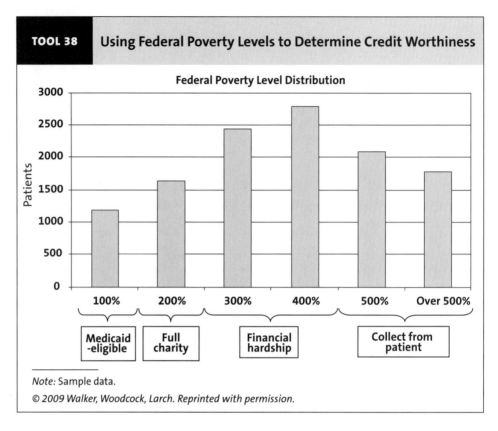

TOOL 38 | **Using Federal Poverty Levels to Determine Credit Worthiness**

Note: Sample data.

© 2009 Walker, Woodcock, Larch. Reprinted with permission.

Create a Policy and Procedure to Manage Bad Checks

Checks with non-sufficient funds (NSF), often referred to as "bounced" or "bad" checks, create significant challenges for a billing office. The funds are insufficient, so the account remains outstanding, and staff must embark on efforts to pursue the payment — again.

To avoid NSF checks, train staff to make sure the check is complete and correct, including the medical practice's name, dollar amount, and the check holder's signature. For patients who pay by check at the time of service, ask for photo identification (ID). Check to make sure that the ID — picture, description, and signature — matches the check holder. Record a telephone number, driver's license number, and address on the check. Promptly deposit checks, and request timely communication from your bank regarding any problems. Charge an NSF fee, typically $25.00 to $50.00 (consistent with your reprocessing costs and as documented in your financial policy provided to your patients) per incident. Try contacting the patient who wrote a bad check immediately, and flag the account for collections if you have no response.

To avoid NSF checks at the time of service, your medical practice can contract with a check verification or guarantee service. The vendor performs an electronic verification of the patient's account to determine whether the check holder has sufficient funds to clear the payment. Available at a higher price, vendors also offer check guarantee services, which essentially turn a personal check into a debit card, thus transferring the funds from the patient's bank account to your medical practice's bank account at the time of processing.

Finally, your medical practice may wish to consider eliminating payment by personal checks altogether. Since most patients now use credit and debit cards, many businesses have simply stopped accepting personal checks. Discontinuing the acceptance of personal checks allows your medical practice to avoid the problems with bad checks without a lot of downside. If your medical practice discontinues accepting personal checks, make sure you inform your patients of this policy during your registration process.

Include Billing Service Questions on Patient Satisfaction Instruments

Include questions on patient satisfaction surveys or in patient focus groups that are directly related to the revenue cycle to determine the patient's perceptions of (1) service quality, (2) clarity of the patient statement, (3) courtesy of staff, and (4) access to the billing office. Initiate improvements where indicated and include these measures in your staff performance management process and performance evaluations.

In the era of increasing patient financial responsibility, the patient collections process is of critical importance to your medical practice. Take steps to ensure that you have established the best process for your medical practice — and your patients.

STAFF WORKLOAD RANGES

The staff workload ranges for the patient collections process that we typically expect are provided below. The ability to perform within these ranges may vary due to internal practice-specific factors, as well as the scope of work delegated to the staff. The workload ranges are based on a staff member performing these functions approximately seven hours of productive time per day (allowing one hour for breaks, interruptions, and other down time). Note that the workload ranges reflect quantitative performance levels. Qualitative performance — accuracy, completeness, appropriateness, and quality of these functions — should also be measured. When issues of quantity versus quality arise, we strongly recommend that quality be emphasized, even if the performance workload ranges for a particular function must be relaxed from these levels.

Staff Function	Accounts	
	per day	per hour
Self-pay follow-up	70–90	10–13
Correspondence processed	90–105	13–15
Patient billing inquiries (by telephone or correspondence)	56–84	8–12

Note: Institute these workload ranges only if accuracy can be assured in this time frame. If not, you may need to increase the time to perform the function in order to avoid mistakes.

LEADING PERFORMANCE INDICATORS

Use the following indicators to assess the performance of your patient collections process. We refer to these measures as "leading" performance indicators. If your medical practice is successful in achieving these levels in the patient collections process, you are on the correct path to optimizing your revenue cycle.

The quality of your self-pay receivables depends upon your payer mix and the type of self-pay accounts you have, as well as your success in collecting from patients at the time of service.

Responding to patient billing inquiries: Within 24 hours

Assess the following indicators for your medical practice and track this performance over time:

- Patient collections per encounter
- Point-of-service collections as a percentage of fee-for-service collections
- Telephone and online collections as a percentage of fee-for-service collections

THE PATIENT COLLECTIONS DIAGNOSTIC TOOL

The patient collections diagnostic tool provided below helps ensure that the process, people, technology, and quality required for effective patient collections are in place in your medical practice.

Process:

1. What is the timeline for your patient collections cycle? Is it in writing, and do you follow it consistently?
2. What combination of statements, letters, and telephone calls have you adopted? Is there opportunity to shrink your patient collections cycle?
3. What protocol is used to prioritize patient account follow-up?

People:

1. Are staff trained regarding what they can say when contacting patients about their bills?
2. What is the inbound telephone volume for staff?
3. Do all staff take inbound telephone calls from patients or is this a focused responsibility?

Technology:

1. Is a predictive dialer used to facilitate contact with patients?
2. Are you attempting to collect from the patient on the telephone via credit or debit card? If so, how much is collected via this process?
3. Have you automated small-balance collections?
4. Do you monitor bad debt write-offs?
5. Have you automated the transfer of accounts to and from the collection agency(ies) with which you contract?
6. Do you offer full-service online bill payment?

Quality:

1. Are you monitoring your payer mix?
2. Are you monitoring the performance of your self-pay accounts receivable, versus your total accounts receivable, which includes both insurance and self-pay categories?

POLICIES AND PROCEDURES

At the end of each chapter, we provide policies and procedures to assist you in developing a policy and procedure manual for your medical practice. Below are four policies and procedures specific to the patient collections process.

Policy 27: Patient Collections

Policy 28: Collection Agency

Policy 29: Financial Hardship

Policy 30: Payment Plan

POLICY 27: PATIENT COLLECTIONS

Policy:

It is the policy of the medical practice that accounts assigned to the responsibility of the patient will receive a series of statements and collection notices. Failure to respond will cause the account to be considered for external collection efforts and the collection agency fee will be submitted to the patient.

Procedures:

1. Patients will receive two statements – one generated on the day that the responsibility is created, followed by a second notice 30 days from that date.

   Thirty days later (60 days following the initial statement), the patient will receive a letter from the medical practice requesting that the patient make payment or contact the medical practice to discuss alternatives. The statements will have dunning notices embedded based on statement number.

   Thirty days later (90 days following the initial statement), the patient will receive a collections letter from the medical practice requesting that action be taken or collections will commence.

   During the period of 90 to 120 days, medical practice staff will alert providers to the status of the outstanding balance by providing an electronic log of the patient's name, outstanding balance, and any applicable notes about the account. Providers will be requested to provide any guidance about these accounts within 10 days on a standard form that can be manually or electronically sent to the appropriate provider. If the provider does not wish the account to be referred to the collection agency, the account information will be forwarded to the billing manager, who will confer with the provider to determine the appropriate action to be taken. During that 30-day period, if resources allow, telephone calls will be placed to patients urging them to pay or make contact with the medical practice.

2. Patient balances will be considered for transfer to the collection agency if the following are applicable:

   a. Patient balance is not paid in full;

   b. Patient balance is outstanding 120 days from date of patient notification of responsibility;

   c. Patient has received four statements and/or collections notices;

    d. Patient balance exceeds $9.99; and

    e. Patient has failed to make payments according to the plan to which he/she agreed or to otherwise meet commitments made to medical practice staff engaged in collection activities.

3. If a patient balance remains after patient balance follow-up, a minimum of 120 days has passed from the date of posting, and it is determined that the patient balance will not be written off, the account will be turned over to a collection agency.

4. The account will be sent to the collection agency or written off using the appropriate adjustment code. See related policy on collection agency.

5. The patient will be notified in writing via certified mail that he/she has been discharged from the medical practice. Appropriate time to find a new provider will be accommodated by the medical practice.

6. The patient account will be flagged as bad debt. This flag will be apparent when a patient attempts to schedule an appointment. The patient will be reminded that he/she has been discharged from the medical practice and an appointment will not be scheduled until full payment is received. Services will be denied except in the case of an emergency.

Patient accounts will be turned over to the collection agency according to the communication required by the collection agency. If possible, such actions will be totally automated through an interface between the medical practice and the agency.

The fees associated with the collection agency recovery will be charged to the patient. Patients will be so notified via the medical practice's financial policy and via the letter sent during the collection process.

POLICY 28: COLLECTION AGENCY

Policy:

It is the policy of the medical practice to utilize external collection efforts through a collection agency(ies). The medical practice will track and monitor the cost of, activities of, and monies recovered by the collection agency(ies) with which it contracts to work overdue accounts.

Procedures:

1. The amount of the account assigned to a collection agency shall be written off to a bad debt account code at the time the account is assigned to the agency.

2. Patient accounts will be turned over according to the communication required by the collection agency. If possible, such actions will be totally automated through an interface between the medical practice and the agency.

3. Collection agencies will provide monthly account activity reports that identify all new accounts received, payments on existing accounts, closed accounts, estate status, skip-trace information, or litigation status. The information from these reports will be documented, when appropriate, to each patient's account.

4. Collection agencies will forward all payments received on a regular and consistent basis. The payments will be posted immediately and included in the daily deposit.

5. Payments received by the medical practice on accounts that have been assigned to a collection agency will be posted to the patient's account using the payment code for bad debt recovery with a secondary code assigned to the particular agency who was assigned responsibility for that account. The collection agency will be immediately notified of the receipt of payment.

6. If applicable, according to the contract with the agency, an adjustment will be applied to the patient's account to reflect the agency's fee adjustment. The amount will be confirmed to assure compliance with the agency contract.

7. A monthly collection agency report will be generated to collectively report all payments received by the medical practice for collection agency accounts. These reports will be forwarded to the appropriate collection agency(ies).

8. The collection agency may deem an account uncollectible upon completion of judicial collection processes. When this occurs, the agency will no longer follow up on the account and will report this determination to the medical practice.

9. The billing manager will closely monitor fees and recovery rates by agency. Contracts and agency(ies) used will be reevaluated annually.

POLICY 29: FINANCIAL HARDSHIP

Policy:

Patients are expected to pay for services rendered. The medical practice will assist patients who indicate they are unable to meet their financial obligations. Patients may be determined as eligible for partial to full discounts utilizing the current poverty guidelines issued by appropriate government agencies.

Procedures:

1. Exclusions from this policy are:

   a. Cosmetic services; and

   b. Services rendered to persons who are eligible, but have not applied for, medical insurance or assistance programs sponsored by federal, state, or local government.

2. Financial hardship may be extended to those who qualify for all four of these reasons:

   a. The patient is not eligible for Medicaid or pending Medicaid approval;

   b. The patient is determined to be unable to pay for services provided;

   c. The patient is unable to accept an installment payment arrangement; and

   d. The patient agrees to make payment at the time the discount is granted.

   For patients who identify themselves or are identified by medical practice staff to be considered for financial hardship/charity care, staff will obtain financial information from the patient. Presumptive eligibility can be based on their current status with federal and state agencies. If not applicable, patients will be requested to submit a copy of their last two paycheck stubs; current-year tax return; and, if applicable, unemployment benefits check stubs. The medical practice will assist patients as much as possible in completing their information.

3. The billing staff will determine eligibility for financial hardship or charity care. Discounts on charges will be calculated as follows:

Percent of state poverty level	Percent discount
300%	30%
200%	50%
100%	75%
< 100%	100%

An adjustment code will be assigned to each level of discount.

4. The granting of the discount will be noted in the patient's account. The patient's account status, however, will never be permanently designated as financial hardship. The patient's status will be reviewed on a regular schedule.

POLICY 30: PAYMENT PLAN

Policy:

It is the policy of the medical practice to offer payment plans to assist patients experiencing financial hardship in paying off outstanding accounts. This may include patients who are unable to provide acceptable health insurance, have no health insurance, are unable to pay their account balance in a single payment, or do not qualify for financial hardship according to the medical practice's financial hardship policy.

Procedures:

1. Medical practice staff will encourage all patients to pay in full. However, if they are unable to make full payment, a payment plan can be created by medical practice staff to pay the outstanding balance over time. Payment plans may be used for outstanding balances or pre-service deposits for procedures, surgeries, or non-covered services.

2. The billing manager or his/her designee will train and assign responsibility to medical practice staff to execute payment plans.

3. Payment plans may be established with patients in person or via telephone. If in person, medical practice staff will ask patients to agree to a payment plan by acknowledging the agreement with a signature.

4. If the balance is less than $500.00, it must be paid within three months. If it is greater than $500.00, it must be paid within six months. Any payment plan requested outside of those parameters must be approved by the billing manager or his/her designee.

5. Once the medical practice staff and the patient have agreed to a payment plan, the particulars will be keyed into the practice management system.

6. Upon establishing a payment plan, a confirmation letter stating the patient's commitment to pay and the particulars of the plan will be generated automatically or manually for the patient. The account will be assigned as a payment plan for tracking and monitoring purposes.

7. Medical practice staff will follow up on all payment plans every month. A listing of delinquent (more than 30 days since last payment) payment plan accounts will be printed each week.

8. Delinquent accounts are given one month to make up the missed payment. If they fail to meet this schedule, the account is no longer eligible for a payment plan, and is expected to be paid in full. If the account is more than 120 days old, it is eligible for collection agency turnover. A standard letter is sent informing the patient of the change in the account status.

CHAPTER 14

Pothole 12
The Contract and Reimbursement Management Process

Although this chapter falls near the end of the book, the contract and reimbursement management process arguably defines the billing process of a medical practice. Every medical practice must decide on the relationships it will have with payers. These relationships set the stage for the professional fee billing process by defining the expected payment (also referred to as the "allowable") for each service, and the opportunity to receive bonus reimbursement, if any, as well as the claims processing and administrative requirements by which the medical practice can pursue the payment upon rendering a service to one of the payer's beneficiaries.

Other issues like credentialing, covered services, medical necessity, appeals process, and so forth are also outlined in the practice-payer relationship. Key documents that describe the practice-payer relationship include the contract itself, the payer's provider manual, and other policies and procedures as outlined by the payer. Traditionally, these documents have been authored, presented, and maintained by the payer and then presented to the medical practice.

Better-performing medical practices review all aspects of payer communications, and negotiate issues that are unfavorable or problematic for the medical practice. They proactively manage their contracts, including coverage, authorizations, payment terms, and the conditions for terminating the relationship. Finally, better-performing medical practices may choose not to have a contract with a payer, instead forming a relationship with the patient directly. Every practice-payer relationship defines the structure of the billing process; rarely are any two relationships alike.

In this chapter, we present the following key topics:

- Practice-payer relationships
- The credentialing process

- Contract negotiation tips
- Internal reimbursement expertise
- Payer reimbursement tactics

PRACTICE-PAYER RELATIONSHIPS

Although each unique payer defines the details of its relationship with a medical practice, there are broad categories of relationships that can be summarized as follows:

Participating Provider

The medical practice and the payer enter into a contract that is signed by both parties. The participating provider agrees to treat the payer's beneficiaries and submit claims for payment to the payer for reimbursement. In turn, the payer agrees to communicate information about the participating provider to its beneficiaries and reimburse the provider for his/her services performed on the payer's beneficiaries at a pre-determined fee schedule. Participating provider is often shortened to "par" when discussing this term (as opposed to non-participating provider, which is often simply termed "non-par").

Non-participating Provider

The medical practice declines to contract with the payer, but may still see the payer's beneficiaries. Because no contract exists, the reimbursement is adjudicated at or near the medical practice's charges. The payer often maintains a separate schedule to pay "non-participating" (also referred to as "non-par") claims. These fees are higher than the allowable provided to participating physicians, and medical practices often accept them (in lieu of the full charge submitted) because the non-par allowances are better than what they could have expected as participating providers. From patients' perspectives, a physician who does not participate with their payer is out of their network of participating providers. Thus, it is common to refer to non-par providers as "out-of-network." The downside for non-par providers is that the payer will not encourage its beneficiaries to utilize the medical practice because of the excess costs it must bear for services provided out of network versus in network.

As we have said, though the medical practice and the payer do not have a relationship, the patient may still present for care. Although not ubiquitous, the medical practice may still file the claim to the patient's payer as a courtesy. As noted in Chapter 11: The Insurance Follow-up Process, the medical practice should only wait 30 to 45 days after the claim has been submitted to the payer before transferring financial responsibility to the patient of a payer with which the medical practice doesn't participate.

If your medical practice decides not to participate with any payer, you can establish and enforce reimbursement rules as you see fit. (Of course, patients aren't going to return if you charge and try to collect $1,000 for an office visit, so the fee schedule you establish must be within local market norms to sustain your patient base.) Medical practices with no payer relationships are often referred to as "cash-only" practices and are growing in popularity throughout the country.

Note that while your medical practice may in theory have the chance for a higher reimbursement if it elects non-participating provider status, the patient's health plan typically requires a greater out-of-pocket obligation to be paid by the patient. The payment paid by the payer is often sent directly to the patient, so your medical practice must often collect both the payer and patient payments from the patient. Your medical practice's ability to successfully collect from the patient will determine if you are indeed able to recognize this higher revenue.

It is worth noting that the Centers for Medicare & Medicaid Services (CMS) has a slightly different definition of non-participating providers. Indeed, CMS defines two levels of not participating with their program.

Medicare non-participating

For Medicare, dropping participation — often referred to as going "non-par" — means that you can charge more than participating physicians, but you cannot charge more than the limiting charge. Medicare-approved amounts are currently 95 percent of the allowances afforded to Medicare participating physicians; the limiting charge, which is set by CMS, is 115 percent of the current Medicare allowance. The Medicare payment is made directly to the beneficiary (typically the patient) if the provider is not a participating provider and does not accept assignment on the claim. When you accept assignment on the claim, your medical practice receives 80 percent of the 95 percent allowable from Medicare, and the remaining 20 percent from the patient or his/her secondary insurer. (Notably, you may choose either to accept or not accept assignment on Medicare claims on a claim-by-claim basis.) Having to collect this extra payment from the patient (or a secondary payer) is one of the most compelling reasons why medical practices do not become non-par. The cost of collecting from the patient is much higher and often has reduced results.

To determine if it's beneficial for your medical practice to go non-par and discontinue accepting assignment, the key is whether you'll be able to collect directly from the beneficiary. Specifically, will your patient payments make up the difference? Analysis by the American Medical Association (AMA) reveals that a physician has to collect the full limiting charge amount 35 percent of the time in order to equal the revenue of participating physicians. If you collect greater than 35 percent of the time, you may be better off as a non-par physician who does not accept assignment, though you should carefully evaluate the financial and other impacts of this option for your medical practice.[1]

Medicare opting out

Discontinuing your relationship with the Medicare program is possible, but it's a decision that is currently binding for two years. You can "opt out" of Medicare to contract directly with your patients without any restrictions regarding

---

[1] American Medical Association, Medicare Participation Options for Physicians. http://www.ama-assn.org/ama1/pub/upload/mm/399/medicarepayment08.pdf (accessed September 19, 2008).

fees. However, you have to stick with your decision; in other words, you can't decide to participate on a case-by-case basis. If you see a patient who is a Medicare beneficiary after you opt out of the program, you need to present a contract disclosing your discontinuation status to the patient. The contract must be signed by the beneficiary and include the fact that Medicare does not pay for the services provided. Further, the beneficiary must acknowledge in writing that he/she cannot bill Medicare or ask the physician to bill Medicare for the services, he/she is liable for all of the physician's charges, he/she acknowledges that supplemental insurance won't pay for the services, and he/she has a right to obtain services elsewhere from physicians who participate with Medicare. Although the decision is binding for two years, the Medicare program currently allows you 90 days to change your mind the first time you opt out, but you must revoke the status change in writing.[2]

Although most physicians participate with payers, it's not a requirement. As your medical practice grows and develops, review your participation status with each payer, at minimum, annually.

Assignment of benefits

An assignment of benefits is a transfer of a beneficiary's interest in policy benefits to another party. The policy generally requires a written assignment by the beneficiary to the provider, allowing the provider to bill the payer directly and receive payment. Assignment of benefits is often confused with participating and non-participating provider status. If you are a participating provider (par), you accept assignment. If you are a non-participating provider (non-par), you do not have to accept assignment. In actuality, assignment of benefits simply directs the payment to the provider of services.

State law differs on assignment of benefits. A summary of the laws for the states of Georgia and Idaho are presented below to give you an indication of the variability of these laws by state.

According to Georgia Code § 33-24-54: Payments to non-participating or non-preferred providers of health care services, "... whenever an accident and sickness insurance policy, subscriber contract, or self-insured health benefit plan, by whatever name called, which is issued or administered by a person licensed under this title provides that any of its benefits are payable to a participating or preferred provider of health care services ... the person licensed under this title shall be required to pay such benefits directly to any similarly licensed non-participating or non-preferred provider who has rendered such services, has a written assignment of benefits, and has caused written notice of such assignment to be given to the person licensed under this title...."[3]

According to Idaho Statute, Title 44: Insurance, Chapter 56: Prompt Payment of Claims, "Nothing in this chapter requires an insurer to accept an assignment of payment by the beneficiary to the practitioner or facility."[4]

---

[2] Ibid.

[3] http://www.legis.state.ga.us/legis/2003_04/gacode/33-24-54.html (accessed June 30, 2008).

[4] http://www3.state.id.us/cgi-bin/newidst?sctid=410560004.K (accessed June 30, 2008).

Because state laws vary, it is important to understand your state law and how it may impact the billing process. Although most assigned claims are paid to the medical practice that submitted them without any problems, assignment of benefits can become an issue particularly when the medical practice is not a participating provider. Services performed in an emergency situation can often result in assignment of benefit challenges (for example, a person traveling from out of state who is in a motor vehicle accident). If the payer reimburses the patient for your services and the patient refuses to pay you, examine your state law regarding assignment of benefits to determine if it can assist you in collecting from the patient.

To ensure efficient and effective contracting and reimbursement management processes, we present proven strategies to enhance your revenue cycle.

ADVANCED PRACTICES: THE CONTRACT AND REIMBURSEMENT MANAGEMENT PROCESS

Facilitate the Credentialing Process

If you agree to participate with a payer, you will be asked to submit group and individual provider applications. The applications and accompanying paperwork are often referred to as the credentialing or enrollment process. Although there is a movement to a universal application process, most payers have separate applications and require different information to be approved as a participating provider.

Figure 14.1 displays information typically requested during a credentialing application.

FIGURE 14.1 ■ Credentialing Requirements

The credentialing data requested from the medical practice about its physician(s) and other health care professional(s) may include, but not be limited to, information and proof of:

- Demographic information such as full name, birthplace, date of birth, current mailing address, and telephone number;
- Medical school and graduate medical education;
- Specialty and subspecialty certification details;
- Drug Enforcement Administration (DEA) registration status;
- Criminal convictions and sanctions;
- State(s) licensure, including issuance and expiration dates;
- Curriculum vitae;
- Hospital privileges and affiliations;
- Residency program certificate;
- Continuing medical education;
- Board eligibility or certification;
- Professional liability insurance information; and
- Malpractice claims history.

Although there are efforts to streamline the credentialing and provider application process, most medical practices find it resource-intensive. Automation is providing relief, as data can be stored and electronically submitted. Furthermore, credentialing software allows a medical practice to integrate alerts for resubmission of data, as most payers require periodic updates to providers' applications. As one can imagine, managing the process for one provider and one payer is simple; hundreds of providers credentialed with hundreds of payers quickly becomes a full-time job. The level of knowledge required to manage the credentialing process has led to the development of organizations that educate and credential staff who manage this process.

Because of its complexity, as well as the seemingly bureaucratic processes of some payers, the credentialing process takes at least 90 days and often up to six months. Two important outcomes of the credentialing process and payer enrollment process are (1) payer provider numbers and (2) national provider identifiers.

Payer provider number

In order to bill for physician services, payers require medical practices to obtain a payer provider number for physicians and a payer group provider number for the medical practice. Payers continue to revise their provider number enrollment policies and procedures. It is very important that medical practices stay current on payers' enrollment rules. Since the enrollment process always takes longer than expected, we highly recommend that all provider applications be carefully reviewed before they are submitted. If supporting documentation is required, make sure it is attached and readable. If the application is not signed and dated by the provider, it is not complete. Without the payer's provider number, the provider cannot bill and be paid for the medical services provided.

National provider identifier

In addition to the payer provider numbers, as of May 23, 2008, all medical practices that use a Health Insurance Portability and Accountability Act (HIPAA)-standard electronic transaction are required to include a national provider identifier (NPI) on the transaction. The NPI is required as part of HIPAA's "administrative simplification" provisions. The NPI is a 10-digit number assigned to each health care provider (NPI Type 1) and organization (NPI Type 2). The NPI is assigned to the provider for life and stays with him/her regardless of where he/she works. When the NPI was originally defined, it was expected that it would replace the payer legacy provider numbers. Providers continue to need payer legacy provider numbers, though they are not always required on claims. The NPI replaces the Unique Physician Identification Number (UPIN) that was historically used to identify physicians on claims.

Develop a Formal Contract Negotiations Plan

The payer establishes the rules and regulations for the relationship with the medical practice in the contract, provider manual, and accompanying communications. Some medical practices just sign on the dotted line, and in fact are not able to cite their contract termination dates, basic contract terms, and other key components of the practice-payer relationship.

Better-performing medical practices develop a proactive contracting position and take the opportunity to negotiate the payer contract terms to make them more favorable to the medical practice. They attempt to increase revenue and/or reduce the "hassle" factor associated with the payer's billing requirements. In this context, these medical practices don't hesitate to gather and present data regarding patient satisfaction and quality of care specific to the payer's beneficiaries. They don't hesitate to report payer claim denial rates, unacceptable customer service from the payer, reimbursement troubles, and other aspects of their relationship with the payer. Better-performing medical practices take a proactive stance regarding their relationships with payers, which helps them to not only enhance revenue, but also reduce billing costs.

It is recognized that the leverage a medical practice has with a particular payer depends on market, practice size, specialty, and other factors. However, proactively developing your medical practice's position on key negotiating issues will help prepare your medical practice to make its "best case" in negotiating with the payer.

Although this context does not allow a comprehensive guide to contract negotiations, we have highlighted some issues that better-performing medical practices typically negotiate.

Timing of contract renewal

Many medical practices have experienced delays in renegotiating contract terms with payers. To mitigate this problem, indicate to the payer that if the contract has not been renegotiated by a specific date, the contract will be considered terminated. This certainly gets the attention of the payer and may permit you to renegotiate terms in a timely fashion, particularly if your medical practice has contracting leverage.

Another approach is to negotiate automatic renewals of the contract. Often referred to as evergreen provisions, these automatic renewals are very common in payer agreements. No medical practice should agree to a contract that automatically renews unless there is an automatic fee escalator built into the contract. It would typically be better to let the contract expire and have to renegotiate it than to let the payer renew the contract with no increase (unless, of course, you are in a highly competitive market and this will result in the loss of a needed contract for your medical practice).

Many medical practices utilize the Consumer Price Index for Medical Care, published and maintained by the United States Department of Labor's Bureau of Labor Statistics,[5] as the benchmark for fee escalators. The medical practice should carefully manage its contract renewal dates and formally determine whether it wants to initiate renegotiation of contract terms.

---

[5] For information about the current CPI for Medical Care, visit www.bls.gov/cpi/.

Fee schedule

Negotiate for increased reimbursement for all fees with a baseline at least at the medical inflation rate. If the payer balks, consider these other strategies:

- Hone in on your high-volume services. Before your meeting with the payer, run a report to pull the top 20 procedure codes billed to that particular payer during the past 12 months.

- Discuss payment for services that the payer has historically not reimbursed. This may include services it typically bundles with evaluation and management services (such as laboratory, injections, and/or supplies), services billed with a modifier, unlisted procedure codes, and surgical assists.

- Identify specific CPT® codes that you use regularly but for which you receive less reimbursement when compared to other payers. These codes may not be in your top 20 most frequent codes but they are also not at the bottom of the list. These have enough volume that low reimbursement is a problem and a successful strategy for these codes will boost your revenue.

- Focus on individual specialties. If your medical practice is a multispecialty practice, you may find focusing on certain specialties to be to your negotiating advantage. If your medical practice has a specialty in short supply in your area, you should be able to be paid more for that specialty's services or more for the codes that are specific to that specialty. Or, there may be one specialty that is really losing money in your medical practice; any improvement you can garner to their fees helps balance your medical practice's performance.

- Don't forget carve outs. Radiology, ophthalmology, mental health, and other areas are often carved out of a payer contract. Either they have a special fee schedule for those services or the payer subcontracts with another entity to handle only those services. You may need to negotiate a separate fee schedule or develop a relationship with the subcontractor.

- Focus on a higher conversion factor. An AMA study of 127 public and private payers covering 123 million patients found that 77 percent of payers use Medicare's Resource-based Relative Value Scale (RBRVS) to help determine what they pay physicians. That is up from a 74 percent adoption rate in 2001 and a 63 percent adoption rate in 1998. Importantly, however, the study, published in *Medicare RBRVS 2007: The Physician's Guide,* found that the majority of payers are not using Medicare's conversion factor (which determines the final payment amount). Fortunately, the conversion factors used by the majority of commercial payers are higher than Medicare's rate.[6] Using Medicare as a benchmark and reflecting on historical rates, negotiate a higher conversion factor for your services.

In summary, attempt to increase reimbursement for the services performed by your physicians at each and every opportunity as you renegotiate your contracts with payers.

---

[6] *Medicare RBRVS 2007: The Physician's Guide.* ISBN 978-1-57947-811-7. Item OP059607. Authors: AMA.

Refund time frames

Establish the shortest time frame possible in which the payer may attempt to take back funds or request a refund. The payer gives you a certain amount of time (for example, six months) within which you can appeal claims denials or underpayments. Ask the payer to establish a similar timeline that applies to refunds back to the payer. Alternatively, if your state has a law limiting the time during which a payer can request refunds, defer to that as the deadline.

Balance billing patients

When you participate with a payer, the contract typically prohibits your medical practice from billing patients for services that are within the payer's purview to pay. But what if the payer denies a claim for information needed from the patient? Your staff might spend many weeks trying to get the correct information from the patient in order to re-file the claim. Protect yourself by negotiating for a maximum non-payment term of, for example, 30 days when patients fail to provide the requested information. When claims are denied because of "information needed from patient," encourage those patients to respond to their payer's request for information. With this provision in your contract, after 30 days of no response from the patient, you could bill the patient directly for the negotiated amount of the service.

All products

Many payers have a standard "all products" clause built into their contract. This clause indicates that the participating medical practice must agree to accept *all* of the plans the payer offers in the market — and the terms that come with them. For medical practices that want to participate with the payer's preferred provider organization (PPO) product but not the health maintenance organization (HMO) product, an "all products" clause is disastrous because the medical practice is forced to accept the PPO *and* the HMO. Several states have already passed laws to prevent payers from including these clauses; however, they are still found in many standard contracts. Review your contracts carefully for the clause, and ask to have it removed or amended so that your medical practice can decide whether or not to accept each product distinctly.

Timely filing

Inaccurate information from the patient at registration can cause a service to be billed to the wrong payer. By the time the mistake is discovered and corrected, the timely filing deadline may have passed. Avoid these unnecessary write-offs by negotiating timely filing in your contract. Seek to have the timely filing period extended whenever a patient fails to provide you with correct information. Support your stance by offering to provide the payer with proof that you filed that claim in a timely manner to whatever health plan the patient claimed to have. An example of such language is as follows:

> In the event that payment of a claim is denied due to untimely filing, the denial will be reversed and payment made if the medical practice appeals within six months after the date of service and can show all of the following:
>
> - that, at the time that payer contract terms required notification or at the time the claim was due, the medical practice did not know and was unable to reasonably determine that the patient was a beneficiary;

- that the medical practice took reasonable steps to learn that the patient was a beneficiary; and

- that the medical practice promptly provided notification, or filed the claim, after learning that the patient was a beneficiary.

Medical necessity

Although your medical practice provides only medically necessary services to patients, a payer may not always agree. Head off lengthy and disruptive appeals by offering to agree to a definition of medical necessity in the next contract. The AMA publishes an invaluable resource for this in its "Model Managed Care Contract," which includes a section on medical necessity that offers ideas on how to describe it in payer contracts.[7]

Consumer-directed health care (CDHC)

Many CDHC plans do not allow you to collect from their beneficiaries prior to the service being rendered even if you know that they have an unmet deductible. Negotiate the ability to collect from the patient at the time of service so that you're not left chasing the money after the payer denies your claim due to the deductible and only gives you permission to collect from the patient months later.

Claim form variation

Payers require providers to submit claim forms on a standard CMS-1500 form for professional services. However, they may define custom requirements for which data fields will be used and how they will be used. Medical practices should compare the different claim formats across major payers and negotiate claim form standards over time across all payers. Variations cause errors and delay payments.

Referral and authorization requirements

Payers change referral and authorization requirements with no notice or no advance notice. Medical practices should negotiate that authorization requirement changes cannot be made without written consent of the medical practice. Medical practices should work to eliminate all pre-authorization processes. If you have evidence that you are approved for the services every time you seek a pre-authorization, you have evidence that you do not need to perform the pre-authorization process. Discuss the expense of the process for your medical practice — and that of the payer.

Denial appeal process

Define the denial appeal process in the contract or in a contract addendum. You want to see what information is required in order to appeal a claim. An advanced practice is to include in the contract the ability to appeal multiple claims through trend data rather than having to appeal each claim with the same issue.

---

[7] American Medical Association Model Managed Care Contract Supplement 1: Medical Necessity and Due Process
http://www.ama-assn.org/ama1/pub/upload/mm/368/mmcc_4th_suppl_1.pdf
(accessed November 27, 2008).

Request for documentation

"As many as 15 percent to 20 percent of commercial claims require additional documentation to support claims … ."[8] Often, staff in the medical practice need to pull and submit a portion of the medical record, such as an operative note or a discharge summary, to send to the payer. In your contract negotiations, determine when medical documentation is required and define an automated approach that allows sharing of documentation with the payer in a streamlined manner.

Payer termination

Hopefully, it will be rare that one of your payers will go out of business, but it does happen. And, there may come a time when the current payer contract ends without a renewal. In these situations, it is helpful if the contract includes information about providers' obligations to continue treating the payer's beneficiaries, and the payer's obligations to pay for care for patients who are in the midst of treatment at the expiration of the contract.

Remember, once the contract is negotiated, it will be up to the medical practice to effectively execute the contract terms. Thus, it is critical that the payer's policies and procedural requirements are known and minimized, where possible. If you negotiate well, the day-to-day operational payer requirements will be lessened.

As you prioritize which terms you want to negotiate in your contracts, it is often helpful to compare each payer to Medicare. Most medical practices are very familiar with Medicare's fees, policies, and administrative requirements. Determine if the payer with which you plan to negotiate is more complex or difficult to work with than Medicare. Are you getting paid a premium — an amount higher than Medicare — that is sufficient to cover your increased cost of doing business? Normalizing fees, as well as terms, to Medicare allows you to compare your relationships fairly.

Stop thinking of your relationships with payers as one-sided affairs. Better-performing medical practices use the contract negotiating opportunity to present equitable terms that can benefit their medical practice.

Develop Internal Contract Review Expertise

After the contract has been signed, it behooves your medical practice to ensure that the payer complies with the terms to which both parties have agreed. Medical practices spend many weeks evaluating and negotiating a contract but often too little time, on an ongoing basis, evaluating whether the payer is living up to the contract terms.

---

[8] Lauer, R., Miller, T., Semko, G., and Welter, T., "Contracting to improve your revenue cycle performance: is the contracting process hurting your hospital administratively and financially? There are things you can do to lessen the pain," *Healthcare Financial Management*, September 2007.

At minimum, review a sample explanation of benefits (EOB) from each payer every quarter. Peruse the EOBs to make sure the payer reimburses you at the fee schedule on which you agreed, as well as any other terms you successfully negotiated.

Most practice management systems allow you to maintain the payer fee schedules (also known as the allowances) to which you have agreed. As staff post payments, the system pulls the corresponding expected allowance and displays it, along with any variance between the payment posted and the payment expected. If the actual amount paid is different than the expected, staff can manually or automatically flag the account to work at a later time or review the nature of the discrepancy in real time.

Taking a sample and relying on payment posters to research and resolve any payment variance from expected payment is very helpful, but medical practices with sophisticated coding and multiple relationships with payers find great benefit in automated contract management. As discussed in Chapter 18: Leveraging Technology to Enhance the Revenue Cycle, there are software products on the market that can maintain your contract terms to the finest detail and present the variances from expected by line item. Most of these products also offer guidance as to the variance (for example, where it is derived and what to do about it), and electronic work files that maintain the status of each variance, the staff member responsible for working it, the actions taken, and the timelines for subsequent activity.

Regardless of the method you use to conduct contract review, don't let your efforts in negotiating a favorable contract go awry. Every payer has thousands of relationships to manage; place importance on protecting your medical practice by monitoring the payer's compliance with the terms you set forth.

Beware of Payers' Problematic Reimbursement Tactics

Medical practices have been the victims of unknown and often unrecognized reimbursement techniques by payers. Whether a computer glitch or a purposeful act, medical practices should recognize and understand these problematic reimbursement tactics. If they occur at your medical practice, pursue correct reimbursement and, depending on the situation, report the payer to your state insurance commissioner, medical society, and/or professional association. You may also choose to pursue legal action. Some of the key problematic reimbursement tactics used by payers are discussed below.

Blending

A reimbursement tactic, blending occurs when a payer pays a single fee regardless of the code submitted and regardless of the contract fee schedule. It most often occurs with evaluation and management codes, particularly at levels "3" and "4." When reimbursement is blended, you are paid the same amount for a 99213 and a 99214 CPT® code. Blending proliferated with the advent of electronic health records. As automation improves physicians' documentation and charge capture, it raises the level of codes they can legitimately bill. In other words, physicians have tended to underdocument and undercode; electronic health records have helped them document and code appropriately. Payers are responding by essentially ignoring the higher (now justified) codes through blending.

Downcoding

Downcoding occurs when a medical practice submits an evaluation and management code, such as a 99214. The payer downgrades the code a level or two (for example, the payer turns the 99214 into a 99213) and pays based on that lower code. Downcoding is often transparent to the medical practice in that there is no remark code on the explanation of payment. The only way to recognize it is to post payments on a line-item basis. The payment poster would see that you charged one code (99214, in this case), but received notice that a 99213 was paid for that service.

Linking

Basing reimbursement on a patient's illness is a payment mechanism linking reimbursement to the diagnosis code(s) you submit with the procedure code(s). Diagnostic codes have typically been utilized to determine medical necessity as part of the payer's policies, but have not been used to determine payment. Traditionally, the fees that a payer agrees to reimburse you are determined by the procedure code. Now, payers are reimbursing different rates for the procedure code depending on the diagnosis with which it is billed. The decision about the payment (that is, which diagnosis constitutes a higher or lower payment) is made by the payer. Usually, the medical practice is not privy to the payer's logic, nor does it have any influence on the decision.

Silent PPOs

When silent PPOs entered the market they created added confusion for billing offices related to claims reimbursement. These entities rent or purchase the contract your medical practice enters into with a payer; subsequently, the PPO then attempts to pay the medical practice at this reduced, discounted rate. Fortunately, the prevalence of these occurrences are now reportedly lower than in the past, yet it still bears reminding readers of the need to be diligent in ensuring that the "network discount" rate reported on the EOB is indeed a discount that you have formally contracted to receive. If you receive EOBs with contractual adjustments for payers with which you did not contract, the services need to be appealed for full payment.

Bill review companies

A similar phenomenon is bill review companies. These companies have been hired by payers to attempt to encourage your medical practice to agree to a discounted price on an individual claim. For example, though you may have a contract for in-state coverage for a particular payer, a bill review company may contact you and attempt to obtain the same discounted rate for a patient who presented with an out-of-state product of the same payer. The communications are often sent via facsimile, with the announcement that the payment will be taken care of immediately ... if the terms are agreed to. Frequently, the communication indicates that agreement for the claim will be binding for future services as well. In an attempt to complete the account follow-up, some billing staff agree to these terms without recognizing the impact of their actions. In these instances, it is important for your medical practice to be diligent and to have a formal process in place with which these requests will be managed.

Don't let these reimbursement practices wreak havoc with your revenue cycle. Be alert for payers that aren't fairly adjudicating your claims.

Consider Participating in Pay-for-Performance Plans

Although capitation — payment per member life — versus services actually rendered exists, it has not achieved the level of popularity or mainstream reimbursement as some policymakers anticipated. Fee-for-service has returned in full force, but it is being supplemented by significant efforts to recognize quality, efficiency, and technology utilization in the care-delivery process. Coming in many different forms, the movement to pay physicians for their quality and efficiency is generally referred to as "pay-for-performance" (P4P). This includes Medicare's Physician's Quality Reporting Initiative's (PQRI's) voluntary reporting program, which links higher reimbursement levels for reporting a discrete set of "quality" measures.

Each payer defines its own terms, but the definition of pay-for-performance can be summarized as follows:

"Pay" relates to the reimbursement you receive for meeting the program's requirements. Pay may come in the form of an increased allowance, a flat fee, the release of a withheld payment, or a percentage of reimbursement. There also may be a cap on the maximum amount you can receive from a pay-for-performance program.

"Performance" is a set of criteria designed to encourage the physicians and other health care providers in your medical practice to provide better care. The criteria for "better care" can vary greatly from program to program and may include health outcomes measurements, technology utilization, usage rates for generic drugs, patient satisfaction, patient safety, and preventive care.

In order to evaluate a P4P plan, your medical practice must understand the nature of how and what you will be paid, as well as how to capture and report performance criteria. Once you understand how the plan works, you'll need to decide whether you want to participate by asking and answering such questions as, Can you identify patients who meet the criteria? Do your physicians agree with the performance criteria and want to comply with it? How will you track compliance with the performance criteria? How will you report your compliance? Many medical practices find that manually performing these tasks is challenging, if not impossible. The key is to automate all aspects of your participation with the P4P plan.

The contract and reimbursement process in physician billing is undoubtedly complex. A solid understanding, coupled with good management and automation, can truly offer a positive return on investment for your medical practice.

THE CONTRACT AND REIMBURSEMENT MANAGEMENT DIAGNOSTIC TOOL

The contract and reimbursement management diagnostic tool below will help ensure that the process, people, technology, and quality required for effective contract and reimbursement management are in place in your medical practice.

Process:

1. What tools are used to manage payer reimbursement levels?
2. What formal negotiations strategy has been developed for each key payer?
3. What data are being captured to make the "best case" for the medical practice?
4. What is the process for identifying a new physician and obtaining the information required for credentialing — in advance of the physician's arrival?
5. What steps are taken to ensure that the medical practice is consistent with contract terms as they relate to the delivery system — for example, authorizations and wait time to appointment?
6. What steps are taken to ensure that inappropriate payment tactics are identified?

People:

1. Who is responsible for developing the medical practice's negotiating position?
2. Who is responsible for tracking the "hassle" factors associated with a particular payer?
3. Who is involved in actually negotiating the contract? Are they familiar with the payer and with the services provided by the medical practice?
4. Who is responsible for announcing that a new physician has been hired? Who is responsible for initiating the credentialing process?

Technology:

1. What software is used to manage the credentialing process?
2. How is technology deployed to facilitate communication with the payer, such as medical documentation requests?
3. What software is used to manage the medical practice's contracts?
4. Does the data include contract termination dates, reimbursement levels by service, authorization requirements, frequency limits, and other important terms?

Quality:

1. What errors have occurred related to timely credentialing of providers?
2. Are there contracting terms that should have been more effectively negotiated?
3. Are there payers with which the practice should have a relationship — or payers with which the practice should terminate its relationship?
4. Is the practice or the payer in violation of contract terms?

CHAPTER 15

Staffing the Revenue Cycle

Do you have the right number and type of staff involved in your revenue cycle? Are they doing the right things to optimize revenue performance in your medical practice? In this chapter, we help you answer these questions — and more — about staffing your revenue cycle.

In this chapter, we provide:

- Key staffing recommendations
- Staffing deployment models
- Organizational structures
- Staff training, competency, and accountability
- Incentive plans

The most effective staffing for the revenue cycle involves a formal structuring of the work processes and handoffs among physicians and staff involved in both front-end and back-end billing and collection processes. It is critical that roles be carefully defined and boundary relationships clearly delineated.

It is also important that the results of the work be shared with staff so that they can be actively engaged in performance outcomes related to the revenue cycle and their particular roles. For example, a biller responsible for insurance account follow-up should know the aged trial balance, days in accounts receivable, net collection rate, and the volume of work being performed for the accounts assigned to him or her. The biller responsible for payment posting should know the number of transactions he/she has posted, the accuracy of that posting, and the contractual and non-contractual adjustments that he/she has generated.

In order to ensure that staff are performing optimally, follow these key staffing recommendations.

DEVELOP PAYER-SPECIFIC KNOWLEDGE

It is important for a medical practice to develop knowledge experts with regard to key payers. For front-end billing, staff based at the practice site need payer-specific knowledge so they can manage patient financial clearance, conduct accurate registration, obtain waiver forms, and collect time-of-service payments.

For back-end billing, payer knowledge is critical for appropriate payment posting, account follow-up, and denial management. Each payer differs with respect to the rules and requirements related to coding and bundling, payment policies, denial and payment codes, and other important factors.

We recommend that the insurance account follow-up staff be organized by payer. A payer may reject claims for coding or other reasons that may not be recognized early if all staff are involved in all payers. This permits early identification of problem claims and problem payer performance. For large medical practices, a further organization can take place along specialty service lines, such as primary care, medical specialties, and surgical specialties, and within that, depending on the claim volume and claim complexity, a further delineation of staff by subspecialty. For example, within the medical specialties follow-up unit, there may be account follow-up staff devoted to a payer (such as Medicare) and then devoted to a specific specialty (such as cardiology). In this fashion, the medical practice delegates work on a functional basis with appropriate responsibility and defined accountability, combined with payer and specialty-specific knowledge.

EMPHASIZE FRONT-END BILLING

Historically, professional fee billing was considered a back-end process. Staff at the practice sites, including schedulers, check-in staff, clinical staff, and checkout staff, were not highly involved in the revenue cycle. Today, the key to a superior revenue cycle largely rests with these staff. They control the financial viability and access to the medical practice. They also play a key role in obtaining full and complete registration and ensuring that payer-specific requirements are met, such as verifying and obtaining authorizations and waiver forms, and meeting similar other required payer rules.

Though many medical practices have begun to recognize the enhanced and vital role played by staff outside of the traditional billing office, we believe that these staff will play an even greater role in the revenue cycle of the future. This is due to consumer-directed health plans and the need to collect higher levels of payments from patients in terms of deductibles, co-insurance, and copayments at the time of service (if permitted by your contracts); the trend to collect patient responsibility payments prior to elective procedures and services; and the advent of real-time claims adjudication, where the information required by the payer in order to adjudicate the claim is entered at the point of care.

Thus, we believe that the staffing of the revenue cycle of the future will largely rest with staff at the practice sites and with staff that are located in proximity to where the patient physically receives care. Indeed, many better-performing medical practices cite evidence that their investment in front-end billing has paid off, with higher percentages of clean claims being submitted and paid by payers — doing it right the first time — resulting in significantly less resources deployed for back-end billing functions and rework.

LINK COMPLEMENTARY WORK FUNCTIONS

We also recommend linkages between some of the functional work areas. Work linkages permit one staff member to have a broader breadth and scope of responsibility. Particularly with the increased volume of electronic payment remittance, linking the work of payment posting and insurance account follow-up is a natural. Both tasks require in-depth payer-specific knowledge in order to recognize under-profile payments and payer denial codes. Each must recognize and interpret the information the payer is attempting to convey through its explanation of benefits (EOB) and the various codes it is using. Since both the payment posters and account follow-up staff require this same knowledge, many medical practices have thus adopted what is called "total account ownership" (TAO), which focuses the work of payment posting and insurance account follow-up with one individual, who is assigned a specific payer and is well versed in payer nuances.[1] Care must be taken from an internal controls perspective to mitigate problems that might arise from one individual managing the entire account; however, with appropriate supervision, challenges to internal controls may be overcome.

EMPHASIZE PROCESS DEPENDENCY

All too often we have visited medical practices and have found that important work is simply waiting for a staff member to return from vacation or sick leave. The problem with this approach in staffing a revenue cycle is that each process step is highly interconnected and revenue can fluctuate at dangerous levels if one of the processes is significantly delayed. So, we advocate a revenue cycle that is "process-dependent" rather than "people-dependent." Practice staff must be cross-trained to ensure that no key process simply "waits."

When work is delayed in any key step in the revenue cycle, it has a profound impact on revenue and the ability to interpret and take action based on revenue cycle performance indicators. As an example, suppose that the staff member assigned to charge entry is on vacation for two weeks. Since charge entry is needed for claims to even be submitted, every back-end billing process will be affected due to this staff's absence. Importantly, once charge entry is brought to a current state, each staff member's workload along the revenue cycle continuum will experience high fluctuations. If management reports are produced during this same period, the medical practice could mistakenly be alarmed at what it believes is a significant decline in patient volume, when the problem is simply due to the fact that no provisions were made to manage the charge entry work in this employee's absence.

A process-dependent revenue cycle not only helps you provide knowledge transfer throughout the revenue cycle via cross-training, but it also reduces revenue fluctuations for your medical practice.

DEPLOY STAFF BY FUNCTION

There are many underlying sources that influence the actual staffing deployment model of the revenue cycle; however, most medical practices organize staff on a functional basis, with staff assigned to perform a specific scope of work.

---

[1] Woodcock, EW: "Total account ownership. A new model for streamlining your business office staff," *MGMA Connexion*, January 2007, pp. 28–33.

Front-end Billing

Front-end billing functions include the following key areas:

Credentialing and enrollment — The process of submitting applications to payers to become a participating provider with the payer, permitting the medical practice to bill the payer for the physician's services.

Registration and scheduling — The process of obtaining patient demographic and insurance information from the patient and scheduling the patient for his/her appointment.

Patient financial clearance — The process of verifying insurance and benefits eligibility, obtaining authorizations, and identifying expected payment levels by payers and patients.

Patient check-in and check-out — The process of verifying patient demographic and insurance information, and collecting and posting payments at the point of care.

Coding — The process of translating physician documentation into appropriate procedure and diagnosis codes to submit on claims.

Charge capture — The process of ensuring that all charges have been captured and entered to the billing system, involving verifying charges with source documents, logs, frequency analyses, and charge capture audits.

Charge entry — The process of entering the procedure and diagnosis codes to the practice management system.

Back-end Billing

Staff are typically deployed to perform the following key back-end billing and collection functions:

Claims and claim edits — The process of printing, reviewing, and submitting all paper and electronic claims to payers. Includes research and resolution of up-front claim edits prior to submission to payer, and coordination of all attachments (for example, medical documentation and primary payer EOB) submitted with claims.

Payment posting and cashiering — The process of capturing all incoming patient and payer payments; submitting and reconciling deposits to the bank, practice management system, and general ledger; and sorting and preparing payment batches for posting to the practice management system. Also includes manually posting payments and denials to the billing system, along with overseeing processing of electronic remittance files and resolution of all electronic payments and denials requiring manual intervention for posting.

Refunds — The process of researching and resolving all credit invoices.

Insurance follow-up and denial management — The process of researching and following up on all outstanding insurance receivables. Also includes researching and resolving all claims that were denied by payers, including correcting errors, deleting charges from the system, and modifying data for rebilling to payers and/or patients.

Patient follow-up and collections — The processes of receiving, researching, and resolving all patient inquiries via telephone, written correspondence, or face-to-face communication with patients; researching and following up on all outstanding receivables due from the patient or guarantor; monitoring payment plans; providing on-site financial counseling; preparing accounts for small claims court; managing returned checks and returned mail; and readying accounts for collection agency.

Other Staff Roles

In addition to the core functions listed above, the following responsibilities are also performed by staff involved in the revenue cycle:

Reimbursement analysis — The process of reviewing billing and collection financial data for purposes of monitoring payments for contract compliance and providing feedback to management and physicians to maximize reimbursement and improve revenue cycle performance.

Source document storage and retrieval — The process of capturing and storing (via paper, imaging, or other media) all source documentation required to support billing and collections activities, and responding to all requests for source documentation.

Practice management system support — The process of "closing" (typically day-end, month-end, and year-end) that determines the data that will be reported for a defined time period, maintaining and updating practice management software, and managing system back-up protocols.

Training and quality assurance — The process of orienting and providing continuing education to staff involved in the revenue cycle regarding issues related to billing and collections. The process of reviewing samples of work to evaluate quality and quantity.

Liaison — The process of coordinating data and information exchange between the billing office and practice sites.

Clerical support — The process of providing clerical support, including managing incoming and outgoing mail, filing, duplicating, and scanning.

Finally, there may be managers, as well as supervisors and leads for these functions. The management structure typically depends on the size of the medical practice and the number of revenue cycle functions that have been internalized in the medical practice (as opposed to outsourced).[2]

---

[2] The above list of revenue cycle functions is not meant to be exhaustive or reflective of the full scope of work performed in each of these areas, but rather, a compilation of responsibilities most often found in front-end and back-end billing and collection processes.

Determine Staffing Volumes for Key Work Functions

Just how many staff are needed to manage the revenue cycle? The answer depends on a number of internal, medical practice-specific factors, such as productivity, payer mix, and use of technology. If physicians produce significantly above their peers based on market data, we would expect the revenue cycle to be staffed at higher levels to reflect this enhanced productivity. The more productive physicians are, the more claims will be produced on their behalf. We present an approach to determining the number of staff needed in the billing office and the number of staff required for each key back-end billing function later in this chapter. For now, it is important to recognize that internal medical practice-specific factors can and do influence the constitution of the billing office in terms of its size and its work processes.

The staffing volumes and staffing deployment models also vary based on a medical practice's philosophy regarding prevention or correction. Many medical practices devote resources inappropriately by focusing on *correcting* problems rather than resolving the root cause, and *preventing* problems from occurring in the first place.

For example, some medical practices focus on claim denials by allocating additional staffing resources to work the claim denials. Their motto seems to be, "Just add one more person to fix the problem." The following case example depicts a scenario found in many medical practices.

Case Study: Staffing Deployment Model

Medical Practice Anywhere has the following claims track record:

100,000 claims per year submitted

20,000 claims per year (20 percent) denied due to the following reasons:

- 5,000 due to registration errors;
- 7,500 because diagnosis does not support medical necessity;
- 5,000 due to invalid procedure/diagnosis codes; and
- 2,500 because of various other reasons.

Should the medical practice add more staff to rework the denied claims based upon this case example? Many medical practices do.

But we strongly recommend that a medical practice allocate resources to diagnose and treat the disease, not the symptom. That is, rather than add more employees to work a complex or broken process, identify the causes of the denials and correct them before you submit the claim. In this case study, you could choose to add or identify a staff member to perform insurance verification for every patient. Or, you could bring in a coding specialist to review and update charge tickets and demonstrate how proper coding can reduce denials due to medical necessity.

Efficient and effective staffing for the revenue cycle involves much more than simply adding staff to fix the problem. If the performance outcomes are substandard, rather than have more staff involved in checking and re-checking work, train staff and provide them with additional tools and resources so they can do their work right the first time, increasing quality.

In an optimally resourced revenue cycle, we see the right number of staff performing the right tasks and processes to minimize rework, reduce the time to payment, and optimize revenue performance.

Benchmark Staffing Levels for Back-end Billing

Based on our research, the optimal staffing for back-end billing is approximately 10 staff members per 100,000 claims.[3] If you have 100,000 annual claims in your medical practice, you should have approximately 10 full-time-equivalent (FTE) staff involved in back-end billing functions. (Notably, there is variation by specialty; the data reported herein is for all professional fee services.)

The steps outlined in Tool 39 will help you determine whether you have the right number of staff in your billing office.

TOOL 39   **Determine the Number of Staff for Back-end Billing**

5-STEP PROCESS:

Step 1. Determine how your staff spend their time.

Step 2. Compare overall staffing with available benchmarks.

Step 3. Determine benchmark measure of choice and identify specific full-time-equivalent (FTE) levels required for tasks.

Step 4. Determine equitable distribution of work.

Step 5. Identify performance workload ranges and compare these with suggested ranges to determine if there is opportunity for change.

© 2009 Walker, Woodcock, Larch. Reprinted with permission.

The following section provides an example of using the staffing tool to determine if Medical Practice Anywhere has the right number of staff devoted to back-end billing.

Step 1: Determine how your staff spend their time

Request that staff members estimate the number of hours devoted per day to particular tasks. Total the hours of all staff members and calculate the FTE levels associated with major billing and collection functions. Determine the hours that your staff spend on:

1. insurance denial and follow-up;
2. patient inquiries and follow-up;

---

[3] Woodcock & Associates surveyed 70 practices in 2007 regarding billing office staff involved in back-end functions. The median staff per 10,000 claims is 0.98.

FIGURE 15.1 ■ Staff Time Devoted to Key Billing Functions

Medical Practice Anywhere

Major billing function	Hours/week	FTE*
Insurance denial and follow-up	80	2.00
Patient inquiries and follow-up	80	2.00
Credit resolution	20	.50
Payment posting/cash management	60	1.50
Claims	30	.75
Other	40	1.00
Total	**310**	**7.75**
Total annual claims	**100,000**	

*Full-time-equivalent based on a 40-hour work week

3. credit resolution;

4. payment posting and cash management;

5. claims; and

6. other (including clerical support).

See Figure 15.1 for an example of Step 1.

To assist with this project, consider contacting the industrial engineering department of your local university and ask if a student is available to conduct the study for you.

Step 2: Compare overall staffing with available benchmarks

In Figure 15.2, we have made a comparison of staff volume per 100,000 claims. The claim is considered the preferred measure to use when staffing a billing office, as the claim itself is the unit of work around which most of the other tasks revolve. Whether the claim is for $100.00 or $1,000, similar billing functions are required to capture the charge, enter the charge into the practice management system, submit the claim, follow up on the account, and post the payment.

FIGURE 15.2 ■ Staffing Levels Compared to Benchmarks

Staffing indicators	Medical Practice Anywhere	Benchmark**
Billing FTE* per 100,000 claims	7.75	10.00
Claims per billing FTE	12,903	10,000

*Full-time-equivalent based on a 40-hour work week

**Source: © 2009 Walker, Woodcock, Larch. Reprinted with permission.

Based on the above data, Medical Practice Anywhere has a total of 7.75 staff involved in billing functions compared with the benchmark of 10.00 staff. One should ask a number of questions at this stage in the staffing process, such as the following:

- Is Medical Practice Anywhere outperforming benchmark levels by having lower but more productive billing staff?
- Does Medical Practice Anywhere deploy technology more effectively than its peers?
- Does Medical Practice Anywhere have sufficient staff to carry out billing functions in an optimal fashion?

Step 3: Determine benchmark measure of choice and identify specific FTE levels required for tasks

Now that we know the overall staffing required for back-end billing, by applying Step 3 we can determine the number of billing staff *by function* that are required for the key back-end billing functions. This approach is demonstrated in Figure 15.3.

FIGURE 15.3 ■ Staffing Levels by Function with Comparison to Benchmarks

Function	Medical Practice Anywhere FTE per 100,000 claims	National benchmark* FTE per 100,000 claims
Insurance denial and follow-up	2.00	3.54
Patient inquiries and follow-up	2.00	1.32
Credit resolution	.50	.43
Payment posting/cash management	1.50	1.23
Claims	.75	.54
Other	1.00	2.97
Total	7.75	10.51

© 2008 UHC-AAMC FPSC Billing Office Survey. Reprinted with permission.

Individual categories for benchmark data do not sum to total because median data reported for all categories. Billing staff does not include charge entry, chart abstraction, or registration; includes supervisors and managers.

These staffing analyses can assist Medical Practice Anywhere in identifying areas in which resources may be allocated differently than they are at peer medical practices. These benchmarks will not provide Medical Practice Anywhere all of the answers to its staffing questions, but they will give the medical practice the data to determine where there may be opportunity for staffing improvement.

Step 4: Determine equitable distribution of work

The previous table outlined the total number of staff on a per 100,000-claims basis. But simply assigning staff based on claims volume alone does not take into account the *difficulty of the work* associated with each payer.

Traditionally, accounts have been assigned to various staff members based on volume. That is, if there are five employees, everyone is assigned approximately 20 percent of the work. But each payer requires a different level of work. For example, the work involved in workers' compensation claims is more complex and time consuming than the work required for Medicare. In order to provide each staff member with the opportunity to perform at optimal levels, the work should be divided equitably. An equitable division must account for the difficulty by payer.

Figures 15.4, 15.5, and 15.6 demonstrate how to assign work fairly to staff involved in account follow-up functions. In Figure 15.4, the actual difficulty of the work by payer is acknowledged and a "total difficulty index" is calculated for each payer.

In Figure 15.5, the claims are then "weighted" by the difficulty index.

In Figure 15.6, we are now able to assign the work to specific staff members based on the difficulty and weights. In this fashion the medical practice has

FIGURE 15.4 ■ Calculation of Total Difficulty Index (TDI)

Function	Payers					
	Medicare	Medicaid	BCBS	Managed Care USA	HMO One	Workers' Compensation
Electronic payment remittance	10	10	10	20	10	25
Website functionality	10	30	5	0	0	25
Adherance to stated reimbursement	10	10	15	15	15	10
Adherance to stated payment policies	10	10	20	20	25	10
Relative prevelance of pended caims	10	25	10	10	20	25
Relative prevelance of denied claims	10	15	15	15	15	20
Communication processes	10	20	5	15	5	20
Relative prevalence of overpayment	10	0	15	15	15	10
All contract terms provided in writing	10	10	25	15	20	10
Total Difficulty Index (TDI)	100	140	135	140	145	180

Key:
   10   Same as Medicare
  > 10 More difficult than Medicare; the higher, the more difficult
  < 10 Less difficult than Medicare; the lower, the less difficult

Source: Woodcock, EW, "Total account ownership: A new model for streamlining your business office staff," *MGMA Connexion,* January 2007, pp. 28–33.

FIGURE 15.5 ■ Weighting Claims with the TDI

Payer	Unweighted		TDI Weighted*	
	# of Claims	% of Claims	# of Claims	% of Work
Medicare	32,500	40.57	32,500	32.46
Medicaid	7,900	9.86	11,060	11.05
BCBS	23,300	29.09	31,455	31.42
Managed Care USA	5,700	7.12	7,980	7.97
HMO One	6,100	7.62	8,845	8.83
Workers' Compensation	4,600	5.74	8,280	8.27
TOTAL	80,100	100.00	100,120	100.00

*TDI Weighted = The sum of the TDI (calculated in Figure 15.4) multiplied by actual number of claims divided by 100.
Source: Woodcock, EW, "Total account ownership: A new model for streamlining your business office staff," *MGMA Connexion*, January 2007, pp. 28–33.

FIGURE 15.6 ■ Staff Assignment Based on Work

Employees	Assigned Payers	% of Work
Nancy	Medicare	16.23
Sally	Medicare	16.23
Robert	HMO One/Managed Care USA	16.80
Joe	BCBS	15.71
Jill	BCBS	15.71
Lilly	Medicaid/Workers' Compensation	19.32
TOTAL		100.00

Source: Woodcock, EW, "Total account ownership: A new model for streamlining your business office staff," *MGMA Connexion*, January 2007, pp. 28–33.

more equitably distributed the workload among the staff involved in account follow-up in order to recognize the difficulty and complexity of the work, as well as the quantity of work.

Step 5: Identify performance workload ranges and compare staff activity with the ranges to determine areas of opportunity

Like Medical Practice Anywhere, your medical practice may have questions about the opportunity to improve your staffing deployment model. In order to further analyze this opportunity, in Step 5 we now want to analyze the staffing levels based on the expected staff workload ranges to identify if there is further opportunity to improve staffing of the revenue cycle.

Below are three case studies demonstrating this step involving the use of staff workload ranges to "build" the number of staff required for a particular revenue cycle function. Each case study reflects a comparison of a medical practice's actual performance workload ranges with that of expected workload ranges.

By performing this type of analysis, a medical practice can then question the current work processes of the staff, identify issues that may be associated with problem payers, provide educational opportunities for staff, pursue technological advances, or take other action that may improve the staff's ability to perform within the expected staff workload range.

Important questions to ask in each of these case studies include:

- Why are the staff performing at levels that vary from the expected range?
- Is there opportunity to improve performance?
- How many functions have been delegated to the staff? Is this multitasking impacting the efficiency of staff in performing any single function?
- What is different about our medical practice that others may not experience? There may be valid reasons a billing office appears to be overstaffed. If, for example, one of your primary payers is workers' compensation, which requires medical documentation at periodic intervals and other in-depth manual intervention, your billing office may require more staffing resources for billing and collection processes.
- Are the work processes to which the staff adhere encumbered or streamlined?
- Should we explore how other medical practices perform this function so we can see new ways to improve the process?
- Does our practice management system offer the functionality that we need to perform at optimal levels? Are we using it appropriately? Do we deploy other technology available in the industry to leverage our human resources?

Answering these questions will help you review the tools and resources provided to the staff, as well as the current processes established for each billing function. Conduct this type of analysis for each function of the billing and collection process to find areas where you can streamline the key processes of your revenue cycle.

Case Study 1
Payment posting (manual)

Expected staff work level*:	525–875 transactions/day
Actual observed staff work level:	125 average transactions/day
Staff utilization rate:	14–24 percent

---

* Assumes a seven-hour productive day with staff devoted to this function.

© 2009 Walker, Woodcock, Larch. Reprinted with permission.

In Case Study 1, when the medical practice asked itself why the staff was performing at a utilization level less than 25 percent for payment posting, the medical practice was able to see the impact of a policy decision it had made. This medical practice let each of its practice sites and specialties maintain its own database in the practice management system. Consequently, the payment posters had to post to 40 different databases. When you analyze the quantity of the work the staff are able to perform at this functional level, the financial impact of the policy decision is readily apparent.

Case Study 2
Insurance follow-up — Research correspondence and resolve by telephone

Expected staff work level*:	42–84 accounts/day
Actual observed staff work level:	30–40 accounts/day
Staff utilization rate:	48–71 percent

* Assumes a seven-hour productive day with staff devoted to this function.

© 2009 Walker, Woodcock, Larch. Reprinted with permission.

In Case Study 2, when the medical practice asked why the actual performance workload ranges were low, it realized that the accounts receivable for this medical practice were old, with many of the accounts older than two years. The medical practice decided to declare some of the old receivables uncollectible and instead focus on the newer accounts. When the medical practice implemented this decision, it recognized not only an enhancement in staff morale, but also an improvement in revenue as staff were able to collect in an accurate and timely fashion on current account balances rather than waste time on accounts that had a very low probability of success.

Case Study 3
Patient telephone inquiries

Expected staff work level*:	56–84 patient inquiries/day
Actual observed staff work level:	45 average patient inquiries/day
Staff utilization rate:	54–80 percent

*Assumes a seven-hour productive day, with staff devoted to this function.

© 2009 Walker, Woodcock, Larch. Reprinted with permission.

In this medical practice, all of the billing staff were responsible for answering the telephone whenever they could. Whoever was available to pick up the telephone did so. After performing this workload analysis, the medical practice determined that a focused unit to manage the patient inquiries would enhance staff productivity. In addition, the medical practice decided to publish an e-mail account to permit patients to correspond with the medical practice electronically when they have questions about their accounts.

In summary, by examining staffing levels using the above five-step process, a medical practice is able to determine if it has the right number of staff devoted to the right functions in order to optimize revenue cycle performance.

Note that a medical practice can also use the performance workload ranges to determine the staff hours needed to perform billing and collection functions and/or to correct past problem performance.

The additional case study below demonstrates the use of performance workload ranges to determine the estimated time to work the credit balance report for a medical practice.

Case Study 4

How long should it take to work the credit balance report?

Expected staff work level*:	60–80 accounts per day
Basis of expectation:	Time to review account, investigate account, obtain EOB, copy backup, prepare refund request
Current state:	2,500 accounts in credit status
Calculation:	2,500/60 = 42 days
	2,500/80 = 31 days
Range:	31–42 days

Conclusion: It would take 1.00 FTE working 31 to 42 business days to completely resolve 2,500 accounts that are in credit balance status.

_____

* Assumes seven-hour productive day, with staff devoted to this function.

© 2009 Walker, Woodcock, Larch. Reprinted with permission.

Evaluate Staffing Levels for Front-end Billing

While there is industry data relative to the staffing volumes and staffing deployment for back-end billing functions, these benchmarks do not exist for front-end billing. The reason is that there is a high degree of inter-practice variability regarding the use and deployment of staff involved in the front-end billing functions, due to the size of medical practices, centralized versus distributed functions, payer mix, use of technology, and many other factors.

It should be recognized that the unit of work for front-end billing is different from back-end billing. In back-end billing, as discussed earlier in this chapter, the unit of work is the claim. In front-end billing, the unit of work is typically the service, such as a patient visit, procedure, or surgery. Due to the process variation among medical practices and the focus on productivity as the unit of work, we determine staffing levels for front-end billing functions based on projected staff workload ranges, essentially, "building" the staffing needed based on the work to be performed.

Patient financial clearance — Many different approaches are used by medical practices to register patients, perform insurance and benefits verification, ensure prior authorizations, process referrals, and notify patients of pre-determined patient financial responsibility or patient balances on the account. The staff workload ranges outlined in Figure 15.7 provide expected staff workload ranges for these functions; however, each medical practice must determine its own expectations, given its staffing deployment model.

FIGURE 15.7 ■ Staff Workload Ranges by Activity

Staff activities	Per day	Per hour	Per transaction
Insurance verification			
▪ Via Website	n/a	n/a	1 to 3 minutes
▪ Via telephone call	n/a	n/a	2 to 10 minutes
Benefits eligibility			
▪ Via Website	n/a	n/a	3 to 10 minutes
▪ Via telephone call	n/a	n/a	5 to 20 minutes
Registration with insurance verification (on-site or pre-visit)	60 to 80	9 to 11	
Patient check-in			
▪ With registration verification only	100 to 130	14 to 19	
▪ With registration verification and cashiering only	75 to 100	11 to 14	
Appointment scheduling			
▪ With no registration	75 to 125	11 to 18	
▪ With full registration	50 to 75	7 to 11	
Referrals (inbound or outbound)	70 to 90	10 to 13	
Check-out			
▪ With scheduling and cashiering	70 to 90	10 to 13	
▪ With scheduling, cashiering, and charge entry	60 to 80	9 to 11	
Coding			
▪ Evaluation and Management codes	n/a	15 to 20	3 to 4 minutes
▪ Surgeries and procedures	n/a	6 to 12	5 to 10 minutes
Charge entry line items			
▪ Without registration	375 to 525	55 to 75	
▪ With registration	280 to 395	40 to 55	
Resolving pre-adjudication edits			2 to 10 minutes
Payment and adjustment transactions posted manually	525 to 875	75 to 125	
Refunds researched and processed	60 to 80	9 to 11	
Insurance account follow-up			
▪ Research correspondence and resolve by telephone	n/a	6 to 12	
▪ Research correspondence and resolve by appeal	n/a	3 to 4	
▪ Check status of claim (telephone or online) and rebill	n/a	12 to 60	
Self-pay account follow-up	70 to 90	10 to 13	
Self-pay correspondence processed and resolved	90 to 105	13 to 15	
Patient billing inquiries (by telephone or correspondence)	56 to 84	8 to 12	

n/a = not applicable.

© 2009 Walker, Woodcock, Larch. Reprinted with permission.

Time-of-service collections — Typically, check-in and/or check-out staff are involved in collecting payments from patients at the point of care. The role of these staff vary among medical practices, and the collection of time-of-service payments is typically only one of many tasks the staff are asked to perform. Figure 15.7 provides expected staff workload ranges for various combinations of check-in and check-out tasks that may be assigned to these staff.

Coding — A medical practice may have no certified coders or many. In addition, the coders may be assigned to code only operative reports or perform full chart abstraction, involving reading the full medical chart and extrapolating the services to be billed. Some coders only code, while others perform charge entry. Full chart abstraction and complicated surgical procedures obviously require more time, while outpatient visits may require less time than this projected work level, so it is important to recognize the type of service that is coded in order to appropriately develop workload ranges for your medical practice. As we presented in Chapter 6: The Coding Process, we typically expect coders to code 15 to 20 encounters per hour for evaluation and management codes and 6 to 12 per hour for surgery and procedure coding.

Charge capture — Staffing the charge capture process may leverage technology or it may involve manual verification of services with source documents, such as verifying charges submitted with the labor and delivery log, the operative log, the hospital census report, and many others. Each medical practice needs to build its own expected workload range for this function by identifying the typical time required to perform this function by service.

Charge entry — The number of staff involved in charge entry in a medical practice varies based on technology. If a medical practice has an electronic health record, for example, the staff involved in charge entry will be quite low. If the medical practice has delegated this function to the practice site staff in the outpatient setting, the other work functions of these staff must also be taken into account. As discussed in Chapter 7: The Charge Entry Process, if the staff perform "heads down" charge entry, a medical practice will likely have less staff than a medical practice that also requires charge entry staff to perform registration, insurance verification, authorization verification, and other similar tasks. Recognizing these variations in work assignment, we typically see staff entering 55 to 75 charges per hour (assuming "heads down" charge entry).

In summary, staffing for front-end billing is highly variable by medical practice. As we have noted, medical practices now focus on front-end billing to a heightened degree, due to the need to perform patient financial clearance and collect more (and higher dollar) patient payments at the point of care.

Benchmark Staff Workload Ranges

Throughout this book, we have provided staff workload ranges by function. Figure 15.7 is a summary of these ranges. These ranges can be helpful in determining opportunities for improvement, as well as analyzing your staffing needs. As noted previously, the ability to perform within these ranges may vary due to internal practice-specific factors (such as facility layout, telephone system, EHR, and practice management system). The workload ranges are based on a staff member performing these functions approximately seven hours of productive time per day (allowing one hour for breaks, interruptions, and other down time). Note that the workload ranges reflect quantitative performance levels. It should be recognized that qualitative performance — accuracy, completeness, and appropriateness of these functions — should also be measured.

When issues of quantity versus quality arise, we strongly recommend that quality be emphasized, even if the performance workload ranges for a particular function need to be relaxed from expected levels.

DETERMINE ORGANIZATIONAL STRUCTURE FOR THE REVENUE CYCLE

Figures 15.8, 15.9, and 15.10 outline different types of organizational structures for a medical practice's revenue cycle. The key to each of these formal structures is to have discrete billing and collection functions assigned to specific individuals so that you can establish and monitor accountabilities and performance expectations. When medical practices attempt to multi-task staff without setting clear expectations, there is a tendency for tasks and responsibilities to fall through the cracks because no single person is responsible for the performance of a specific function.

We offer these organizational charts to give the reader examples of different typologies. Each of the organizations has established specific roles and responsibilities in the area of charge entry, account follow-up, reimbursement management, and data controls. These typologies also reflect the importance of separation of duties to permit adequate internal controls.

Structure A outlines an organizational structure that small medical practices frequently adopt. We address the delineation of work functions and separation of duties through the formation of four separate units within the billing office: (1) data control, (2) charge entry and registration, (3) account follow-up, and (4) coding and compliance. In this example, we identify leads for each of the first three units, with the billing office manager involved in coding and compliance functions.

We generally recommend Structure B for a medium-sized medical practice. The billing manager works actively with an assistant manager in leading and directing four separate work units: (1) data control; (2) insurance billing/posting/follow-up; (3) customer service; and (4) audit and compliance. Front-office staff involved in patient scheduling and patient check-in processes have a dotted-line reporting relationship to the assistant manager in the billing office. We have delineated an educational and training function, with the billing manager leading educational efforts. As demonstrated in this structure, total account ownership — the linkage of payment posting and account follow-up — has been adopted.

The final example of an organizational structure for a revenue cycle is found in large, multi-site medical practices. In this structure, the practice sites have

FIGURE 15.8 ■ Revenue Cycle Organization — Small Medical Practice

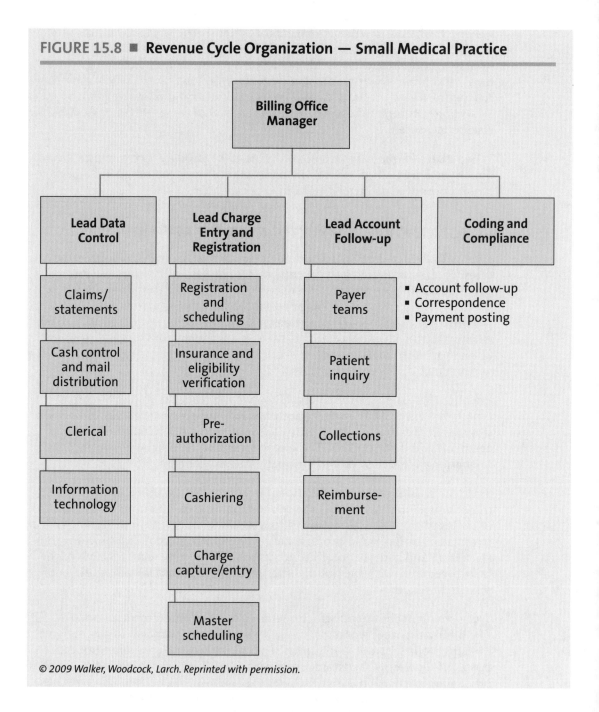

a billing lead position responsible for overseeing the billing and collection functions — patient scheduling, registration, cashiering, and charge entry — performed at each practice site. These individuals have a dotted-line reporting relationship with the training and compliance office and serve as liaisons between the billing office and the practice sites. Within the central billing office, account follow-up and data control units provide separation of duties and permit oversight of focused roles and responsibilities.

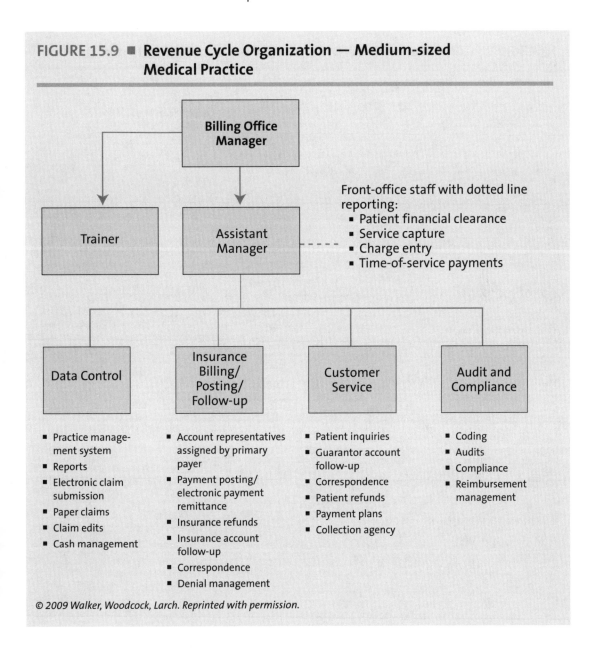

FIGURE 15.9 ■ Revenue Cycle Organization — Medium-sized Medical Practice

Billing Office Manager

Trainer

Assistant Manager

Front-office staff with dotted line reporting:
- Patient financial clearance
- Service capture
- Charge entry
- Time-of-service payments

Data Control
- Practice management system
- Reports
- Electronic claim submission
- Paper claims
- Claim edits
- Cash management

Insurance Billing/ Posting/ Follow-up
- Account representatives assigned by primary payer
- Payment posting/ electronic payment remittance
- Insurance refunds
- Insurance account follow-up
- Correspondence
- Denial management

Customer Service
- Patient inquiries
- Guarantor account follow-up
- Correspondence
- Patient refunds
- Payment plans
- Collection agency

Audit and Compliance
- Coding
- Audits
- Compliance
- Reimbursement management

© 2009 Walker, Woodcock, Larch. Reprinted with permission.

The organizational structure you develop for your medical practice will depend upon the size of your practice and the number of staff devoted to front-end and back-end billing functions. It will also depend upon your practice management system and the technology you have adopted for specific billing functions. As we noted earlier in this chapter, medical practices that increase their resources devoted to front-end billing will typically have far less staff involved in back-end billing, due to their higher success in getting paid at the initial claim submission. They are doing work right the first time, thus minimizing resources needed for account follow-up, denial management, and rework.

FIGURE 15.10 ■ Revenue Cycle Organization — Large Medical Practice

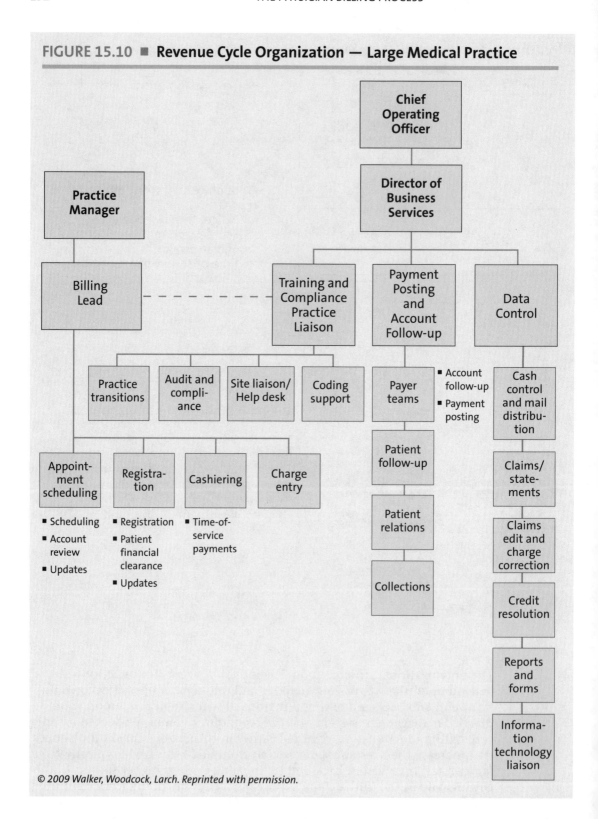

© 2009 Walker, Woodcock, Larch. Reprinted with permission.

DEFINE STAFF EDUCATION, COMPETENCY, AND ACCOUNTABILITY

Staff Education

If the local job market makes it difficult to recruit well-trained and knowledgeable staff, you need to conduct internal training to develop competent employees. Ongoing education is necessary as well because coding and payer policies change rapidly.

Develop a formal training program for each functional area. Schedule regular updates in the form of seminars, tools, Webcasts, audioconferences, online education, reading material, staff meetings, and assignments to keep employees updated.

Competency Assessments

Conduct formal competency assessments before an employee uses the practice management system with "live" data. An untrained payment poster can wreak havoc on a system by inadvertently creating credit balances, selecting improper adjustment codes, and failing to flag EOBs for appeal, thus requiring a great deal of time to reconstruct accounts on the system. An untrained employee performing patient check-in can select an improper payer for the patient, fail to recognize the need for a pre-authorization, and fail to collect time-of-service payments, thus creating rework, escalating the cost of billing, and resulting in lost revenue.

Conduct periodic competency assessments for current staff, not just new staff. Changes in billing and collection regulations, updates to the practice management system, and revisions in payer requirements underscore the need to provide ongoing competency evaluations.

Competency exams for billing and collection activities are available from a number of sources. We also provide examples of competency assessments for critical functions in billing and collections throughout this book. The sample competency assessment shown in Tool 40 relates to general payer knowledge that all billing staff would be expected to demonstrate. The use of competency assessments ensures that staff have the knowledge and understanding of key workload components.

Accountability

The key to performance management of billing and collection staff is holding individuals accountable for results. When staff are multitasked without specific expectations established, you will have a difficult time assessing who is responsible for specific functions, problems, or stellar results. By developing a performance management process that takes into account expected performance outcomes, as well as specific functions and tasks, you can focus on accountability for performance.

Managing performance involves not only a job description outlining functions and tasks, but the outcomes expected of the staff member. You can include the

TOOL 40	Competency Assessment: Payer Knowledge

Demonstrate the following activities requiring general insurance knowledge:

	Competency Level	
	Satisfactory	Unsatisfactory
1. Knowledge of payer types and products	_____	_____
2. Determining eligibility	_____	_____
3. Determining primary/secondary coverage	_____	_____
4. Determining copayments, deductibles, co-insurance	_____	_____
5. Identifying when waivers are needed	_____	_____
6. Prior authorization – how and when needed	_____	_____
7. Interpreting an insurance card	_____	_____
8. Explaining a statement to a patient	_____	_____

Action plan: _____

_____

_____

_____

© 2009 Walker, Woodcock, Larch. Reprinted with permission.

staff workload ranges in the performance management process, holding staff accountable for this quantity of work. More importantly, assess the *qualitative* indicators related to accuracy of work functions that we have cited in each of the potholes chapters of this book. You can do this using a sampling of a staff member's work product. For example, you can assess the workload accuracy of a payment poster via a sampling of EOBs throughout the month. You can assess the workload accuracy of a staff member responsible for registration information relative to claim edits and claim denials. Include these types of performance indicators as a formal part of the performance management process. After all, your medical practice needs performance outcomes to optimize reimbursement.

Consider implementing specific performance indicators per employee as part of the performance management process. On a weekly basis, track statistics by employee via user codes. Some common indicators include the following:

- Dollars collected by payer according to collector responsibility;
- Aged accounts receivable by payer;
- Percentage of accounts receivable by payer over 90 days;
- Account adjustments by category; and
- Bad debt percentage by collector responsibility.

EVALUATE INCENTIVE COMPENSATION PLANS

Some medical practices establish incentive compensation plans for their staff involved in the revenue cycle. These plans have tended to focus on only one or a select few measures in the billing and collections process. For example, a popular incentive plan rewards billing staff for enhancing collections by a predetermined percentage target (for example, 2 or 5 percent). Unfortunately, this type of incentive plan has drawbacks, as staff may set aside other important billing and collection tasks if the aim is solely to enhance short-term collection performance. Further, it also does not recognize that all staff in the medical practice have some role in the success of the revenue cycle, not simply the back-end billing staff.

Another type of incentive plan for billing staff consists of a collection of measures at the individual, team, specialty, and/or medical practice level. Here are three examples of this type of incentive plan:

Incentive Plan 1

Billing staff are eligible to receive both individual and group performance bonuses for a total of $250 per quarter. Each quarter, $125 is available for individual performance. It is awarded for the following performance outcomes:

- Days in accounts receivable is less than 40 on the accounts for which the staff member is responsible (here's where there may be some variance depending on your specialty and/or payer);
- Percentage of accounts receivable greater than 90 days is less than 20 percent on the accounts for which the staff member is responsible (again, perhaps there will be some variance depending on your specialty and/or payer); and
- A review of 10 sample accounts pulled at random results in 100 percent of accounts appropriately worked and documented.

In addition, another $125 is available each quarter based on practice or team performance. The performance outcomes for this portion of the incentive include:

- Days in accounts receivable is less than 40 (at the practice or team level);
- Percentage of accounts receivable greater than 90 days is less than 20 percent (at the practice or team level); and
- Cash collections are greater than $500,000 (the dollar threshold obviously depends on your medical practice).

As demonstrated in this example, a combination of individual and practice or team incentive is used to provide financial recognition and rewards for billing and collection performance outcomes.

Incentive Plan 2

In this plan, individuals are able to earn up to 10 percent of their gross salary each year based on individual, team, and medical practice goals.

- Sixty percent of the plan is tied to the individual's performance based on his/her job-specific competencies; the medical practice identifies individual goals at the beginning of the year. Based on the individual's performance, the employee can earn 0 to 6 percent of his/her gross salary. The employee must attain a minimum level of individual performance before he/she is eligible for the team or total medical practice incentive.

- The team (or specialty) incentive is 30 percent of the bonus plan and is tied to team collections, percentage of claims suspended on edit lists, charge entry lag, and percentage of accounts receivable over 90 days. These elements are weighted in importance. The team incentive criteria are not tied together, so a staff member may be eligible for a portion of the team incentive. For example, if the charge entry lag hits the target and none of the other targets are reached, the staff would still receive a portion of the bonus.

- The final goal measures a performance outcome that is practice-wide. The incentive payment equals 10 percent of the potential incentive. In this example, the practice-wide incentive is based on overall net collections — because the medical practice has to collect enough cash to fund the incentive pool. The practice-wide goal is a stretch goal for the entire group that is not always reached.

Incentive Plan 3

In this incentive plan, all staff in the medical practice participate in the incentive plan and the measures used are expanded to include other important areas that have an impact on the revenue cycle and its performance.

Result	Point Level
Patient visit volume	10 points
Patient satisfaction survey results	20 points
Claim pre-adjudication errors/edits	10 points
Claim post-adjudication denials	10 points
Time-of-service collections	10 points
Non-contractual adjustments	10 points
Net collection rate	15 points
Accounts receivable > 90 days	15 points
Total points that may be earned	100 points

A goal is established for each result, and points are awarded if the medical practice reaches the goals. Dollars per point are determined and communicated to staff each quarter based on the profit from the previous quarter.

When you're developing an incentive plan for billing and collection staff, ask (and answer) the following questions:

- Who should we reward? Because the entire revenue cycle involves all levels of the organization, who should be included in the incentive plan? What are the pros and cons of establishing a plan for only the billing office versus the entire medical practice?

- Should we reward individual or team/unit performance? Should individuals be incented for their own work or should the performance of the overall team or unit be the focus for the incentive? Or both?

- Should we reward short-term or long-term goals? Should our medical practice incent monthly performance, or should we take a more long-term view of performance?

- Should we provide financial rewards or are non-financial rewards more (or equally) important? Are there ways to reward our employees — and motivate them — that don't involve money?

- When should the rewards be given? Should the rewards be granted immediately — for example, weekly — or should they be granted at year-end? Will a delay in rewards permit the staff to connect the reward with their performance?

- Should the incentive plan for the billing office be a component of a reward system that we establish for the entire medical practice?

- How will we finance the incentive plan? What if we fall short of our goals?

- How will we communicate the plan to staff?

Incentive plans can be motivating, but consider your long-term strategy before implementing one. You don't want to be left with an incentive plan that loses its motivation — and becomes an expectation. Regular review of the performance expectations is necessary to keep the plan current. Most medical practices' priorities change over time, and you want your incentive plans tied to current priorities. The review of your incentive plan must include a review of the rewards. In the examples above, staff and managers are eligible for monetary rewards. Not all people are motivated by money. Younger generations, in particular, are looking at lifestyle improvements and are interested in extra days off, or the potential to earn larger prizes (for example, vacations). An incentive plan is a dynamic part of your compensation plan that requires careful development and ongoing management oversight.

ENGAGE STAFF IN REVENUE CYCLE PERFORMANCE

It is important to actively engage the staff in the performance of the revenue cycle. Many of these staff have excellent ideas for improvements to process performance. Similarly, many of the staff perform work that is interconnected with that of their colleagues and can voice issues that will improve the process handoffs between staff involved in the revenue cycle.

Problem-solving and Decision-making

Involve staff in problem-solving and decision-making regarding billing and collection functions and tasks. Encourage staff to bring suggestions for resolution along with the problem. Share information with staff, to include accounts receivable status, payment posting status, time-of-service collection percentages, administrative dashboards, credentialing status, payer updates, and more so they can understand the full revenue cycle and its many interconnected parts.

Staff Forums

Hold weekly meetings with all staff. Use these meetings to educate staff on specific billing issues and to share key data related to performance expectations involving the entire revenue cycle. Share data from front-end and back-end billing functions with all staff so they can see their performance in relation to their peers and manage their workload with appropriate priorities. To maintain policies and procedures, review a billing policy or procedure each week to (1) sustain knowledge currency among staff and (2) update the policy consistent with changes in payer and regulatory guidelines.

Data Transparency

In medical practices that actively engage staff in process improvement efforts and in leading change, staff can cite current billing performance. For example, they know the days in accounts receivable and the percentage of receivables greater than 90 days. Routinely share this type of data and identify action items, responsible party, and deadlines to take actions to improve performance, if needed, in order to meet targeted goals and expected outcomes.

Your staff need to be actively engaged in your revenue cycle. You need the right staff doing the right things in order to achieve optimal revenue performance. Ongoing education, effective communication, and competency assessments ensure that staff have the knowledge and tools to perform the key functions of your revenue cycle.

CHAPTER 16

Internal Controls for the Revenue Cycle

Each medical practice is responsible for establishing and managing internal controls. Internal controls are a set of processes approved by the medical practice's governing body to provide reasonable assurance that key objectives are achieved, including efficiency and effectiveness of medical practice operations, fiduciary responsibility, reporting reliability, and compliance with payer requirements and laws and regulations applicable to the revenue cycle. The "controls" are the policies and procedures that are established to achieve the objectives. The size and complexity of the medical practice and its level of business risk tolerance determine the amount of internal controls that are instituted.

Internal controls outline specific actions that must be taken to minimize business risk. Control activities include approvals, reconciliations, review of procedures, and segregation of duties. These controls need to be monitored through evaluations and audits. When internal control deficiencies are identified, they must be presented to the medical practice's governing body so that solutions can be defined and implemented. Thus, internal controls can help a medical practice prevent loss of resources and ensure credible financial reporting.

In this chapter, we cover:

- Segregation of duties
- Safeguarding cash
- Evaluating business risk
- Internal audits
- Physical security measures
- Red flags for fraud

Each medical practice needs written policies and procedures to support its business processes. In financial and billing arenas, these policies and procedures are even more critical. Written policies provide employees with clear instructions as to *who* is responsible for which task and *how* each task should be handled.

To ensure efficient and effective internal controls, we present proven strategies to enhance your revenue cycle.

ADVANCED PRACTICES: INTERNAL CONTROLS FOR THE REVENUE CYCLE

Log Money Received

Any money received via the mail (for example, insurance or patient checks) should be recorded as received. Typically, insurance checks are logged by payer and check number, while patient payments are logged by batch (for example, the number of checks and the amount of the checks in the mail are totaled and recorded on the log). The amount that was received via the mail should be reconciled with the amount posted to the practice management system, and then further reconciled with the money that has been deposited to the practice's bank account. Too often we have witnessed the checks simply being distributed to staff for payment posting, bypassing the login process. This is a lapse in internal controls. In addition to ensuring that all monies received have been accounted for, the log permits the medical practice to view at a glance when the last payment from a payer was made and the amount of that payment so that it can quickly pursue payment delays.

Stamp Checks for Deposit

The billing office and every front office should have a bank endorsement stamp that reads "For Deposit Only." Staff must stamp the checks as they are received. This limits the check being used for any other purpose other than depositing into the medical practice's bank account.

Issue Receipts

When patients pay at the time of service, it is optimal to have the staff post the payment as it is received and then generate an electronic receipt and pro-vide it to the patient. If your medical practice does not have electronic receipt capability, a manual receipt book should be used that involves pre-numbered receipts, with the original receipt provided to the patient and a copy main-tained by the staff. New, unused receipt books should not be in the custody of front office personnel. Staff should be instructed to ask their supervisor for a new book when the previous one is finished. The person with custody of the new receipt books should be keeping a log of the receipts book and receipt numbers used, issued to the front office staff, and unused books on hand.

Deposit Money Daily

Money on hand, such as checks, cash, and credit card payments, should be turned in by the front office daily and counted in the presence of the person receiving it. Deposits should be made daily on pre-printed deposit slips with the name of the patient or the payer noted next to the dollar amount on the face of the deposit slip. Regardless of the amount, any cash should be secured in a locked area during office hours and in a safe at night. The distribution of keys to the locked area should be limited.

Reconcile Payments

The amount of money deposited to the bank should be reconciled to the bank statement and the practice management system. Staff members from the finance office and the billing office should be involved so that the individual making the deposit is not the same person who reconciles the accounts. This will reduce the risk of collusion, which involves several individuals working together illegally. In a small medical practice, it may be difficult to have duties assigned to separate individuals. If that is the case, the practice executive needs to more regularly review those processes to ensure policies are appropriately followed.

Optimize Electronic Payment Remittance

As discussed in Chapter 10: The Payment and Denial Posting Process, the use of electronic remittance means that a "live" check is not sent to the medical practice. Instead, the money is electronically sent to the practice's bank account. This eliminates check handling in the medical practice and minimizes the opportunity for fraudulent cash management.

Use a Lockbox

If electronic remittance is not used by the majority of your payers, your medical practice should consider the use of a lockbox. Payments are directly sent to a separate location — typically a vendor (for example, a bank) where envelopes are opened and checks are deposited. Every effort should be made (through communication to your patients and payers) to make sure payments are routed through the lockbox. A lockbox is more secure than a medical practice, the money gets to the bank faster, and it saves staff time in receiving and logging payments.

Adopt Remote Deposit

Another cash management option is to acquire a scanner that permits checks to be directly scanned to the practice's bank account. Remote deposit allows the number of checks and the dollar total of the checks received at the medical practice to be reconciled to the number and dollar amount of the payments related to checks posted to the practice management system.

Define Accountability

The medical practice may wish to consider a policy that makes each collector in the billing office and the front office responsible for maintaining his/her own receipt book, cash box, envelope of payments, and change fund (often referred to as a "change bank"). This system increases individuals' accountability. In the event of any discrepancy, it is easier to identify the source of the error. The change fund should always be a pre-established amount and accounted for during the daily closing process.

Avoid Bad Checks

Utilize a check verification service if challenges arise related to checks being received with insufficient funds. Alternatively, maintain information in the practice management system about patients who have provided bad checks in the past. Do not accept checks from these patients in the future. As the procedure is implemented, counsel such patients that they need to bring cash, a money order, or a cashier's check with them the next time they present. A patient who has bounced a check should have a comment noted in his/her billing account and it may be appropriate to create a patient alert in your scheduling system.

Avoid Signature Stamps

Do not create a stamp of your physician's signature unless the physician is ready to assume responsibility for its use. Signature stamps may be an acceptable form of medical record authentication, depending on the payer's requirements and your state's regulations. But in order to utilize them, the physician has to attest that he/she is the only person allowed to use the signature stamp and the signature stamp is securely stored to prevent unauthorized use. To reduce your business risk, we recommend that physicians sign the notes rather than utilize a signature stamp. The same or greater risk involves signature stamps used in your disbursement or refund check process. Again, signature stamps expose your practice to unnecessary risk.

Implement Employee Policies

Many problems can be avoided by screening prospective employees. Verify previous employment and verify references from at least two or three prior jobs. If a previous employer hesitates to recommend a candidate or, certainly, if you receive negative information, it's better to pass on that applicant.

Many medical practices run criminal and credit checks on all applicants, in addition to screening for violations of federal programs.[1] You may also want to consider bonding your employees. For any staff members who handle money, to include all billing office staff, many medical practices bond these employees. A medical practice can enter into contracts that protect it against financial loss due to employee actions.

New employee orientation should include information on the medical practice's internal control policies. One of those policies should be a required vacation policy for all staff employees. This will avoid one person handling a specific function alone for a year. It will allow other staff to handle their duties while they are absent, which can be enough time to identify fraudulent processes. This allows the billing manager to review pending work that has been assigned to this employee and that is residing both on and in his/her desk. This will assist in identifying inappropriate processes and/or delays that

---

[1] Screening for violations of federal programs can be conducted through the Department of Health and Human Services exclusions database at oig.hhs.gov.

may present concerns from a fraudulent business practices perspective or, more commonly, recognize issues associated with delayed revenue performance.

Reconcile Charge Tickets

If you have an electronic health record (EHR), your medical practice typically has eliminated paper charge tickets, since the charge capture is conducted after the service has been documented in the EHR. If your medical practice does not have an electronic health record, it likely uses paper charge tickets for charge capture and coding; however, some medical practices utilize other electronic tools, such as personal digital assistants that automatically uplink to their practice management system.

Regardless of what type of charge ticket is in use, we recommend that you reconcile all charge tickets with patient visits to ensure complete charge capture. One way to conduct this in a non-EHR environment is to pre-number the charge tickets. A gap in the numbering sequence typically means that there is a misplaced ticket; however, it can also signal a situation where an employee is attempting to cover up theft. If the charge tickets are not pre-numbered, other methods to reconcile charge tickets include (a) reconciling the tickets against the patient sign-in sheet (if used) and (b) reconciling the tickets against the daily arrived appointment list. If charges are entered at the time of service, another reconciliation method is to create a missing charge ticket report from the practice management system that denotes patients who received services for which there is no corresponding charge. Regardless of which process you adopt, a missed charge ticket needs to be found and the patient's account for that date examined to ensure that it reflects the charge and payment (if applicable).

Reconcile Payments Received

Beyond reconciling charges to arrived visits to ensure complete charge capture, a medical practice needs to ensure that all payments are accounted for. This can be accomplished by reconciling payments received against a sign-in sheet or appointment schedule, as well as comparing them to the record of daily receipts. All patients should receive a receipt for their time-of-service payments — either electronically from the system or from a manual receipt log book that creates a copy of the original receipt. The cash receipt log can be reconciled with the daily deposit ticket to ensure all payments were deposited.

Control Adjustments

Few people should have the ability to enter charge adjustments, write-offs, or refunds on the account. Control these functions by limiting the transactions to a few, trained staff members or closely monitor the transactions. A physician owner or medical practice executive should review and approve all adjustment, write-off, and refund transactions over a certain threshold. Significant revenue can be lost if an employee wants to embezzle in this way and has the opportunity.

1. All adjustments, write-offs, or refunds should have supporting documentation explaining why the payer (insurance or patient) paid what it did. It is also a good idea to categorize adjustments by major payers so that adjustment trends can be tracked for inconsistencies. The medical practice should have a written policy and procedure so the employees have guidelines to follow when making adjustments to accounts and for monitoring and oversight of these adjustments.

2. Another control is to periodically review selected accounts. We recommend that your practice management system identify accounts with certain characteristics for review, such as any account that has been adjusted off entirely in the last year.

Involve Physicians

It is important that physicians be familiar with the practice's internal control policies so that they also can be on the alert for potential problems. For example, in some medical practices, a physician is tasked with opening the unopened bank and credit card statements each month and reviewing the month's transactions. Though the physician will seldom be involved in the actual reconciliation, having the physician open and review statements is a great fraud deterrent.

ESTABLISH SEGREGATION OF DUTIES

Segregation of duties is the process of assigning work to two or more individuals to prevent fraudulent activity and to minimize error occurrence. In other words, your medical practice should "segregate the duties" performed by staff. For example, no one person should determine what payments are due, collect the payment at the time of service, and then deposit that money in the bank. Implement separation of duties in each major function within the revenue cycle. If you prevent one person from performing all transactions on the account, for example, charge entry, charge correction, account follow-up, and payment posting, you lower your business risk.

The following are some examples of separation of duties that medical practices should establish:

Segregate Cash-related Functions

No one person should have authority over all cash transaction processes. Divide responsibility for duties such as opening the mail, posting the payments, and completing the deposit slip, as this will help minimize opportunities for fraud. Not only does this prevent a single person from inappropriately manipulating patient accounts, it also helps reduce inadvertent errors.

Segregate Payment Posting and Account Adjustments

Many medical practices segregate payment posting and account adjustment functions to ensure that the person who posts the payment also does not have access to perform an adjustment on the account. If your staffing deployment model links payment posting and account follow-up, implement appropriate supervisory controls to ensure that the account adjustments that are made are appropriate. We also recommend that a specific adjustment policy be developed that outlines the adjustment codes to be used and the approval authority by dollar and type of account adjustment.

An area where segregation of payment posting and account adjustment is obviously important is collection agency recovery. The accounts that have been submitted to the collection agency are written off the accounts receivable and no one is actively "looking for" the money collected on these accounts. If the same person who adjusts the account to the collection agency is also responsible for posting any payment to the account that is recovered by the agency, there is an obvious lack of work segregation needed to ensure an appropriate level of internal controls.

Another area ripe for problems is the refund process. If the same person who orders or generates the refund payment is also the person who is responsible for adjusting off the account, a refund could conceivably be provided to a friend or relative. In either case, no one would be the wiser.

Segregate Duties Related to Check Controls

Medical practices can take steps to safeguard their own checks and the checks they receive. Check-signing authority should be limited to a very small number of people, maybe even to one physician owner. In addition, ensure that access to blank checks is restricted. Imagine an employee adjusting an account and writing a refund check to a family member. Segregating the functions of check writing and check signing will help to prevent such an occurrence.

Typically, the smaller the medical practice, the more difficult it is to segregate duties among staff. If it is not possible to separate some duties, the medical practice executive should regularly review some parts of those processes and immediately institute an investigation if unexpected results occur. For example, if the daily deposit for copayments is lower than expected, the practice executive should review all paperwork for that day to ensure that monies have been appropriately accounted for.

SAFEGUARD CASH

Cash management is often subject to internal controls in a medical practice. While everyone knows that cash should be safeguarded, not everyone knows the specific steps to take to ensure effective internal controls. Many physicians fully delegate the handling of cash payments to their staff with no oversight, which is problematic. A medical practice needs to keep close track of cash and protect it from theft.

Most cash thefts in a medical practice occur at the front office because that is where the practice typically handles cash. Employees have been found to pocket cash that patients have paid at the time of service. An electronic or written receipt must be issued for every payment (whether cash, check, or credit/debit card), with a copy of the receipt maintained in the system or in the medical practice's records. Those receipts should add up to the total payments received and posted. Medical practices should have a sign posted stating that patients should expect a receipt for any payment made and that if they do not receive one, they should ask to speak to the practice executive.

Note that this receipt process is not fail safe. That is, an employee could still accept and pocket the money and not produce a receipt (especially if the receipt is a manual process). However, if a receipt is expected for each transaction, it makes it more difficult to carry out this fraudulent scheme, as, in theory, someone will more likely notice an employee who does not issue receipts to patients. Be on the alert for any patients who contact the medical practice regarding their statements to complain that they paid their copayment at the time of service, yet the statements indicate the payment is outstanding.

Evaluate the strength of your cash controls by answering "yes" or "no" to the question in Tool 41. A process that receives a "no" response could indicate a process that needs to be strengthened to ensure that your internal controls are keeping your medical practice safe.

EVALUATE YOUR BUSINESS RISK

The Association of Certified Fraud Examiners (ACFE) publishes a report each year summarizing its findings. It continues to rank health care as a high-risk industry for fraud. A recent report found health care ranked third out of 21 industries in the incidence of fraud based on case frequency.[2] The report also states that small organizations (less than 100 employees) are more vulnerable to fraud. In small organizations, furthermore, problems are most often identified by accident.

The ACFE report highlights frequent types of fraud that one should look for in any industry and a subset of these is provided below. In assessing your business risk, evaluate each function listed below and identify what policies and procedures your medical practice maintains related to that function. Define how you provide oversight and monitoring to reduce your business risk. Please note that the specific fraud terms and definitions are derived from the ACFE;[3] however, the examples provided are specific to physician billing.

Skimming: Cash is stolen from a medical practice *before* it is recorded in the practice management system and financial records.

Examples:

1. Employee accepts copayment from patient but does not record the payment.

2. Employee posts a charge but does not post the payment and then writes off the charge.

---

[2] http://www.acfe.com/documents/2008-rttn.pdf (accessed November 30, 2008). 2008 Report to the Nation on Occupational Fraud-Abuse by Association of Certified Fraud Examiners.

[3] Adapted from ACHE. 2008 Report to the Nation on Occupational Fraud-Abuse by Association of Certified Fraud Examiners.

TOOL 41	Internal Controls Checklist

YES	NO	CASH FUND
___	___	Petty cash or change is maintained and monitored.
___	___	A custodian is responsible for the petty cash fund.
___	___	The fund reimbursement is made directly to this custodian.
___	___	Custodian has no access to accounting reports.
___	___	Custodian has no access to cash receipts.
___	___	Fund storage takes place in a physically secure place.
___	___	Surprise audits are conducted periodically.
___	___	No employees are permitted to cash checks.

CASH RECEIPTS

YES	NO	
___	___	All cash custodians are bonded.
___	___	All cash is deposited daily.
___	___	A daily list of mail receipts is created.
___	___	Daily reconciliation of cash collections is required.
___	___	Cashier personnel are separated from accounting duties.
___	___	Cashier personnel are separated from credit duties.
___	___	The bank account is properly authorized.
___	___	The bank has been instructed not to cash checks made by the practice to the practice.
___	___	Comparisons are made between duplicate deposit slips and detail of accounts receivable.

CASH DISBURSEMENTS

YES	NO	
___	___	Recording, authorization, and check-signing functions are completely separate.
___	___	Documentation to support payments is provided and reviewed prior to check disbursement.
___	___	Control is exercised if a check signing machine is used.
___	___	There is limited authorization to sign checks.
___	___	Check signers have no access to cash records or receipts.
___	___	Detailed listing of checks is required.
___	___	No checks payable to cash are allowed.
___	___	Checks are pre-numbered.
___	___	Physical control over unused checks is provided.
___	___	Mutilation is required for all voided checks.
___	___	All disbursements are made by checks unless specifically authorized by petty cash.
___	___	Control over and prompt accounting for interbank transfers are exercised.

BANK RECONCILIATION

YES	NO	
___	___	Reconciliation between receipts, bank, and practice management system is conducted at least monthly.
___	___	Reconciliation between bank and accounting records is conducted at least monthly.
___	___	Person responsible for reconciling bank statements is independent from accounting or cashier duties.
___	___	Bank statement is sent directly to the person responsible for reconciliation.

Source: Modified from *Financial Management for Medical Groups*, Ernest J. Pavlock, PhD, CPA, 2nd Edition, MGMA, 2000.

Cash larceny: Cash is stolen from a medical practice *after* it has been recorded in the practice management system and financial records.

Examples:

1. Employee steals cash and checks before they are deposited to the bank.

2. Employee steals cash and checks from daily receipts and then "borrows" cash and checks received in the next mail delivery. The employee then deposits these in the prior day's deposit to "hide" the fact that the money has been stolen. In this case, the employee writes a check for a small amount to ensure that the deposit is the same as expected. The only way to uncover this scheme is to actually look at the individual checks in the deposit.

Fraudulent billing: An employee causes his or her employer to issue a payment by submitting false data.

Examples:

1. Employee knowingly bills payers for services not provided.

2. Employee creates a plausible vendor company and bills the medical practice for non-existent services.

Fraudulent expense reimbursements: An employee makes a claim for reimbursement of false business expenses.

Examples:

1. Employee files a fraudulent expense report.

2. Employee uses the medical practice's corporate credit card or a physician owner's credit card without approval.

Check tampering: An employee steals his or her employer's funds by forging or altering a check on one of the medical practice's bank accounts, or steals an outgoing check.

Examples:

1. Employee steals checks from the medical practice and makes them payable to him/herself.

2. Employee fails to mail an outgoing check to a payee and instead, endorses and deposits it into his/her own bank account.

Understanding the types of business risk associated with your revenue cycle will help you design and implement appropriate supervisory oversight and internal controls.

CONDUCT INTERNAL AUDITS

A critical part of your internal controls process is auditing performance. Each medical practice needs to determine processes in which embezzlement or fraud can occur. Not every revenue cycle function needs to be audited every quarter or every year; the functions that you audit may change each year. As part of the audit process, take each of your internal control *policies* and evaluate your medical practice's actual internal control *practices* in relation to each policy.

In addition, identify patient accounts at random and follow these patients through the entire revenue cycle, following the paper or electronic revenue cycle trail, to assess the reliability of your internal controls.

To demonstrate, let's look at three revenue cycle functions that are considered high risk by most medical practices: payment posting, account adjustments, and refunds.

1. *Payment posting*: Auditing payment posting is an excellent way to evaluate your payment posters' productivity and accuracy. Conducting an audit also allows you to evaluate the broader risks of whether a staff member could have mishandled payments. Figure 16.1 describes some of the ways that a payment can be mishandled and the consequences for the medical practice.

FIGURE 16.1 ■ Impact of Mishandled Payments

1. If the payment are not posted:
   a) accounts receivable are overstated;
   b) revenue is understated;
   c) collection ratios are inaccurate; and/or
   d) revenue is potentially misappropriated.

2. If the payment is not posted in a timely fashion:
   a) accounts receivable are overstated;
   b) revenue is understated; and/or
   c) gross and net collection rates are inaccurate.

3. If the payment is posted to the wrong account:
   a) patient balances are inaccurate; and/or
   b) patient complaints are probable.

4. If the payment is double-posted:
   a) credit balance is created but overstated; and/or
   b) refunds are processed when no money is due.

5. If the payment is posted using the wrong "code" per the practice management system:
   a) revenue is not properly classified; and/or
   b) reports to leadership are inaccurate.

© 2009 Walker, Woodcock, Larch. Reprinted with permission.

2. *Account adjustments*: Auditing your account adjustments (often referred to as "write-offs") is also a key part of managing your business risk. Each medical practice needs a policy indicating who is authorized to write off accounts, at what dollar thresholds, and for what reasons. Then, the medical practice executive or billing manager needs to regularly review those write-offs to confirm that the policy is being followed. Figure 16.2 delineates the four major ways that account write-offs adversely affect a medical practice.

FIGURE 16.2 ■ Impact of Incorrect Account Write-offs

1. Staff who post payments also have the ability to write off accounts:
   a) misappropriation of payments received; for example, an employee deposits insurance payment in his/her own account and writes off the account with a non-cash adjustment bringing the account to zero;
   b) collectible amounts are written off; and/or
   c) adjustment amounts are inaccurate.

2. Write-offs are posted against the wrong code:
   a) monthly reporting is inaccurate; and/or
   b) operations analysis of the medical practice's performance is inaccurate.

3. Write-offs are posted to the wrong account:
   a) account balances are inaccurate;
   b) accounts that should be billed are not billed; and/or
   c) the medical practice experiences a loss of revenue.

4. Write-offs are not reviewed by management:
   a) misappropriation of payments received;
   b) write-offs are not properly posted; and/or
   c) the medical practice experiences a loss of revenue.

© 2009 Walker, Woodcock, Larch. Reprinted with permission.

3. *Refunds*: The process of reviewing credit balances and determining if refunds are due to the payer or patient presents a potential business risk to a medical practice. Make sure someone is assigned to review and take action on the credit balances, as failure to return overpayments is a business risk to your medical practice. Yet, a medical practice also must ensure that its refund process has inherent internal controls to minimize opportunity for fraud. Figure 16.3 describes two areas in which refund management can adversely affect your medical practice.

FIGURE 16.3 ■ Impact of Incorrect Refund Management

1. Refunds not reviewed prior to processing:
   a) refund amounts are not accurate;
   b) refunds are sent to improper recipients; and/or
   c) refunds are sent to fictitious recipients.

2. Refunds are not properly posted:
   a) account balances are inaccurate;
   b) duplicate refunds are processed;
   c) the medical practice experiences a loss of revenue; and/or
   d) expenses increase due to staff processing duplicate refunds.

© 2009 Walker, Woodcock, Larch. Reprinted with permission.

As demonstrated by the above discussion, internal audits conducted on a systematic basis are critical to ensure that funds are appropriately collected and accounted for by the medical practice. After performing an internal audit, a medical practice should design and prioritize its interventions that may include staff re-delegation and the development of new policies and procedures. Once steps are taken to reduce business risk, a follow-up to the audit should be conducted to determine that interventions are successful in preventing a breach of internal controls.

ADOPT PHYSICAL SECURITY MEASURES

Medical practice executives are responsible for ensuring that physical security controls are developed, implemented, maintained, and adhered to by all employees. This ensures that cash, checks, and other sensitive information are properly secured to reduce the risk of theft.

The following scenarios are considered failures of physical security measures related to cash management:

- Cash, credit card receipts, and/or checks are stored on top of the desk, inside an unlocked drawer, or in an unlocked office;

- Cash and checks are stored in a locked box; however, the locked box is kept inside an unlocked drawer;

- The medical practice has a safe to store cash, checks, and other documents. The safe's instruction manual containing the combination and the keys are stored inside of an unlocked desk drawer. The safe is in an office that cannot be locked; and/or

- The code to the safe is provided to an employee who terminates employment with the medical practice; however, the code is not changed.

Your medical practice should implement safeguards, as well as policies and procedures, for all aspects of physical security.

INVESTIGATE RED FLAGS FOR FRAUD

In a normal day in your medical practice, you may see red flags for fraud that you need to investigate. Situations such as the three highlighted below may alert you to a problem.

Case Study A

A patient calls to complain that he/she paid at the time of service, but your medical practice sent him/her a statement that reflects that the amount paid is still outstanding.

If you have a protocol of giving patients a receipt, the patient should be asked if he/she received a receipt at the time of payment. If the patient did receive a receipt, then it is possible that the payment made at the time of service was not posted in a correct or timely fashion. If the patient did not receive a receipt, then it is possible that a staff member pocketed the money.

It is important that you engage your patients as part of your internal control process. In your financial policies you should indicate that patients should contact the medical practice executive if they have any concerns regarding their bill.

Case Study B

Patient refund checks are being sent multiple times to the same patient.

As discussed earlier in this chapter, it is possible that your refund process has inherent deficits. Not only should you review the refund checks and attached documentation at the time of the refund check request, but you also want to audit refunds in a more general sense. Run reports showing refunds by check payee over 6 or 12 months to determine if refund checks are being sent to the same payee time and time again. A staff member could be collaborating with a patient or the patient name could be fictitious.

Case Study C

An employee refuses to take vacation.

All employees need to take a vacation of at least five consecutive days off. While the person is out, potential red flags may surface. The only way a person or persons can continue a fraud over a long period of time is to have complete control over the process. If an employee must go on vacation, the process will be handled by someone else who is likely to uncover processes that run contrary to established policies and procedures.

In summary, each medical practice must determine its business risk tolerance and develop written policies and procedures for key functions related to financial management. In addition, a culture focused on internal controls should be promulgated throughout the medical practice. Appropriate internal controls allow the medical practice to reduce the risk of asset losses and ensure reliability of financial reporting.

POLICIES AND PROCEDURES

At the end of each chapter, we provide policies and procedures to assist you in developing a policy and procedure manual for your medical practice. Following are four policies specific to the internal control process.

Policy 31: Employee Background Check

Policy 32: Time-of-Service Payment Controls

Policy 33: Deposit of Patient Receipts

Policy 34: Bank Statement Reconciliation

POLICY 31: EMPLOYEE BACKGROUND CHECK

Policy:

This policy applies to all medical practice employees.

A. Purpose

1. It is important that the medical practice take actions to protect its funds, property, and other assets.

2. This policy is intended to support the verification of credentials, criminal history, credit status, and other information related to employment decisions.

B. Statement of General Policy

1. It is the policy of the medical practice that all new employees have certain credentials and criminal and other background information verified as a condition of employment.

2. It is the policy of the medical practice that current employees with fiscal management responsibility have their criminal and other background information verified as a condition of continued employment.

C. Background Checks and Verifications

The following checks and verifications may be performed:

1. Credit history check: checking the credit history of the employee or applicant. (Federal laws prohibit discrimination against an applicant or employee as a result of bankruptcy.)

2. Criminal history check: verifying that the applicant or employee does not have any undisclosed criminal history in every jurisdiction where the applicant or employee currently resides or has resided.

3. Educational verification: ensuring that the applicant or employee possesses all educational credentials beyond high school listed on the application, resume, or cover letter. This expressly includes all professional certifications.

4. Employment verification: ensuring that the applicant or employee actually worked in the positions listed on the application, resume, cover letter, or otherwise cited by the candidate that qualify the individual for the position sought, as well as all employment during a period of at least seven years immediately preceding application. This verification should include dates of employment and reasons for leaving each position.

5. Limited criminal history check: verifying that the applicant or employee does not have any undisclosed criminal history in the jurisdiction where the applicant or employee currently resides, or where the applicant or employee last resided, if the applicant or employee only recently moved to a location near the medical practice.

6. Tax payment check: verifying that the selected applicant or employee is current in payment of state taxes.

POLICY 32: TIME-OF-SERVICE PAYMENT CONTROLS

Policy:

It is the policy of the medical practice to ensure timely and accurate tracking, reconciliation, and deposits of all payments received (checks, cash, and credit/debit cards) at the time of service.

Procedures:

1. A charge and payment entry staff member logs on the practice management system using his/her personal log-on identification and password.

2. If the staff member takes a break during the shift, he/she must log off. If applicable, the replacement staff member enters charges and payments under his/her own log-on identification number and password.

3. All patient charges and corresponding payments are entered into the system at the time of patient check-out, unless otherwise designated to be the billing office's responsibility.

4. Every check received is endorsed with the medical practice's bank endorsement stamp at the time of check-out.

5. Credit card payments are transmitted daily in accordance with the service procedure found at each credit card terminal.

6. At the end of the shift, each staff member entering charges and/or time-of-service payments runs a daily system summary in the practice management system, showing all patient charges and payments (cash, check, and credit/debit card) by log-on identification number.

7. Each staff member responsible for charge and/or payment entry must balance patient charges, as well as receipts for his/her allotted shift as follows:

    a. Total all medical practice charges or fees on each charge ticket to arrive at the total charges for each patient seen during the shift.

    b. When totaling charges, the employee shall not confuse patient charges with charge card receipts; charge/debit card receipts are considered payments.

    c. The grand total of charge tickets (run on a calculator tape) and the grand total of payments (run on a calculator tape) must match the daily summary of charges and payments, respectively, for the shift.

    d. The employee running the tapes shall resolve any discrepancies.

    e. When discrepancies are resolved, the staff member attaches the tapes to the front of the stack of charge tickets and receipts, and staples them together.

    f. For each of these batches, the staff member responsible for keying and balancing completes a Daily Summary of Charges and Payments form. (See below.)

8. The cash/change drawer must balance to $100.00 at the end of every shift.

9. The charge tickets (unless charges were automatically interfaced), cash, check, and credit card receipts and the corresponding daily summary are then placed in a locked safe.

10. Each shift repeats the same process.

11. At the end of the day, all patient charge tickets are cross-referenced with the master patient schedule for that day, verifying that an encounter has occurred and that a charge ticket has been generated with every scheduled patient (including any add-ons for the day).

12. "No shows," "cancellations," and "reschedules" are noted on the schedule.

13. A list of "no shows" and "cancellations" is provided to the appropriate clinical assistant designee for follow-up and notation in the medical record.

14. The master patient schedule is given to the billing manager or designee with the batch.

15. See the related policy on appointment reconciliation.

16. At the end of the business day (or the next business morning at the latest), the billing manager or designee prepares the deposit as follows:

    a. Dates the deposit slip with the date of service.

    b. Totals all cash and writes the amount in the cash area on the deposit slip.

    c. Lists each check by check number on the deposit slip.

    d. Writes the total of cash and checks to be deposited in the appropriate space on the deposit slip.

    e. Does not list credit card payments on the deposit slip.

    f. Writes the name of the originating practice site on the lower-left corner of the deposit slip.

    g. Removes the white and yellow copies of the deposit slip from the deposit book; retains the pink copy in the deposit book for practice records.

    h. Paper clips the original copy (white) to the cash and checks and places the copy in a white envelope.

    i. Attaches the yellow copy to the Daily Deposit Log. (See below.)

17. The deposit total plus the credit/debit card charges must balance to the daily summaries.

    a. If it does not, the practice executive or designee reviews all charge tickets, daily summaries, and cash/check totals.

    b. The review will be repeated until balance occurs.

    c. If balance does not occur, notify the practice executive or designee.

    d. Separate and detailed documentation must support the error requiring attention and adjustment.

e. The billing manager or designee shall submit the error documentation on the Request for Edit/Correction form on the day of the corresponding daily deposit information. (See p. 317.)

18. The practice executive or designee shall enclose checks, cash, and the deposit slip for a single date of service in a white envelope stamped with the date of service, the total of the deposit, and the name of the originating office.

19. Use a separate envelope for each date of service and seal it.

20. The billing manager or designee shall place all envelope(s) in the site-specific, numbered bank pouch, and lock the pouch.

21. The billing manager or designee shall keep the bank pouch in a locked safe for pick-up by the courier.

22. The bank pouch is given to the courier, who initials and dates a courier deposit log acknowledging receipt of the envelope.

23. Each deposit must be listed on the daily deposit log by date and amount.

24. The practice executive or designee shall attach the yellow copy of the deposit by paper clip to the log sheet.

25. Each individual credit card total (by credit card type) is noted daily as a line item under the cash/check deposit for the day on the calculator tape to ensure balancing to the transmitted credit card charges.

26. A copy of this tape is marked "Total Credit Card Charges," dated with the date of receipt, and attached to the deposit log with the cash/check deposit slip for the day.

DAILY SUMMARY OF CHARGES AND PAYMENTS FORM

Name: _____   Date of batch: _____

Total charges/fees: _____

Total cash: _____

Total credit cards: _____

Total checks: _____

Total payments: _____

Note: "Total payments" must be the sum of "total cash," "total credit cards," and "total checks."

Attach charge tickets, payments, and tapes to the back of this form, and return the form to your supervisor.

DAILY DEPOSIT LOG

Practice site: _____

Date	Deposit Total	Prepared By
12/1/10	$500.00	EWW
12/1/10	MC $50.00	EWW
12/1/10	VISA $50.00	EWW
12/1/10	Discover $35.00	EWW

REQUEST FOR EDIT/CORRECTION

Account number: _____

Patient name: _____

Date of service to be edited: _____ _

Requester: _____

Date: _____

Approval granted by: _____

Date: _____

Notes of approval not granted: _____

_____

Please attach any available, appropriate documentation.

POLICY 33: DEPOSIT OF PATIENT RECEIPTS

Policy:

It is the policy of the medical practice that all staff follow appropriate and consistent procedures for handling and depositing patient receipts.

Procedures:

For all funds collected directly from patients, the following guidelines apply:

For practice sites with five or more providers:

1. During operating hours, all cash funds are maintained in a locked drawer that is inaccessible to patients, as well as to unauthorized employees. The drawer is always locked when unattended. At the end of the business day, a reconciliation of the cash drawer is prepared to ensure accuracy.

2. As part of this reconciliation process, all checks and cash in excess of the cash fund balance are prepared for deposit to the bank.

3. A deposit slip is prepared and checks are properly endorsed with a stamp.

    a. If the bank is still open, the deposit is taken to the bank for inclusion in the nightly sweep account.

    b. If the the bank is closed, the deposit is placed in the night drop box at the bank.

4. The medical practice bank account(s) should reflect this deposit the next day.

5. An alternate deposit procedure is to prepare a daily deposit by 3 p.m. This ensures that the deposit is included in the nightly sweep, which enhances cash flow.

6. Any money collected after 3 p.m. is securely stored overnight and deposited the following day by 3 p.m.

For practice sites with less than five providers:

1. The same procedures issued for sites with five or more providers are followed. However, deposits are made when there is greater than $500.00 on hand for deposit, or at the business weekend, whichever is sooner.

2. At the end of the business day, the money must be maintained in a locked, fire-proof safe for security purposes.

3. At the end of the business day, copies of the receipts are submitted to medical practice staff assigned to post payments or to the billing office for posting to patient accounts.

POLICY 34: BANK STATEMENT RECONCILIATION

Policy:

It is the policy of the medical practice to reconcile bank statements as part of month-end closing procedures. The purpose of this policy is to ensure the timely performance of month-end closing.

Procedures:

1. Bank statements

   a. Bank statements must be reconciled as part of the month-end closing procedures.

   b. This procedure is completed for each bank account.

   c. The following is an example of the recommended reconciliation format:

Bank balance at month end	$xxxx
Plus deposits in transit	xxx
Less outstanding checks	(xxx)
Plus/minus other reconciling items	xxx
Balance	$ xxxxx
Balance per general ledger (G/L)	$ xxxxx

2. Deposits in transit (DIT)

   A review of the detail is essential to determine whether there have been any lost or misapplied deposits. Any DIT greater than five days old should be investigated immediately.

3. Outstanding checks

   a. A detailed list of outstanding checks should be maintained.

   b. All outstanding checks more than 30 days old with a balance of $250.00 or more should be reviewed.

   c. A stop-payment should be issued on any outstanding checks older than six months.

      (1) These checks should be investigated immediately as to why they have not been cashed.

      (2) A new check is reissued if applicable.

4. Other reconciling items

   a. The detail is reviewed monthly to determine appropriateness and a method of resolution (for example, journal entry).

   b. There should be no difference between the reconciled bank balance and the general ledger balance.

CHAPTER 17

The Debate: Centralize, Decentralize, or Outsource Billing?

Each medical practice must decide whether to outsource its revenue cycle in whole or in part. This decision is a function of available financial, human, and information system resources, as well as the interest and expertise of internal managers. If the revenue cycle is managed internally, the medical practice must decide which tasks should be operated and managed centrally, and which tasks should be decentralized. A medical practice should revisit these fundamental structural questions on a periodic basis as its market, performance, information systems, staffing, and other factors change from current levels.

Outsourcing involves retaining a company to perform billing and collections services on behalf of the medical practice. The company is not part of the medical practice and may be geographically located close to the practice or across the globe.

An alternative to outsourcing the full revenue cycle is functional outsourcing. Similar to assigning staff based on billing and collections functions (as discussed in Chapter 15: Staffing the Revenue Cycle), many medical practices approach outsourcing from a functional perspective. In contrast to an "all or none" approach, medical practices determine what billing functions make logistical and financial sense to outsource to a vendor. In fact, most medical practices have outsourced one or more revenue cycle tasks, such as using a clearinghouse to edit and process claims, using a vendor to mail patient statements, or sending problem accounts to a collection agency for follow-up.

When billing and collections functions are not outsourced, but are conducted within the medical practice, they are structured in centralized, decentralized, or hybrid structures. A centralized billing office (CBO) typically performs all billing and collections functions by staff members who are in a unit that is separate (often geographically) from the rest of the medical practice staff. In contrast, in a decentralized billing office, all functions stay at the practice site in which the care is provided; for a multi-site practice, each site has its own staff working the accounts for that particular practice site. From a practical perspective, most medical practices that perform their own billing and collection functions have a hybrid structure involving some combination of centralized and decentralized structures.

In this chapter, we discuss:

- Decentralization
- Centralization
- Outsourcing
- Transition and change management

To begin, we review the options to structure an internal billing and collection operation. There are advantages and disadvantages to each approach. We do not intend to indicate a bias toward any method based on the order we discuss them. Each medical practice needs to assess its particular circumstances in order to resolve the debate between centralization and decentralization.

STRUCTURAL OPTIONS

The unit of work in back-end billing, which is a claim, remains largely unchanged whether it is centralized, decentralized, or even outsourced. Economies of scale are challenging to capture in any structural model: staff still have to key the charge, edit and transmit the claim, process the denial, post the payment, and communicate with the payer. Although technology has decreased the staff intervention required for many billing functions, the benefits of technology can be equally distributed to decentralized and centralized structures. Although it's typically easier to stay current with payer requirements in a CBO because of its expanded and focused resources, the actual time to perform the work is the same whether or not it is performed centrally.

Decentralization

A decentralized structure resides the majority of billing functions at the practice site. The key advantage of decentralization is that the billing staff are closer — emotionally and physically — to the site where care is provided. Because the revenue cycle initiates with the patient's registration and scheduling, which is performed or confirmed at the site, and the submission of claims is based on the services performed on site, the physical presence of billing staff facilitates communication and information exchange between the key internal stakeholders of the billing process. This includes communication between physicians and billing staff, as well as the development of a team approach between the front office and billing office.

Two key advantages of a decentralized model are (1) the ability to foster relationships with physicians and (2) ease of communication.

Relationship with the physician

Key components of the revenue cycle are coding and charge capture. Speed and accuracy are critical, and they depend heavily on the physician and his/her ability to communicate with the billing staff. Employees in a decentralized setting can easily ask the physician questions: "Did you mean to put this modifier with this procedure code?" or "Do you have some time to review the linkages of the multiple procedure codes and diagnosis codes for this patient?" Because employees are located "where the action is" and are more actively attuned to clinical practice and the work associated with the delivery of patient care services, it is not uncommon for the billing staff's engagement and loyalty to the organization to increase when billing is decentralized. (Notably, this is particularly apparent when a medical practice transitions to a centralized model where it is difficult to create the same level of staff engagement for those staff who formerly worked directly with physicians.)

This is in contrast to a CBO structure, where interaction with the physicians may require filling out a form and e-mailing it to the physician or creating an electronic task request. In turn, the staff often must wait a few days — or even weeks — for the request for information or clarification to be returned. The staff time, as well as the time the charge is pending, can really add up.

Ease of communication

It is easier to communicate in a decentralized billing office than in a centralized one because the physicians, practice site staff, and billing office staff are based at the same location.

Decentralization offers many advantages. Of course, the outcome depends not only on the structure, but the effectiveness of the people and the processes.

Centralization

There are a number of advantages and disadvantages to a CBO. In general, advantages include focused attention to performance management, compliance, and coding. In addition, the size and scale of a CBO can often serve to justify the purchase of more sophisticated information systems. These advantages need to be weighed against the disadvantages of a CBO, which can include a disconnect between the billing office staff and the provision of care, as well as higher billing costs. The advantages and disadvantages of a CBO are further explored below.

Resources and costs

Because a medical practice may have functioned without a CBO for years, a CBO almost always adds several new resources. These include coding, compliance, reporting, contract analysis, training, and application support. Clearly, medical practices need these activities in today's reimbursement environment, but for many medical practices, they represent new costs. These new resources are not without a price — though they do contribute long-term to better reporting, improved business risk management, and the potential for increased revenue.

Patient collections

If you centralize billing and remove it from the medical practice site, front-office staff can quickly take the "it's not my job" attitude. Many front-office staff assume that since their billing colleagues have been shipped down the road, so too has the work. Freed of billing duties, they have no qualms about telling patients to call the CBO if they have questions. We have witnessed front-office staff refusing to accept payment of prior account balances; they tell the patient to "send it to the CBO." At the same time, the CBO is desperate to get these same patients on the telephone. Thus, account follow-up work may expand at the CBO, even though the front-office staff could easily collect payments at the time of service. Unfortunately, this situation is more a function of attitude than process, which is more difficult to correct. However, it is fairly common and must be managed well, particularly if a transition of billing structures occurs.

Ease of communication

Because the billing staff are under one roof, communication about billing issues can be swift and effective. If a payer bulletin publishes information about billing for a new service, staff or managers can communicate it very quickly throughout the CBO. However, in contrast to direct communication with physicians described in a decentralized model, in a CBO, paper, telephone calls, and e-mails must fly back and forth between the practice site and the CBO. When places of business are disjointed, communication is difficult to maintain and informal communication is replaced with multiple meetings. Typically, a CBO management team spends a significant amount of time in meetings, making sure everyone is current with data, information, and reporting. This heightened communication can have its advantages in terms of staying current with coding and reimbursement issues, but also has a cost in terms of staff time and resources. Fortunately, technology is reducing the time and resources that must be dedicated to communicating among multiple parties.

Compliance

In a large organization without centralization, it is difficult to keep compliance in check. There are a number of ways that the billing process can become non-compliant. It is critical to recognize that the medical practice is responsible for everything that happens in its billing process. By centralizing the refund process, monitoring coding, managing internal controls, and standardizing policies and procedures via centralization, the organization may reduce its business risk. (For more information on billing compliance, see Chapter 20: Regulations Impacting the Revenue Cycle.)

Performance monitoring

By forming a CBO, a medical practice takes tasks that multiple staff members once performed and locates them into single functions so that one employee (or a focused team) performs only these tasks. The CBO can therefore track and monitor performance, including accuracy rates and productivity measures.

Expert management

A medical practice with a CBO can employ a manager who is focused and professionally trained to manage billing and collection operations rather than a manager who has this responsibility as one of many. Sophisticated management has the potential to improve performance.

Education

A CBO can perform targeted orientation and training that can bring results. As the professional fee reimbursement environment becomes increasingly sophisticated, it is harder to train on the job. A CBO can offer training and expertise to new employees, as well as competency assessments for all employees. Although this is possible in a decentralized environment, it is much easier in a centralized model.

Information systems

Typically, capital for information systems and technology is more readily available in large, centralized practices. To pay off, however, those "bigger and better" systems really have to save money by automating processes or improving revenue by catching mistakes. Medical practices are often sold by the fact that technology can perform such tasks, but the implementation or processes often do not capture these positive effects because the training, implementation, or even the users are inadequate.

Shared accounts

If the medical practice is billing for multiple physicians who cross specialty lines, a CBO can work accounts that are shared by different specialties. For example, patients who undergo surgery are also likely to have anesthesiology, pathology, and radiology services. A medical practice can organize billing and collection teams to include surgical specialties with these referral-based specialties, with this integrated team fully working the account.

A centralized billing structure has the potential to achieve economies of scale, but the management and information systems must be effective to ensure a positive outcome.

Hybrid Models

Some medical practices have recognized challenges associated with exclusively decentralized or centralized models and have overcome many of the obstacles by creating "hybrid" models that involve some degree of both decentralization and centralization. A hybrid model often consists of the following characteristics.

Charge entry

Given the distributed technology of most practice management systems (including the increase of Web-based alternatives), charge entry activity is often delegated to staff physically located at the practice site. These staff are closer to the physician and can ensure that all services are captured and entered to the system.

Clean claims

Through automation, a centralized model can integrate responsibility for creating a clean claim at the practice site, instead of congregating problems exclusively in the CBO. In recent years, charge scrubbing technology has become so sophisticated and efficient that requests for clarification and information can be integrated into the coding and charge capture processes via pre-adjudication edits. In this case, physicians and charge entry staff are alerted to problems as charges are captured. (For more information about charge scrubbing technology and pre-adjudication edits, see Chapter 7: The Charge Entry Process.)

Time-of-service collections and posting

The practice site staff often have a clear advantage over a CBO in collecting time-of-service payments. There is no reason they should not also be delegated the posting of these payments rather than hand off this task to a staff member located in the CBO.

Patient collections

The centralized model can delegate patient follow-up to the practice staff. The practice staff are more likely to have success collecting from patients via telephone and/or in person as they are face-to-face with the patient and may have developed a relationship with the patient. They are also most likely to know the patient's individual circumstance.

Process commitment

In a hybrid model, confusion may arise as a result of the number of people and processes involved in the revenue cycle. In order to mitigate challenges that result from uncertainty in roles and responsibilities, establish a code of commitments for physician billing. See Figure 17.1 for a sample code of commitments.

There is no right answer as to how to structure your revenue cycle, yet the medical practices with the most successful accounts receivable performance have found effective results from a hybrid model that combines the best features of both decentralization and centralization.

Outsourcing

For those of you contemplating outsourcing your entire revenue cycle or a portion of your revenue cycle, we recommend that you conduct a formal analysis of your medical practice to see if outsourcing billing is the best option. An outsourcing arrangement must ensure that the dollars invested generate a positive return. That is, you should outsource only if you are going to boost revenue or save money.

Some medical practices, however, elect to outsource their entire revenue cycle or portions of their revenue cycle due to resource constraints or competing priorities. For example, a small medical practice may elect not to invest in the infrastructure and resources to establish its own internal billing operation. As another example, a medical practice that has just opened its doors may determine that its initial priorities will be better placed in marketing and growing its patient base, electing to outsource its billing until it has achieved a more mature state in its evolution. Notably, referral-based specialties, such as neonatology, radiology, anesthesiology, pathology, and those physicians specializing as hospitalists, rely on registration conducted elsewhere (for example, at the hospital or other facility in which

FIGURE 17.1 ■ Code of Commitments for Physician Billing

Focus areas for practice sites:

- We will notify the billing office when we make employment offers to new providers.
- We will utilize the practice management system for all patient appointments and surgeries.
- We will obtain complete registration, including demographic and insurance information, prior to the date of service.
- We will obtain required referrals and authorizations for services rendered.
- We will review and follow through on notices on patients' accounts when patients present to determine if information or payment needs to be gathered.
- We will collect copayments, co-insurance, unmet deductibles, and prior balances due at the time of service.
- We will ensure that all services provided are accurately captured and coded.
- We will resolve all pre-adjudication edits related to front-end errors in a timely fashion.
- We will receive notification regarding claim denials related to front-end errors and take action to prevent these errors from occurring in the future.
- We will work collaboratively with our partners in the billing office to ensure timely exchange of information necessary to support reimbursement.

Focus areas for the billing office:

- We will enter charges in a timely and accurate fashion.
- We will resolve back-end claim edits to ensure clean claims.
- We will post payments and denials in a timely and accurate fashion.
- We will notify the practice sites regarding front-end edits and denials.
- We will resolve denials due to back-end errors.
- We will follow up on outstanding receivables to maximize collections.
- We will flag patients' accounts when information or payment is needed for account resolution.
- We will review credit balances and request refund checks.
- We will provide reports to measure progress towards targets.
- We will work collaboratively with our partners in the practice sites to ensure timely exchange of information necessary to support reimbursement.

© 2009 Walker, Woodcock, Larch. Reprinted with permission.

services are rendered) and services are most often performed distinctive of the location of the billing office. Many of these specialties have found outsourcing to be a compelling option.

Next, consider the outsourcing service or product. Consider four basic factors: management, performance, communication, and cost. To illustrate, we will review the four factors in terms of outsourcing your billing operation.

Management

Physicians should expect the highest quality of the outsourced product or service. This is especially important with professional fee billing, a process for which physicians are responsible whether it is managed in-house or at an outside billing service. Thus, the issue of management and oversight is critical in an outsourcing arrangement. Performance expectations must be clear, and the vendor must be able to effectively communicate information regarding those expectations and make improvements if performance is not up to agreed-upon targets. The medical practice, on the other hand, must be willing to delegate work to the vendor and hold it accountable for performance. If a medical practice not only expects high performance, but wants to micromanage the process, an outsourced relationship will not be effective.

Performance

To achieve a positive outcome, the performance of the outsourcing service must be equal to or greater than that of the in-house service. Achieving high performance is certainly possible, particularly if the in-house operation is plagued by untrained staff, poor management, unsophisticated information systems, or high staff turnover. Even if the medical practice is not experiencing these challenges, vendors may be able to offer higher performance as a result of specialty- or payer-expertise, or more refined information systems. Prior to selecting the vendor, gauge its performance by requiring it to report its performance with other clients related to key revenue cycle indicators, including percentage of accounts receivable over 90 days, days in receivables, net collection rate, claim denial rate, and credit balances, against historical performance and industry standards. This indicates the current level of performance and the opportunities for improvement. Including the credit balance performance in these measures will ensure the vendor is focused on quality and compliance, as well as how much it collects each month.

The contract itself should include performance targets; better-performing medical practices that outsource their billing tie the price to reaching certain targets. Agreements may include baseline targets that must be reached; if any one of the baselines is not met for a specified period of time (for example, three months in a row), the billing fee is reduced until performance is corrected.

Communication

No matter what product or service is being considered, effective communication is essential. By its nature, outsourcing hampers the communication channel, but hiring a good internal manager or having an effective external manager can bridge the gap. Ask for and call the references of the billing vendor to inquire about the effectiveness of its communication methods.

Cost

The cost of the product or service must be equal to or less than the cost of managing the product or service in-house, unless the medical practice can rely upon the vendor to generate additional revenue. The cost of the billing operation is typically calculated as a percentage of collections or revenue. Typical billing costs for back-end billing range from 4 percent for surgery practices to 13 percent for emergency medicine practices, with primary care and most medical specialists somewhere in the middle around 6 to 9 percent. (See Chapter 19: Measuring and Analyzing the Revenue Cycle and Figure 19.8 for a detailed discussion of billing costs.) Comparing your costs against these industry averages should indicate whether there are opportunities for improvement.

After analyzing these four factors, ask yourself the following questions:

- What degree of oversight must we have over the management of this service? Can we afford to delegate and give up some control?
- What is the current performance of our internal billing operation? Do we have the option of fixing it? Are the needed fixes related to the front office or billing office? Do we believe that someone else can do it better? How much better?
- What level of communication do we need to manage the service? Can the vendor offer us that level of communication? How?
- What is the current cost of managing the service? Do we believe that we can operate the service at a lower cost by outsourcing it? How much lower?
- Which is most challenging for our medical practice — front-end billing or back-end billing? If our medical practice has challenges with its front-end billing, can an external vendor provide added value?

Look for a compelling answer to all of these questions — and others that will certainly arise. Be sure that the overall performance of the outsourced billing service will be improved and the cost will be lower. If one of these two factors is achievable and another is neutral, that may be acceptable as well. However, the control and communication levels must be equally maintained, so make sure that outsourcing does not drop below acceptable levels.

If your medical practice has outsourced its billing and collection process to an external billing vendor, document the scope of services to be performed and the performance expectations of the billing vendor and review these expectations at least annually.

The following billing and collection services are typically included in any billing operation and should be considered in the scope of services for billing vendors:

- *Pricing and coding:* Analysis of codes used, suggestions to improve accurate coding of services performed, fee schedule analysis and recommendations.
- *Registration and charge entry:* New patient registration, demographic and insurance updates, insurance verification, pre-adjudication edits, charge capture and entry.
- *Account management and follow-up:* Accounts receivable evaluation, follow-up on insurance and patient pay balances, telephone follow-up with patients, claims appeals, customer service support with office hours from 8 a.m. to 5 p.m., at minimum, automated services for off-hour and weekend messages.

- *Payment posting:* Line-item posting; ensuring consistency with expected levels of reimbursement; billing secondary payers; timely and accurate validation of bank totals and reconciliation of daily, month-end, and year-end batch runs to deposits; management of credit balances.

- *Cash management/financial:* Development of payment plans, appropriate separation of duties, cash management controls, time-of-service payment programs, banking, lockbox, remote deposit services, financial reconciliation, budget variance analysis.

- *Production:* Patient billing statements, paper claims, and e-claims.

- *Information systems support:* Support for peripheral devices, daily backup/month-end processes, computer and dictionary maintenance, version updates, module updates, new system implementation and support.

- *Compliance and legislative updates:* Established, written compliance program, legislative updates communicated to medical practices and physicians as appropriate.

- *Management reporting:* Standardized reports delivered automatically at specific days following month- and year-end, ad hoc reports as requested.

- *Physician education:* Coding, changes in billing guidelines, chart documentation.

- *Staff education:* Front-office staff related to patient financial clearance, pre-authorization, pre-existing condition exceptions, insurance validation, payment policies, charge entry, time-of-service collections, patient account history, credit risk assessment and segmentation.

- *Meetings with management and physicians:* Monthly meetings to review charges, collections, accounts receivable, collection requests, coding issues, contracting, payer relations.

- *Meetings with administration:* Quarterly meetings to review management reports, problems and issues, additional meetings to discuss and plan for changes to billing and collection practices pursuant to federal or state requirements and payer changes.

The following services, typically considered optional, are often subject to additional fees:

- *Human resources:* Professional organization employing all staff, responsibility for hiring and firing, benefits administration.

- *Enrollment and credentialing:* Enrollment with payers, completion and maintenance of all credentialing.

- *Financial management:* Bookkeeping, accounts payable, internal controls, tax preparation, general accounting duties.

- *Charge capture, charge controls:* Procedures to ensure inpatient and outpatient charge capture; for example, comparison with patient schedules, hospital census reports and operative logs.

- *Contract analysis and negotiation:* Evaluation of payer contracts from an economic and business basis, assistance in negotiating relationships with payers.

- *Physician coding and audit compliance:* Chart audits to determine coding and audit compliance.

- *Managed care analysis:* In-depth review of capitation performance, including utilization management statistics and analysis.

- *Pay-for-performance (P4P) analysis:* In-depth review of P4P contracts, including medical practice reporting and performance outcomes analysis and payment reconciliation between medical practice and payer.

- *Collection agency:* Pursuit of patient payments owed to the medical practice, skip-tracing, legal collections.

The cost of outsourcing varies significantly based on the services that the vendor offers and the medical practice elects. In addition to the services, however, it is critical to evaluate the vendor's performance. Like many products and services, it may be worth it to pay more if your medical practice realizes better quality and performance.

Functional Outsourcing

Many medical practices decide to outsource only a portion of the revenue cycle. In fact, the majority of medical practices send their past-due accounts to a collection agency, which is a form of outsourcing, and many medical practices outsource patient statement processing. There is no formula to guarantee the best results for your investment. You must make a careful review of your internal strengths and weaknesses, as well as the resources available to you before you can select which processes to outsource.

In considering any structural option for your revenue cycle, you need to understand the associated billing costs. When you have your own CBO, the billing costs are often merged into the overall practice overhead. If you want to consider moving your billing out of your office into a CBO or into an outsourced arrangement, you need to separate out your current billing costs from other practice costs so you can provide an "apples to apples" comparison of each option.

If you have an outsourced model (and if you are in a centralized model in which you are formally charged a billing fee), you pay an agreed upon fee to another entity for billing. As mentioned above, you need to determine what services that organization will perform for your medical practice. Furthermore, you need to negotiate the billing fee that you will pay for those services. Billing costs are most often represented as a percentage of collections or cost per claim; alternatively, the cost is cited on a per-transaction basis. If the price is based on transaction, the numbers of charges entered, payments posted, accounts worked, claims submitted, or other transaction are monitored. If you contract exclusively for coding services, avoid a percentage-of-collections arrangement as that might cause upcoding; instead, pay by transaction.

With proper planning and research, you can select the best organizational structure for your medical practice and determine if all or part of the revenue cycle should be managed by an external party.

CREATING AN INTERNAL BILLING OFFICE

Now that we have fully considered the structural options, as well as outsourcing back-end billing in its entirety, we need to consider the steps to transition from outsourcing to moving the operation in-house. If you currently outsource your billing and have elected to transition it to an internal operation, you have a major task at hand.

Beyond deciding on a practice management system and a staffing deployment model, using the same list that you compiled for the vendor regarding the scope of services, create a work plan that clarifies which billing services you will be conducting internally. There may be changes you want to make in the front office at the same time. The front office may need to integrate some functions previously handled by the outsourced vendor into their workflow. You may decide to internalize all billing functions, or you could phase them in over time to minimize any impact to revenue performance. For example, you might transition charge entry for the first three months and then transition payment posting and account follow-up. Deciding what and when to move functions will be based on the contract you have with the vendor, the vendor's willingness to consider a transition over time, and your ability to implement your practice management system and hire and/or train staff for the new work.

As you bring your back-end billing in house, maintain an accounting of your billing costs so that you can continue to evaluate your cost of billing and your billing performance.

TRANSITION AND CHANGE MANAGEMENT

Transitioning from a centralized to a decentralized structure (or vice versa) and outsourcing all or part of a revenue cycle are considered major interruptions in the status quo of a medical practice, and importantly, they have a negative financial impact if the change management process is not well executed.

If you decide to make a change to structure, you should plan for a negative impact to your collections for two to three months, at minimum. No matter how carefully you plan, there will be some timing impacts that cause delays in charge entry and/or account follow-up. Usually there is no actual decrease in revenue — just a slow down. Once the timing is back to normal, you will be anxious to see improved results from your structural change; otherwise you wouldn't have made the decision to change. These improvements will come but may take another six to nine months to impact collections.

What worked well in the past related to the structure of a revenue cycle may not situate the medical practice for optimal revenue cycle performance for the future. We recommend that the structure of the revenue cycle be formally assessed at least annually by asking and answering the following important questions.

1. Does technology permit us to centralize, decentralize, or outsource functions of the revenue cycle?

2. Can accountability and performance be improved by placing staff in

functional roles and/or by outsourcing key revenue cycle functions?

3. Where is the root cause of the errors that are occurring in the revenue cycle? Can a change to structure potentially resolve these errors, or are the required changes needed due to front-end billing alone?

4. What performance improvement can be made if the centralized structure is located "closer to" the physician and/or the patient? If physical proximity is not a possibility, can technology serve as an aid in accomplishing the same goal?

5. Are there vendors that have more sophisticated expertise than the current billing staff and, if so, what are their performance and cost elements?

Change is really the only constant we have in health care today. If the structure of your revenue cycle is not permitting optimal revenue cycle performance, it is time to explore other structural models that may add functionality and/or focus attention on key revenue cycle processes.

CHAPTER 18

Leveraging Technology to Enhance the Revenue Cycle

Technology offers tremendous opportunities to streamline billing and collection processes and save staff time and financial resources devoted to the revenue cycle. At the heart of the billing and collection process lies the practice management system — the software a medical practice uses to register, schedule, bill, and collect from its patients and payers and to generate billing reports. Beyond the practice management system, additional electronic tools can be harnessed to assist managers and staff in ensuring timeliness and accuracy of billing and collection functions. Throughout this book, numerous technologies are identified to improve revenue cycle performance. In this chapter, those technologies are expanded and others are introduced.

In this chapter, we discuss:

- Evaluating technology for your medical practice:
  - Practice management systems
  - Application service providers (ASPs)
  - Issues to consider in technology decisions

- Technology to detect early warning signs:
  - Business intelligence (BI) systems
  - Advanced data analysis
  - Staff performance management
  - Contract compliance

- Technologies to permit patient-focused billing:
  - Online patient portal
  - Online statements
  - Kiosks

- Technologies that help your practice "do it right the first time" and minimize rework:
  - Pre-adjudication edits
  - Demographic verification
  - Referrals and authorizations
  - Tracking information requests

- Technology to permit work to be conducted in real time:
  - Electronic funds transfer (EFT)
  - Electronic payment remittance (EPR)
  - Charge capture and coding
  - Real-time insurance verification
  - Real-time claims adjudication (RTCA)
  - E-mail and instant messaging (IM)

- Technology to ensure effective resource utilization:
  - Document management
  - Electronic data interchange (EDI)
  - Denial management automation tools
  - Telephony
  - Payer interfaces
  - Medical credit scores

The technology available for revenue cycle applications is extensive. Figure 18.1 describes the goals of the available technologies that can be harnessed. Prior to adopting a new technology, it is important to conduct a cost/benefit analysis specific to your medical practice.

EVALUATING TECHNOLOGY FOR YOUR MEDICAL PRACTICE

In this section, we discuss the traditional client-server model of practice management systems and the more recent application service provider model. We also discuss issues to consider when evaluating technology decisions.

Practice Management Systems

A practice management system actually refers to software; it is not a system per se. The traditional practice management system involves the purchase of software from a vendor (or a designated reseller) to perform billing and collection functions. The software can be specific to back-end billing or it can be integrated with other software applications, such as registration and scheduling. Typically, using a practice management system also involves maintaining large sets of data, often organized in files called "dictionaries," including lists of diagnosis and procedure codes, lists of payers, referring physicians, providers, facilities, and much more. Some systems offer additional capabilities, which integrate critical revenue cycle functions into medical practice operations.

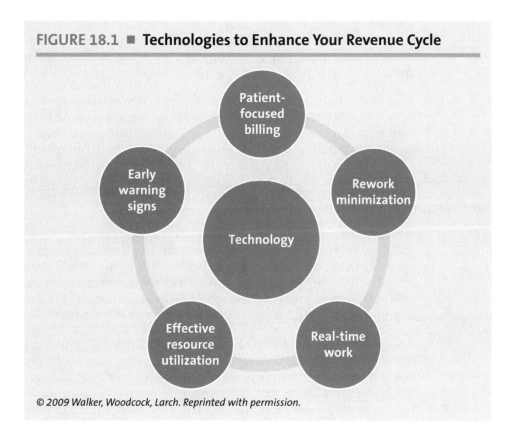

FIGURE 18.1 ■ **Technologies to Enhance Your Revenue Cycle**

© 2009 Walker, Woodcock, Larch. Reprinted with permission.

Key features of a practice management system include the following:

System hardware:	Capability; upgradability; capacity
System software:	Applications specific to billing and collection
	Applications specific to practice operations
Management reporting:	Data search criteria; reports; graphs
Storage:	Location and type of data storage

Further descriptions of the software applications of a practice management system are provided below.

Applications specific to billing and collection

Each practice management system offers different software applications specific to billing and collection functions. Common applications include management of referrals/authorizations, provider file maintenance, claims management, electronic data interchange connectivity, pre-adjudication charge scrubbing, accounts receivable management, collections management, capitation support, expected payer reimbursement schedules, productivity tracking, data access, and reporting.

Applications specific to medical practice operations

In addition to the applications specific to billing and collection, the practice management system may offer expanded applications to facilitate medical practice operations. Common applications include laboratory ordering and re-porting, appointment scheduling, electronic health record, radiology ordering and reporting, prescription ordering and reporting, address label generation, credit card verification, electronic mail, and clinical data transmission.

Your medical practice should regularly review the software applications offered by its practice management system. Software applications typically change with each version of the software. Applications that are offered by your vendor at additional cost may, in fact, provide a positive return on investment if they can be demonstrated to improve the performance of your revenue cycle.

Application Service Provider (ASP)

We have left the era where the only option was to purchase, install, and maintain practice management software within your medical practice (or to enter into a vendor relationship to perform the same). While the client-server model of the practice management system is currently used by the majority of medical practices today, a more recent technology has entered the market that provides medical practices with an alternative to this traditional approach.

An application service provider (ASP) vendor typically hosts software ap-plications on its own Web server. This eliminates the need to install and run the application on the medical practice's computer. ASPs deliver practice management software in a different model than the traditional client-server model. An ASP model remotely hosts a software application most often through a centrally located server via the Internet in a "lease" arrangement. For a monthly "lease," the ASP provides the information technology services supporting the desired software.

An ASP can be a solution to the high cost of purchasing, maintaining, and supporting a practice management system. It alleviates the practice's burden of software maintenance, ongoing operation, and support. Using an ASP also can reduce the initial one-time purchase of expensive practice management software.

Using the medical practice's existing hardware and connecting to the Inter-net offers medical practices a wide variety of applications that are hosted on the Internet. In addition to the initial cost savings, medical practices often consider an ASP because of its flexibility and connectivity to other software ap-plications. Some examples include:

- Real-time access from multiple practice sites;
- Ability to easily outsource certain functions such as statement production or collections;
- Access to payers' online patient authorization systems; and
- Access to real-time online referral or eligibility.

Companies hosting ASPs provide secure and redundant information technol-ogy (IT) architecture with assurances that your data will be protected and backed up. In addition, they typically offer help desk support, training, disaster recovery, and other similar functions as part of the monthly fee. This eliminates the need for a medical practice to employ an IT staff member(s). ASP practice management applications typically include all the basic forms, reports, and so forth to run the administrative aspects of a medical practice.

Issues to Consider in Technology Decisions

Selecting a technology solution for your professional fee billing operation is challenging. There are hundreds of practice management software systems, even though smaller systems continue to be merged into larger ones. With small financial margins, medical practices need to evaluate the return on investment before they move forward. Medical practices need to understand the costs, risks, and timetable for implementation. They also must consider the disruption to their business, if any, and the implications of that disruption associated with system implementation.

The client-server model of a practice management system typically includes an initial fee and monthly maintenance fees. Often, any new versions of the practice management software are also subject to additional fees, as is any ad hoc reporting that requires vendor intervention and that cannot be produced by the medical practice.

With ASPs, medical practices are usually charged a monthly fee and they avoid large initial fees, to include hardware purchases, licensing fees, and other costs. But, medical practices need to consider the potential cost savings with an ASP versus the long-term cost of ownership. With an ASP, the medical practice realizes significant up-front savings and then pays a monthly fee that is usually based on the number of users. If you are a large medical practice with many ASP users, your practice might end up paying a larger total cost over time compared to purchasing the software and installing it internally. There are usually no up-front implementation costs if you choose an ASP, but the trade-off can be a less specialty-customized product.

Regardless of whether you elect the client-server model or the ASP model for your practice management solution, as part of the due diligence process in determining the "right" system for your medical practice, key questions should be formulated in each of these categories:

- Vendor qualifications;
- Software functionality;
- Vendor financials;
- Customer service;
- Security and data protection;
- Contract terms;
- End-user training and support;
- Similar clients — number and contacts; and
- Market share and presence in your regional market.

If your medical practice elects an ASP model, doing business with an ASP should be approached as a business relationship rather than as a software solution. In selecting an ASP, it is very important to consider the amount of time the ASP has been in business and to also contact a number of users for their references. This is a competitive environment; the amount of time an ASP has been in business may signal its financial stability. Evaluating the ASP's privacy and security protocols is of critical importance, though the majority of companies have worked to resolve these issues due to their critical nature. Your vendors are not covered by the Health Insurance Portability and Accountability Act (HIPAA) regulations, so don't forget to put a Business Associate Agreement (BAA) in place with each one. These should be completed as part of your contracting process. See Chapter 20: Regulations Impacting the Revenue Cycle to read more about BAAs.

TECHNOLOGY TO DETECT EARLY WARNING SIGNS

In the next section, we discuss technology to measure performance so that you can recognize early warning signs — what we call "leading" indicators — in your revenue cycle. In this section, we discuss:

- Business intelligence (BI) systems
- Advanced data analysis
- Staff performance management
- Contract compliance

Business Intelligence (BI) Systems

The practice management system contains valuable data that is needed to support financial, business, and operational decisions of the medical practice. Unfortunately, the data that is needed is often difficult to abstract and analyze via standard reports that are generated from the practice management system. BI tools are used by medical practice executives who need information that a practice management system simply is not designed to provide.

BI tools, which are available through software that can be interfaced with the practice management system or as a module within the practice management system, allow users the ability to access and manipulate data at their desktops. Most BI tools are multidimensional and are used for analysis, administrative dashboards, and management reporting. Some of them allow data to be downloaded to a spreadsheet format, such as Microsoft® Excel, or a database program, such as Microsoft® Access. Users can track a whole host of measures, including physician productivity, payer trends, rejection and denial trends, and market demographics that are needed to inform decision-making.

Advanced Data Analysis

New technologies are available to permit more effective recognition of data patterns. Moving to these new tools helps you analyze "if, then" relationships among various data points. Accounts receivable valuation and self-pay segmentation are two examples of how these types of predictive technologies can influence the performance of your revenue cycle.

Accounts receivable valuation: Accounts receivable valuation can help a medical practice more easily and accurately value its accounts receivable. A medical practice can use database analytics to consider factors such as reimbursement rates and payment cycles. Performing accounts receivable valuation assists in proactively identifying risks associated with various types of accounts and accurately budgeting projected revenue for the medical practice.

Self-pay segmentation: Risk segmentation of self-pay accounts can help medical practices determine where to assign their collection resources. This analysis involves consideration of each patient's estimated financial condition (including potential eligibility for financial hardship) and can result in determining a collection risk profile for a patient — the likelihood of the patient paying your medical practice. Once you have calculated the patient's level of risk, it is common to use that data with the account balance to display your patients in different segments. For example, patients with low risk and a high account balance are flagged as high-priority accounts because they are likely to be worth extra collection efforts. Segmenting patients on the basis of demographic and other variables can help medical practices increase self-pay collections and reduce the aging of self-pay accounts. This technology drives the application of credit worthiness as discussed in Chapter 3: The Patient Financial Clearance Process and Chapter 13: The Patient Collections Process.

Staff Performance Management

Technology to track and report staff performance is readily available. Avoiding financial losses in the billing office by monitoring staff activities is particularly important in the case of an overwhelmed or uneducated staff. The technology, which can track data by employee, including the type and volume of accounts worked, is often easy to use and truly beneficial in supervising employee performance.

Beyond performance management, technology can be leveraged to create electronic work files for staff. Rather than work a 600-page accounts receivable report that is printed in alphabetic order by patient last name, for example, an electronic work file is provided to a staff member that has prioritized his/her work by date of service, date of entry, account balance, date last worked, or other established queuing algorithm. Staff can focus on carrying out their job functions rather than devoting time to simply prioritizing their work. Furthermore, management effectively ensures that the staff devote the time and attention to the work it believes is important to achieve a successful revenue cycle.

Contract Compliance

The complexity of the professional fee reimbursement system challenges medical practices' reliance on manual processes to monitor payments. The majority of medical practices deal with dozens of payers' fee schedules and reimbursement policies, and hundreds of procedure codes. It's impossible for a staff member in the billing office to memorize all of them. Under-profile payments are a serious risk to optimizing the revenue cycle. There is software available that matches actual payments against projected payments. In addition, expected reimbursement schedules from your key payers can be loaded onto your practice management software so that the adjustment that is automatically taken as a contractual adjustment when the payment is posted is contract-specific. Ask your practice management system vendor about its ability to help you identify underpayments and explore contract compliance software that can be integrated into your practice management system.

TECHNOLOGY TO PERMIT PATIENT-FOCUSED BILLING

The next technologies we review are those that permit patient-focused billing. These include:

- Online patient portal
- Online statements
- Kiosks

Online Patient Portal

A patient portal is an electronic access avenue for your patients to communicate and interact with your medical practice. If you examine the online patient portals created by medical practices, you will see variability in their functionality. Before investing the time and the money in creating an online patient portal, you must first determine what objectives you are trying to achieve. Many medical practices start online patient portals to improve patient satisfaction through increased patient convenience and communication, as well as to enhance patient engagement in their health and treatment. Other medical practices utilize online patient portals to support their revenue cycle functions, including:

- Registration and insurance: Patients can register online and keep their insurance information current;
- Online payments: Patients can pay their bill online utilizing a credit card;
- Patient inquiries: Patients with questions regarding their accounts can access their patient billing history and send e-mail messages to the billing office; and
- Payer information and practice policies: Patients can access your medical practice's policies and, if made available, payer-specific information.

If you decide that you want a patient portal, your medical practice needs to determine the type of portal and evaluate its return on investment. Options include a practice-created online portal (typically in conjunction with an electronic health record), an ASP or Web-hosting service, and/or an integrated patient portal offered via your practice management system. It is important to note that there is also an administrative element necessary to support a patient portal, including communicating with patients about this new offering (such as via a new patient brochure) and maintaining and issuing passwords for portal access.

Online Statements

Paper statements are expensive to generate and send via mail, and the cost can add up quickly. Many medical practices have outsourced the production of patient statements, which eliminates staff printing, folding, and mailing statements. In order to reduce costs and increase cash flow, better-performing medical practices are automating the entire process by offering statements online. By sending an e-mail with a link to a password-protected area, a patient can be directed to a secure location on the medical practice's Website or online patient portal to view and print his/her statement, and mail it in with payment.

Alternatively, medical practices can offer a full-service online payment system to patients. An online system allows patients to manage all of their account-related activities online. Patients can communicate with the billing office via e-mail, update personal information, and pay online with a secure credit card transaction. Permission for posting statements online or a full-service online bill payment system can be obtained by requesting patient approval during the registration process.

Kiosks

A kiosk is a stand-alone monitor that permits patients to personally announce their arrival to the medical practice and self-perform basic check-in functions. Vendors have designed kiosk systems especially for health care organizations. Kiosks integrate with existing practice management systems to make the check-in and check-out processes more convenient for patients, and they reduce costs and errors for the medical practice.

By swiping a membership card, credit card, or driver's license[1] at the kiosk, patients are identified as arrived and placed on an automated list. Kiosks have proven to minimize wait times and lines at the front office, reduce the need for the clipboards given to patients for their handwritten completion of documents, and lessen the risk of patient misidentification and clerical errors at data entry. Scheduled appointments can be presented on the kiosk to allow patients to confirm scheduled appointment(s) and to check in. Patients at check-out can use the kiosk to schedule future appointments.

HIPAA, consent, and other forms can be included in the kiosk. Patients read the information online and sign the forms using an electronic signature pad at the kiosk.

At the kiosk, patients can use a credit card to pay their copayments. In addition, the kiosk can present and request payment for patients' outstanding balances and other patient payments, such as unmet deductibles.

---

[1] Note that the ability to use a driver's license is state-specific, depending on whether or not a magnetic strip is affixed on the license.

TECHNOLOGY TO MINIMIZE REWORK

We now move to technologies that help you "do it right the first time" and minimize rework. These include:

- Pre-adjudication edits (also known as claims scrubbers)
- Demographic verification
- Referrals and authorizations
- Tracking information requests

Pre-adjudication Edits

As discussed in earlier chapters, there are automated systems employed by the payers that scrub or edit claims as they come in the payer's door. Payers use sophisticated technology to edit claims before adding human edits to them.

Medical practices can also use software to identify pre-adjudication edits, essentially scrubbing the claim prior to submitting it to the payer. See Chapter 7: The Charge Entry Process for a detailed discussion of this technology. Instead of waiting for a claim to be denied by the payer and returned to the medical practice due to incorrect or missing information, a medical practice can proactively edit its own charges and improve the likelihood that a clean claim is submitted to the payer.

Demographic Verification

Demographic errors cause an increase in returned mail, lead to denied claims, increase aging of receivables, and delay payments. Many vendors offer solutions for address checking. Some demographic verification systems are already integrated with some practice management systems, so your medical practice should investigate its technology options for address verification.

Through individual query transactions or batches processed at patient registration, your medical practice can send patient information to a database of addresses. This process may also be performed prior to statement submission by your medical practice or by the vendor who handles statement mailing on your behalf. Within seconds, you receive a response verifying patient demographics using permissible data sources. The vendor validates and corrects a patient's demographic information, including name, address, social security number, date of birth, and telephone number. Returned demographic information is designed to meet the United States Postal Service (USPS) formatting and abbreviation standards.

Referrals and Authorizations

If you accept referrals or authorizations from a referral source, technology can be leveraged to assist in securing the information you need to bill the claim. One approach is to put your referral forms on a CD-ROM and drop it by your referring physicians' offices. Ask them to complete the form each time they refer a patient and e-mail it via an encrypted, secure link to you.

Within your own medical practice, when patients are added to your schedule during the day and need an authorization, send an internal e-mail to all staff involved, including the billing office or staff who will process the referral or authorization. Attach the particulars about the patient's account and flag the e-mail as important so the referral authorization process can take place expeditiously — preferably before the service is performed.

Referrals and authorizations can also be maintained on an online patient portal, which is described earlier in this chapter. Ideally, the portal is interfaced directly with the payers. Thus, when your medical practice needs a referral or authorization, the request can be automatically submitted to the payer. Furthermore, the information can be received and maintained on the portal.

Tracking Information Requests

Technology can help a medical practice track information requests within a medical practice that are delaying encounter forms, claims, and appeals processing. Before a medical practice determines which technology is needed for this tracking, the following questions must be asked and answered:

- What is your current process for transmitting charge tickets to the billing office?

- How many calls does the front office currently receive from the billing office with questions about charge tickets, notes, and other documents?

- How long does it currently take for the front office, providers, and other persons being queried to get the information back to the billing office?

- How many charge tickets are currently suspended due to incomplete or inaccurate information?

- How much time does it currently take to answer queries and respond to them?

Figure 18.2 demonstrates an example of tracking incomplete information and identifying the percentage of charge tickets that are missing in a medical practice.

As demonstrated in this figure, 9.80 percent of the charge tickets were submitted with missing information and 6.08 percent of the charge tickets are still outstanding. This delays cash flow and increases the likelihood of write-offs due to missed timely filing deadlines.

As you examine Figure 18.2, it is important to ask and answer the following questions:

1. Where are those pending documents residing? Are they in your practice management system on an edit list or are they sitting on a staff member's desk?

2. How much is it costing for the requests to be incomplete?

3. Is it possible that these charges are never entered? Is there a process in place to ensure they are?

FIGURE 18.2 ■ Rework Associated with Incomplete Process Handoffs

	Charge tickets received from front end	Charge tickets entered in charge entry	Incomplete charge tickets	Information received for incomplete charge tickets	Cumulative charge tickets outstanding
Monday	100	90	10	1	9
Tuesday	150	135	15	4	11
Wednesday	90	81	9	0	9
Thursday	125	113	12	12	0
Friday	45	41	4	2	2
Total	510	460	50	19	31

Charge tickets entered at first submission: 90.20 percent

Charge tickets incomplete at first submission: 9.80 percent

Charge tickets still outstanding at week-end: 6.08 percent

Note: Sample data.

© 2009 Walker, Woodcock, Larch. Reprinted with permission.

The first priority is to identify the causes for the recurring errors or omissions. The next priority is to track these pending charge tickets, age them, and use that data to make the necessary changes to work processes in your medical practice. For example, it may be that the medical practice can reduce or automate process handoffs between staff in order to resolve the delays. Furthermore, the medical practice can work on why the charge tickets are being held in order to resolve the root cause of the problem and prevent its recurrence.

When additional information is needed by the billing office in order to submit the claim, work the pending accounts receivable, or appeal a denied claim, determine the most efficient way to make that request and track the response. A medical practice can create a spreadsheet or database tool that resides on its intranet that allows the staff to enter requests online. The request can then be routed to the front office, provider, or other person with whom the request is being made. A tracking mechanism can include the request, the requestor, and the date the request is sent. The tool can offer a report that allows a manager to track how long the responses have been outstanding and where, if any, follow-up is necessary. In this fashion, you can see at a glance all of the outstanding information requests to a particular practice site, provider, or staff member and can track the information requests to ensure that they are resolved and nothing falls through the cracks. The benefit of this automated worksheet approach is that the timeliness of request and resolution can also be tracked and monitored so that the medical practice avoids writing off accounts due to missed claim filing or appeal deadlines.

TECHNOLOGY TO PERMIT WORK IN "REAL TIME"

In this section, we discuss technologies to permit your medical practice to perform the work in real time rather than batching and delaying the work. These technologies include:

- Electronic funds transfer (EFT)
- Electronic payment remittance (EPR)
- Charge capture and coding
- Real-time insurance verification
- Real-time claims adjudication (RTCA)
- E-mail and instant messaging (IM)

Electronic Funds Transfer

Manually processing checks can take hours, if not days, even in the most efficient billing offices. Electronic funds transfer (EFT) and electronic payment remittance (EPR) offer medical practices cost and time savings.

Traditionally, the payment receipt and deposit process involves opening mail, logging in payments, stamping checks for deposit, and preparing the deposit. In addition, a courier is assigned to take the deposit to the bank. This staff time is costly, and may be unnecessary if the payers with which a medical practice contracts offer EFT.

With EFT, the payer directly transmits the funds it owes a medical practice to the medical practice's bank account. Instead of a live check, the payer sends along an "electronic remittance advice" (ERA) — a document that informs the medical practice how much has been deposited and to what accounts the money belongs. It eliminates internal control concerns because the medical practice is not handling the live check. Furthermore, EFT means faster cash flow because checks are deposited to the bank faster than can be handled by daily bank runs.

Electronic Payment Remittance

Just as the manual processing of checks is time-consuming and inefficient, so is the manual posting of payments. Additionally, a single incorrect keystroke can mean a tremendous amount of staff time required to research and fix the error. The payment posting process must be done with complete accuracy; yet payment posting is where new — and untrained — billing staff often start their employment with a medical practice. Under pressure to key in as many payments as possible, the environment can breed mistakes.

A medical practice can automate the payment posting process with EPR. EPR posts the payment in the practice management system, eliminating manual payment posting altogether. Most payers, to include Medicare and most Medicaid plans, offer EPR.[2] Any payments that are not posted in your practice

---

[2] The steps required to implement Medicare EPR are outlined at http://www.cms.hhs. gov/ElectronicBillingEDITrans/ (accessed November 27, 2008).

management system automatically, for whatever reason, are reported so that you can manually intervene to resolve these exceptions. It is important to note that even though the payment posting process is automated, staff still must ensure that the payments are reconciled appropriately and that the payment levels and contractual adjustments provided via the EPR are accurate.

Charge Capture and Coding

As coding rules have become more complex, numerous electronic tools have been introduced on the market to help medical practices muddle through the complexity by providing templates, coding definitions, and coding rules. Use one of the many software programs for coding and charge capture on a workstation, smart phone, personal digital assistant (PDA), or other mobile device — or develop your own. Look for a coding and charge capture product that allows for a direct interface with your practice management system.

If you have an electronic health record, it is important that you develop intelligent tools that assist providers in charge capture and coding. With an electronic health record, the physician can utilize these tools in real time as they are documenting and coding the services performed.

Also consider add-on tools to help your coders answer questions more quickly and help your billing office follow up on rejected claims in a timely fashion. Vendors offer online dictionaries that can validate medical necessity throughout the patient experience — pre-service, at coding, and post-service. These online dictionaries include Local Coverage Determinations (LCDs) and National Coverage Determinations (NCDs) and they may also include payer coverage policies. They can also generate waivers when alerted.

Real-time Insurance Verification

Real-time insurance verification is the process of verifying the patient's insurance coverage to determine if the patient is covered by the payer on the service date.

Real-time insurance verification can be processed in a number of ways. A common method is for a payer to send a health insurance card to its beneficiary and to provide a swipable card machine to the medical practice. When a patient checks in to the medical practice, staff can use the machine to verify insurance by swiping the magnetic stripe on the health insurance card, or keying in the patient's identification number and birth date on the device. Assuming the patient is insured, the device then informs the medical practice as to whether or not the patient is covered by that payer for a particular service date. It may also inform the medical practice of the specific out-of-pocket payment requirements of the patient based on his/her coverage.

Real-time Claims Adjudication

Real-time claims adjudication (RTCA) permits the medical practice and patient to know the amount the payer allows for the service. Furthermore, RTCA formulates the amount the payer will pay, and therefore, the amount that is patient responsibility. As the patient is being checked out, the medical practice submits claims through a stand-alone device or an Internet-based processing system. The claims are adjudicated in real time, producing a report that indicates the allowances for the service(s) rendered and the amount for which the patient is financially responsible. Furthermore, funds are released from the payer to the medical practice through EFT or a check is manually issued to the medical practice.

While the technology that supports real-time claims adjudication is available, many payers do not yet offer this option and the RTCA processes offered by payers often require extra work for the medical practice. Today, most real-time claims adjudication systems require a medical practice to enter claims twice — once in the payer's system and again in its own practice management system.

As new operational models become prevalent, medical practices need to evaluate the return on investment for using the technology associated with both real-time eligibility and real-time claims adjudication. Utilizing either of these new tools requires a change in workflow at your front office. If you elect not to handle these functions during front-end billing, however, then you certainly will be required to perform this work on the back end. For example, your medical practice must manage claim denials due to ineligibility if eligibility is not verified up-front. Furthermore, your medical practice must conduct insurance and patient account follow-up efforts if claims are not adjudicated in real time.

In order to take advantage of these real-time technologies, evaluate how you will electronically connect to each payer. Recognize that this connectivity involves exchanging confidential patient health information (PHI), which requires extra protection. (See Chapter 20: Regulations Impacting the Revenue Cycle for a further discussion of HIPAA privacy and PHI.) Medical practices can utilize secure, shared channels on the Internet, which are referred to as virtual private networks (VPNs). VPNs require an agreement between two parties on how they will communicate. One party will distribute the "key" to the network, which limits access to only authorized individuals.

E-mail and Instant Messaging (IM)

Use e-mail and instant messaging (IM) to communicate internally about staff meetings, policy changes, or general announcements. Instant messaging can also be handy to alert staff to immediate issues, such as when a patient with bad debt presents to the front office. The receptionist can IM the billing office to ask a staff member to come to the front office to meet with the patient. Instead of potentially causing an awkward situation for the patient at the time of check-in or violating the patient's confidentiality, the communication to the billing office can be handled with ease. That said, recognize that these channels may not be secure; add encryption software or implement policies to avoid transmitting a patient's PHI.

TECHNOLOGY TO ENSURE EFFECTIVE RESOURCE UTILIZATION

In this final section, we present technologies to ensure effective resource utilization in your medical practice. We discuss:

- Document management
- Electronic data interchange (EDI)

- Denial management automation tools
- Telephony
- Payer interface
- Medical credit scores

Document Management

A medical practice can save staff time and overhead costs by better managing the mounds of paperwork handled and processed by the billing office every day. Document management, available through a dedicated system or integrated with an electronic health record or practice management system, allows electronic access to records. Staff can store and query documents — or the image of them — electronically. That is, staff don't need the actual paper.

Document management offers a multitude of uses, the most prevalent of which are highlighted below.

- *Access to insurance information.* A medical practice scans patients' insurance and identification cards at registration. The medical practice sets up the document management system to attach electronic images of the cards to the patient's account. The billing office, and other staff working remotely, can access the image without having to pull the patient's chart to find the photocopy of the card. Available as a stand-alone system, the terminals and software needed to perform card scanning are cost effective.
- *Retrieve documents for appeals.* Better-performing medical practices appeal denied claims; included in each appeal is a copy of the medical record documentation of the encounter. Instead of searching medical records for operative reports or office notes, staff can pull the images from a document management system.
- *Retrieve explanations of benefits (EOBs) for secondary claims.* For a medical practice that submits secondary claims, a document scanning system allows staff to efficiently retrieve the primary payer's EOB and attach it to the secondary claim prior to submitting it to the payer.
- *Locate authorizations/referrals.* Many payers require referrals, authorizations, pre-certifications, and waivers that are often on paper. Medical practices typically create elaborate filing systems to store and retrieve these documents. The forms can be scanned directly into a document management system, or into an electronic template designed to capture the information. When a claim needs an authorization number, staff can locate it in a document management system instead of a filing cabinet.
- *Electronically post via optical character recognition (OCR).* If a payer does not offer EPR, electronic posting may still be available through a sophisticated document management solution. OCR uses a template that is based on the layout of the payer's EOB to facilitate automatic payment posting into your practice management system.
- *Reproduce patient statements.* For medical practices that receive a high volume of inquiries from patients about their accounts, or patients asking for copies of their statements at tax time, the document management system can accommodate scanned patient statements.

- *Store data.* Because storage can be expensive, many medical practices scan documents that need to be stored for their financial records via document management systems. Electronic storage consumes a fraction of the space that is required by the original papers. Registration forms, charge tickets, EOBs, and appeal letters are examples of documents that medical practices can store electronically. Querying electronic documents is also often more efficient than locating a document stored in a manual file.

Document management systems essentially allow a medical practice to scan, store, and query any piece of paper in the medical practice.

Electronic Data Interchange (EDI)

Electronic data interchange (EDI) permits two or more parties to electronically exchange data. Formal standards exist for this electronic data transmission.[3]

Maximizing your use of EDI transactions improves your medical practice's revenue performance. The HIPAA transaction and code sets define a set of transactions that all payers and providers must be able to exchange between them. Many payers have been slow to offer these transactions, which are often referred to as "codes." The following HIPAA transactions are critical to your medical practice's future performance:[4]

- 837/835: Claims/Remits
  - Claims: The 837 HIPAA transaction is used when a physician or other health care provider files an electronic claim for payment for the delivery of care.
  - Health care payment to provider (with remittance advice): The 835 transaction is used by payers to make a payment to a financial institution for a provider (sending payment only) or to send an EOB or remittance advice directly to a provider (sending data only).
- 270/271: Real-time interactive eligibility or batch mode
  - Eligibility: The 270 (inquiry) and 271 (response) transactions are used to inquire about the eligibility, coverage, or benefits associated with a benefit plan, employer, plan sponsor, subscriber, or a dependent under the subscriber's policy.
- 278: Referral and authorizations
  - Referral certification and authorization: The 278 transaction is used to transmit referral information between providers and payers. It is used to obtain authorization for certain health care services from a payer.
- 276/277: Claim status/Response
  - Claim status request and response: The 276 and 277 transactions are used by providers and recipients of health care products or services to request the status of a claim or encounter from a payer.

---

[3] For current standards and formats see www.wedi.org (accessed January 7, 2009).

[4] http://www.cms.hhs.gov/EducationMaterials/.

See Chapter 20: Regulations Impacting the Revenue Cycle for a further discussion of HIPAA transactions.

Denial Management Automation Tools

Use automated standard appeal letters that allow your staff to easily describe the specifics of the claim your medical practice is appealing. In addition, take advantage of any automated collection tools available within your practice management system. Some practice management systems can flag accounts that have been denied and appealed and then add a reminder for when the next phase of follow-up is needed. There are stand-alone denial software packages that help you automate portions of your appeals processes.

If you don't want to purchase expensive software, other, simpler automated solutions can assist with enhancing the efficiency of your appeal process. For example, set up the appeal letter templates in a word-processing program. As another example, instead of keeping a manual calendar for reminders to follow up on appeals or to determine if payments have been made as expected, use the calendar function that is bundled with your e-mail system.

Telephony

Traditionally used exclusively by telemarketers, predictive dialers are now being deployed by medical practices to aid in the management of patient collections. Instead of spending hours of staff time just to reach patients' voice mail, a predictive dialer can automatically dial the telephone number of the patient. A patient file with telephone numbers can be extracted from the practice management system and fed to the predictive dialer. The predictive dialer, working in accordance with a designated work queue, automatically calls the patient. These systems allow you to customize who you want contacted — by account balance, account age, patient's home zip code, and other criteria. When a patient picks up the telephone, the call is transferred automatically to a staff member to handle the call. Interactive voice response technology can handle small balances, allowing a medical practice to program voice prompts that instruct the patient to pay, without any staff interaction at all. The prompts can feature information about how to make a payment, including gathering information regarding the patients' credit card to complete the payment transaction via the telephone.

Payer Interfaces

If your practice sends claims through a clearinghouse, you may want to investigate direct transmission of claims. A number of payers offer direct transmission at little or no cost. Some even accept claims through their Website or Web portal. This will save your medical practice (and payers) the costs associated with clearinghouse utilization.

Medical Credit Scores

Medical practices are harnessing new technology to determine a patient's credit worthiness. Through predictive modeling, analytical tools establish "medical credit scores" for patients. As discussed in Chapter 3: The Patient Financial Clearance Process and Chapter 13: The Patient Collections Process, medical credit scores assist medical practices in segmenting accounts into categories based on patients' financial situations. At the time of service or following the service, the medical practice can determine the most appropriate collection protocol.

INFORMATION TECHNOLOGY SUPPORT

No matter what technologies you deploy, you need solid technological support for your practice management system so you can minimize system downtime. The technology is sophisticated enough that your information technology (IT) specialist should be versed in medical practice software. For small medical practices, an outsourcing arrangement may work best. Larger medical practices often realize the benefits of having their own on-site support. Those medical practices with ASP practice management systems are often supported by the ASP's technology staff.

To ensure that the revenue cycle receives appropriate levels of priority by your IT department or unit, maintain a running priority list of projects, the responsible party, and deadlines. Medical practice leaders should regularly review this list, noting priority discrepancies, with the appropriate individual held accountable for performance results. In some medical practices, the billing office is not afforded the same priority in terms of technology needs as is, for example, an electronic health record. In the case of a medical practice affiliated with a hospital, often the hospital's IT needs receive priority. You may need to bring the IT issues associated with your billing office to a medical practice leader who can give priority to professional fee billing.

Patient-focused technology will continue to advance. Witness self-scheduling, self-registration, kiosk check-in, and online patient access and bill payment. With the shift toward consumer-directed health care, medical practices need systems that are patient-friendly and readily accessible, such as those via the Web and based in the exam rooms. Your entire revenue cycle can benefit from new technology applications — from simple to sophisticated.

CHAPTER 19

Measuring and Analyzing the Revenue Cycle

How do you know you are doing well? That is the question that most physicians and medical practice executives want answered in order to ensure that their medical practice is in a state of financial health.

In this chapter, we help you benchmark both the performance and cost of your revenue cycle. We provide a detailed discussion of the reasons for low collections and the importance of tracking and monitoring what we term *leading* performance indicators in your medical practice. We help you develop an administrative dashboard so that you can quickly see changes to key billing and collection processes and take proactive steps to implement change.

In this chapter, we present:

- Key impacts to revenue cycle performance
- Benchmarking revenue cycle performance
- Benchmarking the cost of your billing office
- Leading financial indicators
- Administrative dashboard
- Techniques for reimbursement management
- Keys to management reports
- Policies and procedures for the revenue cycle

KEY IMPACTS TO REVENUE CYCLE PERFORMANCE

Before we present the key performance metrics, it is important to understand the impact of four key areas on the performance of your revenue cycle. These areas include (1) payer mix, (2) physician productivity, (3) "clean" data, and (4) technology.

Payer Mix

Beyond obvious differences in net collections for your medical practice based on payer mix, often overlooked is the compliance of the payer and the work required to interact with the payer in order to get claims paid. Your medical practice's payer mix determines the level of difficulty required to collect revenue due your practice, the staffing deployment model and staffing levels required for front-end and back-end billing, and your ability to meet benchmark norms associated with leading performance and cost indicators used to assess your revenue cycle.

If a medical practice has a payer mix heavily weighted toward government payers, it can essentially streamline its back-end billing process. Typically, claims are submitted electronically and claims are paid via electronic remittance. Also, for Medicare, in particular, the timeliness of this process is faster than for many other payers. Thus, a medical practice with a greater preponderance of Medicare in comparison to its peers will typically have less staff involved in payment posting and in insurance account follow-up, but potentially more staff involved in billing of secondary claims, requiring attention to coordination of benefit issues. This medical practice will also typically be able to outperform the benchmarks related to accounts receivable aging, given a lower turnaround time for claims adjudication, in part related to electronic processing of claims and payments.

On the other hand, a medical practice with a payer mix that is heavily weighted toward commercial plans will likely have a more difficult time collecting revenue owed to the medical practice. This is a result of the various requirements by payers related to authorizations, supporting documentation, and other "managed care" requirements, as well as the need to recognize new plans that involve high deductibles, along with a medical practice's success (or lack thereof) in collecting that money from the patient at the point of care. Thus, these medical practices will likely require more staff to be involved in insurance and patient account follow-up activity, as well as patient financial clearance. These medical practices will also likely have a greater aging of accounts receivable, due to the fact that multiple interactions with the payer (and patient) are often required to ensure the claim is adjudicated and paid by the payer and to ensure that the patient has paid his or her portion of the allowable.

Physician Productivity

Physician productivity also influences the staffing of a revenue cycle and the level of accounts receivable when compared to benchmark normative data. Physicians who outperform the productivity of their peers will typically have higher claim volumes. As we discuss in Chapter 15: Staffing the Revenue Cycle, the claim is the unit of work in back-end billing; thus, more staff may be required to manage the back-end billing processes, recognizing that back-end billing staff are essentially a "step-fixed" cost — at some point, additional staff may be needed simply due to greater claims volumes.

Additionally, when physicians perform at greater production levels than their peers, we expect that some of the measures of revenue cycle performance will differ from the norm. For example, for accounts receivable per full-time-equivalent (FTE) physician and other similar measures, a medical practice that has higher productivity than its peers will also be expected to have higher receivables per FTE physician than the norm, given the physicians' greater production level. As another example, the accounts receivable itself may be growing; however, this could be due to new physicians, new services, and the higher work volumes performed.

"Clean" Data

We discuss the importance of "clean" claims throughout this book. It is critical that all revenue cycle data be "clean" in order to optimize the resources devoted to the revenue cycle and to ensure that the performance measures are accurately computed.

For example, if a medical practice maintains a significant portion of its accounts receivable at greater than 180 days, the accounts receivable itself will be cumbersome to work. The need to essentially rebuild and/or interpret an account history consumes additional staff resources in comparison to a billing staff who is able to focus on current accounts. As another example, if the line items and accounts have a number of credit balances, this complicates the process of working the accounts receivable. In addition, this disguises the "true" accounts receivable, as credits at the line or account level will understate the accounts receivable. As a final example, a medical practice that has not been diligent in ensuring that its contractual and non-contractual adjustments are appropriately detailed has a difficult time accurately measuring the performance of its revenue cycle, given the need to discretely manage these two adjustment types when computing a net collection rate.

Technology

The final key impact to a medical practice's ability to measure and monitor its revenue cycle in relation to its peers is the use of technology. A medical practice that has redundant paper systems, is not able to scan an insurance card and link it to a patient account, has not availed itself of electronic remittance with payers, has not installed pre-adjudication claim edit software, does not use electronic work files for account follow-up, has not loaded expected reimbursement schedules by payers to its practice management system, and does not leverage other similar technology to facilitate a streamlined revenue cycle will be at a distinct disadvantage related to staffing and performance.

The use of technology also extends to the ability to produce management reports at a detailed level that permit appropriate management and oversight of the revenue cycle. For example, some practice management systems make it difficult to "take it to the desktop" to produce ad hoc management reports. As another example, depending on the report parameters that are used, a very different conclusion can be drawn relative to revenue cycle performance.

A management report that is produced by date of service (the date the service was rendered to the patient) is very different from a management report that is produced by date of entry or process date (the date the charge was entered to the system).

Furthermore, it is very important that a medical practice determine if its accounts receivable reports are "re-aged." In some practice management systems, when a change in financial status of the account is made, this also signals a change to the aging of the account. For example, if an account is initially billed as Blue Cross/Blue Shield, but the claim is denied due to coordination of benefits and the need to bill Medicare as the primary payer, when the account is changed to Medicare, the account is re-aged and again placed in the 0- to 30-day aged trial balance "bucket." Thus, a medical practice that re-ages its accounts will typically have a lower accounts receivable aging than a medical practice that does not re-age accounts.

If a medical practice re-ages its accounts and has not conducted its front-end billing to a high level, it is possible for an account to shift from payer to patient to payer to patient, and so forth, as the billing staff attempt to determine who is responsible for the payment. In this example, the account may re-age to the medical practice's detriment, in that it looks "current" when it is actually a "problem" account that is significantly aged. Of course, this scenario can be remedied by having a good front-end billing process and by conducting insurance verification at the time a change is made to the account status prior to claim submission.

As a general rule, we recommend that a medical practice not re-age its accounts receivable when it is seeking to benchmark the timeliness and effectiveness of its accounts receivable with other similar medical practices (though we recognize that some practice management systems are "hard-wired" to re-age the account). When analyzing the performance of specific billing functions, a medical practice may, however, wish to run reports based on various aging parameters. For example, if an account has been denied and is pending appeal, the medical practice may want to evaluate the length of time it takes for that appeal to be processed.

We recommend that a medical practice evaluate each of the above four key impacts to its revenue cycle — payer mix, productivity, "clean" data, and technology — before a specific goal or target is determined relative to the performance of the revenue cycle. In this fashion, a medical practice can recognize its staffing and performance advantages — and also potentially its limitations — when it benchmarks its revenue cycle to its peers.

BENCHMARKING REVENUE CYCLE PERFORMANCE

The financial viability of a medical practice depends on the performance outcomes of its physician billing process. In this section, we provide benchmarks for key performance measures so that you can determine whether your revenue cycle is performing at optimal levels.

Net Collection Rate

The net collection rate (NCR) lets you know how much money you *actually* collected of the money you *could* have collected. It is a ratio of cash to the net charges. Net charges are gross charges minus the contractual adjustments that were agreed to as part of the medical practice's contracts. For example, if the procedure code is priced at $125.00, but the contractual adjustment (the money that you have agreed to write off as a function of your contract) is $50.00, then the billing office should be held accountable for collecting $75.00 ($125.00 minus $50.00) rather than the full price of the code (in this example, $125.00). The $75.00 is commonly referred to as the "allowance" for the code, and responsibility for payment may reside with the payer and/or the patient (for example, the patient may owe a co-insurance or deductible). The net collection rate should be calculated for each major payer and at the overall practice level involving all payers.

Many benchmarking sources use a definition of the net collection rate that permits deductions for non-contractual adjustments, bad debt, charity care, and other similar adjustments. By adding deductions beyond contractual adjustments, the medical practice is essentially "accepting" its current level of bad debt and non-contractual adjustments rather than minimizing these types of adjustments. When you compare your medical practice's net collection rate with benchmark sources, read the data definitions carefully and adjust your calculation accordingly to ensure accurate benchmarking.

Calculation: Net collections (collections less refunds) divided by net charges (gross charges less contractual adjustments).

Expected outcome: We recommend an overall net collection rate of 97 percent or greater. When you examine a collections analysis report that matches gross charges with collections by dates of service, you should see an increase in the net collection rate over time. In other words, in month one, you will have only collected a small percentage of what you will eventually collect in month two or three. The difference between the net collection rate and 100 percent includes non-contractual adjustments, bad debt, accounts receivable in transition, and administrative errors. If your medical practice experiences a higher volume of financial hardship accounts than the norm, it is difficult to achieve a net collection rate in the high 90s.

Note that we do not recommend that you benchmark your *gross collection rate* to other medical practices. The gross collection rate is calculated as net collections divided by gross charges. This rate is highly subject to changes in your charges or fee schedule. In the current reimbursement environment, if you increase your gross charges, your net collections don't necessarily follow suit. Thus, the gross collection rate drops. The decrease in the rate, however, is not a reflection of the performance of the billing and collection operation. The gross collection rate can be used to compare relative reimbursement by payer within a time period in which the charges remained unchanged; however, the net collection rate represents a more advanced performance indicator and lets you benchmark billing outcomes against other medical practices, even those with dissimilar fee schedules.

Days in Accounts Receivable

Days in accounts receivable (also known as days in receivables outstanding or DRO) translates the dollar value of the current accounts receivable into the number of days of gross fee-for-service charges. It expresses the business you have outstanding, as measured in days. (Note that you can also express your receivables outstanding in months.) Calculate it by taking the total accounts receivable and dividing it by the average daily gross charge.

Calculation: Total accounts receivable divided by the average daily charge (12 months of gross charges divided by 365).

Expected outcome: This varies by specialty and payer mix. However, approximately 35 to 40 days in accounts receivable is a typical goal for many medical practices. As electronic claims submission and remittance have increased, the time to payment has also shrunk. In addition, as more money is collected at the time of service, the accounts receivable is also reduced. As a general rule, however, a DRO in the range of 35 to 40 days is acceptable.

It is important to note that the selection of the data to be used in the formula and the time frame selected for the formula can impact the actual days in accounts receivable that is calculated. As previously discussed, in many practice management systems, the data that is obtained from the system can be pulled by date of service, date of entry (the date the actual charge was entered), date billed (the date the claim was produced), and even date of last payment. How the data is pulled by the system impacts the results.

For purposes of analyzing your revenue cycle to determine opportunity to improve performance, we recommend that the data be abstracted by date of charge entry. Other tools in this book permit you to look at various charge lag times (for example, the date of service compared to the date of charge entry), but by using the date of entry you can readily see the opportunity within the back-end billing functions to improve revenue cycle performance.

Seasonality of a medical practice also impacts the DRO. For example, in a pediatric practice, there are higher patient volumes in the fall, when children return to school, and also in the winter, during flu season. This seasonality must be taken into account when calculating performance measures as it could signal either better or worse performance than is actually the case. Any major fluctuations in charges will over- or understate your average charges.

The time frame that is used for the days in accounts receivable calculation is important. It is of note that although the industry standard is to calculate the average daily charge over a one-year period (for example, 365 days), this method can lead to misleading fluctuations in days in accounts receivable for medical practices with seasonal variability in production (for example, an allergy practice) or with a fluctuation of physician levels or service volumes.

To control for the fluctuation, management can use the average daily charge based on the last one to three months (for example, 30 or 90 days). It is crucial to choose and commit to a consistent time period. Fluctuating between the use of 30, 90, and 365 days will result in misinformation about your revenue cycle performance.

Some medical practices elect to utilize "moving averages" related to DRO. So, for example, gross charges for three months could be summed and divided by 90 days to obtain an "average daily charge." Total accounts receivable would then be divided by the average daily charge to obtain a DRO. If this calculation is conducted on a moving basis, for example, the oldest month is dropped and the newest month is added, then the medical practice may miss an important early warning sign of a problem related to its billing and collection process.

It is important that the DRO be calculated on a consistent basis, rather than mix calculation methods. If a rolling basis is elected, we recommend that the medical practice also calculate the figure on an annual basis in order to permit benchmark comparison.

Because credits offset receivables, your active credit balances (at the overall account level and at the specific service level of the account) must be added to your receivables to capture a true picture of monies outstanding. We recommend that the medical practice report DRO with and without credits. Typically, a medical practice carries 2 to 5 percent of its total accounts receivable in credit status. Notably, credits include pre-payments for services. Thus, the goal of the medical practice should not be to eliminate credits altogether, but it is important to acknowledge the impact of credits on receivables when interpreting performance.

Finally, it is industry standard to write off balances sent to a collection agency from the accounts receivable. Although these balances are considered "off the books," they should be monitored carefully, as should the recovery rate. (Additional information about collection agency accounts can be found in Chapter 13: The Patient Collections Process.)

Percentage of Accounts Receivable Greater than 90 Days

The aging of the receivables is also an important aspect of receivables management, as a dollar today is more valuable than a dollar in the future. In addition, the longer the accounts age, the more difficult it is to collect the balance due. The higher the percentage of accounts receivable over 90 days, the higher the risk that accounts will be written off to bad debt. The aging of the accounts receivable is calculated by viewing an aged trial balance (ATB).

The ATB is a summary of all receivables by age, and by percentage of total. If an account has been outstanding for 34 days, it is part of the "31- to 60-day" category. Each category includes all accounts that have aged for that period of time. The total dollar of each category is tabulated, as well as a percentage of total accounts receivable outstanding. The ATB allows an observer to determine the dollar volume and percentage of accounts receivable by age.

You should separately calculate the ATB for both insurance and patient receivables. In addition, within the insurance category, you should review the aging by payer in order to identify problem payers and reimbursement. As we noted earlier, it is also important that accounts in credit status (and credits at the service level of the account) be taken into account when examining the aging of your accounts receivable.

The ATB should be reviewed in the following aging categories: 0 to 30 days outstanding (commonly referred to as "current"), 31 to 60 days, 61 to 90 days, 91 to 120 days, and more than 120 days.

It is important to note that just because your practice management system maintains aging beyond 90 days does not mean that you should tolerate aging at these levels. Reviewing the percentage of total accounts receivable that is more than 90 days old and comparing this level against benchmark norms lets you assess the medical practice's aging of accounts compared with its practice counterparts. For further analysis, the category of accounts outstanding over 120 days can be broken down by 121 to 150, 151 to 180, 181 to 210, and so forth. However, even if your practice management system permits this age, your goal should be focused on collecting payment within 90 days.

Calculation: Percentage of accounts receivable greater than 90 days is defined by amounts owed to the medical practice by patients and payers that are more than 90 days old (aged from date of charge entry) divided by the total outstanding accounts receivable.

Expected outcome: Having 15 to 20 percent of accounts receivable greater than 90 days is an acceptable performance indicator.

Again, it is important to note that the aged trial balance that is used in this calculation can be generated either by date of service, date of entry, date billed, or date of last payment. This selection will have important implications for conclusions that are drawn from this data. Most medical practices generate reports that reflect accounts receivable based on date of entry. However, a medical practice may wish to run management reports based on different aging parameters in order to assess the performance of individual functions within its revenue cycle. For example, a medical practice may elect to generate an accounts receivable report by the date of responsibility for the active account on file — that is, if insurance paid and the patient now owes a co-insurance, the account reverts back to "current." Running an accounts receivable report via this method permits a practice executive or billing manager to assess how long an account has been in a particular financial classification — for example, primary insurance, secondary insurance, or self pay.

As discussed earlier in this chapter, it is important for a medical practice to truly understand how its accounts are aged in the practice management system in order to ensure that it is accurately interpreting its performance measures. In addition, as we have noted, the medical practice should examine the aging of its accounts receivable by payer. This will permit a medical practice to better identify its areas of revenue improvement opportunity.

Additional Benchmark Measures

Additional measures of revenue cycle performance can be benchmarked as well. These can also help you determine opportunities for improvement in revenue performance. These performance measures are outlined below.

Matched net collection rates: This measure links the charge and the payment in time. For example, if the medical practice enters $10,000 worth of gross charges on January 1, what percentage of those specific charges are collected in January, what percentage are collected in February, and so forth? The matched net collection rate is typically based on a month's worth of charges, with the collection rate calculated by looking at the amount collected on each charge at 30, 60, 90, and 120 days. So, in this example, the matched net collection rate indicates the percentage of the net charges that are collected in the first 30 days (January), in the first 60 days (January and February), in the first 90 days (January, February, and March), and in the first 120 days (January, February, March, and April). We would, of course, expect the matched net collection rate to increase for each time period.

Bad debt per physician: These data vary based on the payer mix of a medical practice. However, bad debt write-offs are one of the most controllable expenses for a medical practice. To calculate this, divide the amount of accounts receivable written off to bad debt (including collection agency write-offs) by total gross charges for the same time period (for example, 6 or 12 months). Then divide this figure by the number of FTE physicians in your medical practice. Note: Measuring bad debt over time is credible only if you have an established policy and procedure for writing off accounts to bad debt. If you are not consistently applying the policy and are adjusting accounts to the collection agency sporadically, the trend could be misleading.

Total accounts receivable per physician: This measure, which varies depending on the specialty and productivity of your medical practice, is calculated by dividing 12 months of accounts receivable by the number of FTE physicians in your medical practice. Because accounts receivable is a reflection of production (that is, the more charges a physician puts on the books, the more money is earned and owed), the accounts receivable per physician is higher for those medical practices that have higher productivity than their benchmark counterparts — but it should not be older.

Accounts receivable as a percentage of gross charges: Physicians perform at different productivity levels. Thus, it is often difficult to determine if outstanding accounts receivable per physician is at an appropriate level. One would expect a higher level of outstanding accounts receivable per physician for physicians who see more patients. An index that may be used to determine if the accounts receivable is at acceptable levels is to calculate the accounts receivable as a percentage of gross charges. This essentially "controls" for the higher production levels of a particular medical practice. The ratio can assist in identifying opportunities to improve collection timeliness and performance.

Collections per relative value unit (RVU): To monitor the performance of your revenue cycle, calculate net collections divided by total Resource-based

Relative Value Scale (RBRVS) RVUs. The collections-per-RVU measure allows you to monitor the reimbursement you receive per unit of work produced. Break the analysis down by payer to examine the relative contribution of each payer relationship; perform the measurement over time to examine trends regarding your payment for work produced. Obviously, the goal is for this measurement to increase. By evaluating the collections per RVU of each payer, you can determine the value of each relationship and make decisions about participation.

Benchmarking the billing and collection performance of a medical practice requires identifying the source of relevant benchmarks. We provide a list of benchmarking sources in the Additional Resources at the end of this book. It is important to recognize that benchmarking is only a tool to determine performance at one moment in time. Managers and leaders must interpret this data, take action, assign responsibility, determine deadlines, and initiate change in the medical practice to improve performance over time.

The case study that follows can be used as an educational tool to help you identify action items associated with benchmark findings.

Benchmarking Case Study

Practice Anywhere, a multispecialty practice, has performed a benchmarking analysis of its key billing and collection indices. The outcome of this analysis is presented in Figure 19.1.

Case study

- The percentage of accounts receivable greater than 90 days and the days in accounts receivable are higher than median benchmark norms and levels reported by better-performing medical practices.
- The net collection rate is lower than both benchmark sources.

FIGURE 19.1 ■ Benchmarking Case Study

Performance measure	Practice Anywhere	National median	Better-performing practice benchmark
Percentage of accounts receivable > 90 days	25.5	21.73	10–12
Days in accounts receivable	51.15	41.96	30–40
Net collection rate	93.67	98.05	98–100

Benchmark sources:

1. National Benchmark: MGMA *Cost Survey for Multispecialty Practices: 2008 Report Based on 2007 Data, Multispecialty Practices* – All, Median
2. Better-performing Practice Benchmark: Walker, Woodcock, Larch, 2009.

Action plan

If you were the practice executive for this medical practice, what action would you take? Below are some of the action steps we recommend to improve revenue performance for Practice Anywhere:

Review account follow-up activity. Find out if your staff have been able to fully work the accounts receivable report each month. Review account notes for high-dollar balances in the greater-than-90-day category to determine if staff have been systematically conducting account follow-up.

Review aged trial balance by payer. Determine if one payer is skewing the results by making problematic or late reimbursements. Carefully analyze your patient accounts receivable to determine if a change to your collection cycle and/or policy regarding payment plans is in order.

Review net collection rates by payer. Determine if the problematic performance is endemic or if it resides with only one or a few payers. Determine if staff are appropriately recording contractual and non-contractual adjustments by sampling the payment posting activity and comparing it to the explanation of benefits (EOB).

Review credit balances. If you have a high level of credit balances, your accounts receivable may be understated. In this case example, your performance may be worse than the case findings would indicate.

Review collection agency activity. Because accounts are typically written off when they are sent to the collection agency, review the success of the agency in collecting outstanding accounts and the method by which your medical practice records this money in the practice management system.

Review aging by date of service. Try to match your gross charges and collection activity by date of service. (A number of practice management systems provide this analysis for you.) This helps you focus on areas that may need follow-up attention.

Review contract management activity. Make sure your payers are reimbursing at contractually agreed-upon levels.

Verify front-end billing accuracy. Determine the extent to which front-end billing processes are contributing to problematic back-end billing functions by reviewing claim denials. A clean front-end billing process minimizes rework and account follow-up work.

Review payment posting and adjustments. Determine the timeliness of payment posting and ensure that payment posters are flagging $0.00 accounts and accounts that need to be appealed. Make sure payment posters are using the appropriate adjustment codes — both contractual and non-contractual — to the level of specificity needed to analyze performance.

Verify that claims submission is timely and accurate. Verify lag times from date of service to date of claims submission. Determine if claims are being submitted electronically or dropping to paper. If the latter, review the reasons why the claims are not transmitting electronically. Fix the transmission failures with your practice management system vendor, clearinghouse, and payers. Review claim edit reports to determine if a lack of clean claims is contributing to delayed claims submission.

As this case study demonstrates, once you know your medical practice's performance in comparison with the benchmarks, you can evaluate potential problem areas to improve revenue performance. You should undertake benchmarking on a systematic basis (we recommend at least quarterly) to ensure that you are identifying key indicators that impact revenue performance.

Once you have benchmarked your medical practice's performance, you are also in a position to perform a gap analysis.

Performing a Gap Analysis

Once you have benchmarked your performance, a gap analysis lets you identify your revenue opportunity. You can conduct a gap analysis on a number of billing and collection indices to determine the opportunity you have to enhance revenue for your medical practice. This type of analysis is also useful when you are trying to determine the need for additional resources for billing and collection operations. An example of a gap analysis for Practice Anywhere follows:

Case example

Net charges:	$720,000
Net fee-for-service collections:	$600,000
Net collection rate:	83.33 percent
Gap analysis:	
Expected net collection rate:	97.00 percent
Expected revenue if net collection rate were 97.00 percent:	$698,400
Revenue gap:	$98,400

To close the revenue gap, the medical practice needs to take steps to improve its net collection rate. By performing a gap analysis, the medical practice is also in a better position to determine the level of resources to devote to this effort.

You can perform a gap analysis on other billing and collection measures as well. For example, if your medical practice could change its payer mix, you could determine the revenue impact and gap between current and potential revenue. Once you perform a gap analysis for payer mix, you are in a better position to allocate resources for contracting and marketing efforts and to determine whether you want to be more aggressive in managing your payer mix.

LEADING FINANCIAL INDICATORS

While benchmarking is important to permit you to compare your medical practice's revenue cycle with others and to identify areas of opportunity for your medical practice, you'll want to do more than benchmark performance. Once you have measured and reported the above indicators, it is a little late to affect change in revenue for your medical practice. We know of many medical practices that diligently benchmark their billing and collection performance yet are surprised when their revenue takes a turn for the worse. That is because the benchmark measures represent *lagging indicators* rather than *leading indicators* for a medical practice. In this section, we review the reasons for low collections. These serve as early warning signs or leading indicators to identify fluctuating revenue performance. By investigating the reasons for low collections, you can actively manage the performance of your billing and collection operation.

Figure 19.2 outlines a blueprint of possible reasons a medical practice may experience low revenue performance.

When medical practices examine each of these reasons, they often find that there are a number of factors that contribute to the medical practice's fluctuating and/or low collection levels. You should regularly monitor leading indicators so you can anticipate low revenue and take action before revenue declines. For example, if you recognize an increase in payer denials, an effort to improve the percentage of clean claims submitted and/or provide coding education to physicians can minimize or prevent negative impacts to revenue performance.

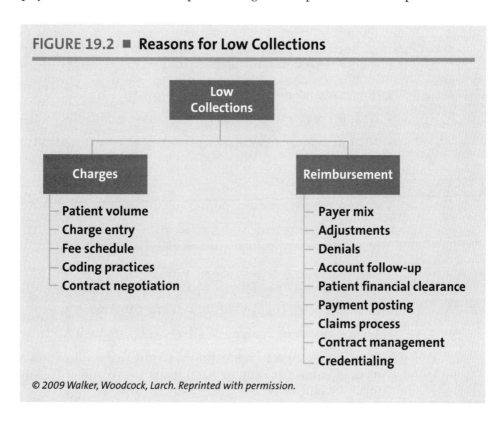

FIGURE 19.2 ■ **Reasons for Low Collections**

© 2009 Walker, Woodcock, Larch. Reprinted with permission.

As another example, by tracking referrals by referring physician, payer mix, and type of case, you can intervene early if you recognize a change in referral patterns. Or, at the very least, you can anticipate a drop in revenue rather than be surprised. We explore the reasons for low collections in two main categories: (1) fluctuating charges and (2) fluctuating reimbursement, and suggest issues to investigate in your own medical practice.

Fluctuating Charges

Your medical practice may experience low collections because of fluctuating charge activity. Varying levels of charges may be due to changes in patient volume, problems with charge entry, your fee schedule or coding practices, or the problem may rest with the payer contracts that you have negotiated or that have been negotiated on your behalf. We explore each of these areas as it impacts revenue for your medical practice.

Patient volume

A change in patient volume impacts revenue performance. Review the ratio of new patients as a percentage of total encounters, procedure volumes, and the type of patients who are presenting to the medical practice. Also review changes to practice style (such as the addition or deletion of services), patient volume per session, physician schedules (including vacation, continuing medical education, and other time off), provider coding, and the referral patterns of the medical practice's key referring physicians. Perform these reviews on an ongoing basis. This allows you to anticipate changes in revenue so that there are no surprises. It also lets you mitigate the impact on revenue performance through such actions as marketing strategies or changes to provider scheduling. Issues to investigate include:

- How many billable services do you provide?
- What is the mix of procedure codes that you bill?
- What percentage of total patient visits are new patient visits?
- Are referring physicians continuing to send the volume and type of referrals as in the past?
- What is the RVU per visit ratio compared with last year — by physician?
- Has a physician changed or altered his/her practice style so that it impacts procedure or visit volumes or type of services performed?
- Has there been a recent change in vacation or leave policies for physicians and/or non-physician providers that is impacting patient volume?
- Has a physician changed his/her coding patterns?
- Are you capturing charges for all services performed?
- What audits are you conducting to ensure that services performed at each place of service are captured, and that all visits and procedures in the office are billed?

- How many surgeries are performed? If you have the same number of surgical cases, has the mix of minor versus major surgery shifted? Have your surgeries moved from the main operating room in the hospital to a stand-alone ambulatory surgery center?

Charge entry

You may find that the charge entry function is backlogged. If physicians hold charge tickets until the end of the week or end of the month, this impacts revenue and provides wide fluctuations in staffing workload and realized revenue. If staff are behind in coding or entering charges and there is a lag time from date of service to date of charge entry, this could also mean reductions in revenue for a particular month or quarter. Issues to investigate include:

- When are office, outpatient, and inpatient charges entered with respect to date of service? Track by physician, place of service, and location.

- Do you have the appropriate number of staff to enter the charges?

- Do you have staff with the appropriate skill mix and tools for charge entry?

- How many charge tickets are stacked on staff desks or electronic task queues? How much revenue is backlogged if you have weeks' worth of forms waiting to be entered? When charges are backlogged, assign a staff member who is cross-trained in charge entry to the task, authorize overtime, or add a part-time staff member to bring charge entry to a current state.

Fee schedule

We often find that medical practices charge fees that are below reimbursement levels for some payers. You can easily quantify this with data available to the practice. Issues to investigate include:

- When did you last review your fee schedule?

- Examine the EOBs for your top 25 codes from all of your payers. Do the allowances match your fees? Are your fees too low?

Coding practices

Coding education is available for physicians and non-physician providers from a number of organizations. These include educational workshops, as well as both on-site and off-site prospective audits performed by certified coders. See Additional Billing and Collection Resources at the end of this book for coding resources. Improved coding ensures that accurate levels of services are billed and appropriate reimbursement is received.

Issues to investigate include:

- Have the codes and/or levels of codes used shifted?

- Have you kept your charge tickets and other coding tools current regarding new or inactive codes?

- How do your coding patterns compare with national data, such as those published by the Centers for Medicare & Medicaid Services (CMS)?

- Are your physicians actually documenting everything they do? Spend a half day observing each one to ensure that they document and code appropriately for the services they render.

Contract negotiation

The initial contract negotiation could have a detrimental effect on revenue performance. If the contract terms initially established do not cover the expenses of the medical practice, for example, revenue will not be optimized. Issues to investigate include:

- When was the last time the contract was negotiated? When is it up for renewal?

- Are you getting the patients and mix of services you expected when you negotiated the contract?

- Do you track problems with the payer so that you can work to resolve them at meetings or at contract negotiation?

- Are you being paid the agreed-upon fee schedule stated in the contract and are the annual increases to your fees effective on the date specified? Ask that a copy of the actual fee schedule for the codes relevant to your specialty be attached to the contract; that way you'll avoid misunderstandings about the meaning of contract language that links reimbursement to a fixed percentage of Medicare allowable and to a specific year of Medicare's fee schedule. Can the payer change your fee schedule without notifying you prior to making the revisions? If the payer must notify you, make sure the contract contact information is current as to who they notify and what address they are to use for this notification.

Fluctuating Reimbursement Levels

In addition to changes to your gross charges, there may be critical indicators of fluctuating revenue because of reimbursement issues and/or lack of due diligence in managing this portion of the revenue cycle. We outline leading indicators for fluctuating reimbursement levels, along with issues the medical practice should regularly investigate below.

Payer mix

If the payer mix has changed in the medical practice so that a lower-reimbursing payer represents more of the business, this decreases revenue. Many medical practices attempt to actively manage their payer mix so that they do not become unduly dependent on one payer for the majority of their revenue stream. Issues to investigate include:

- Is a greater portion of your revenue derived from guarantor or patient responsibility? If so, what is that portion and what is the ATB associated with this accounts receivable?

- What is your payer mix (based on charges) for your top 10 payers during the past 12 months and the prior 12-month period? If your market is changing more rapidly, you should consider comparing the most recent six months to the prior six-month period.

- What is the average gross collection rate for each payer? Use a weighted average to calculate your medical practice's expected gross collection rate and compare variance with actual revenue. As stated earlier, the gross collection rate is not something that we promote as an important benchmarking tool, but it is useful in comparing reimbursement levels by payer.

- Has your payer mix shifted toward payers with lower payment schedules? Has a payer changed its reimbursement methodology (for example, from fee-for-service to pay-for-performance)? Are the more complicated cases being directed toward your physicians without higher reimbursement? Are there services for which your payers have discontinued payment or now consider non-covered?

- Do more of your payers require the patient to pay a copayment, co-insurance, or high deductible? If so, are you successfully collecting these funds?

Adjustments

As we discuss in Chapter 10: The Payment and Denial Posting Process, if the payment posters adjust accounts inappropriately, this obviously has a negative impact on revenue. Payment posters should code adjustments accurately; we recommend instituting a second level of review for adjustments at a particular dollar threshold. Issues to investigate include:

- How do you define a contractual allowance in your medical practice? We consider a contractual adjustment to be uncontrollable, as contractual adjustments were agreed to at the contract negotiation. A missed filing deadline, for example, should not be considered a contractual write-off because you are able to meet this deadline. Determine separate categories for those controllable losses and train staff to identify them.

- What is the amount of contractual adjustments your medical practice made during the past 12 months by payer? How does this compare with the previous period?

- What is the amount of non-contractual adjustments your medical practice made during the past 12 months by type of adjustment? By payer? By place of service? By location? If you see an increase in adjustments for no referral or authorization, for example, stop and make changes to improve those processes.

- Can your practice management system verify that payments from payers received on every claim are appropriate? If not, has a system been instituted manually or electronically to verify payment levels?

- Do your payment posters know how to read an EOB and how to select the appropriate adjustment code? Are you performing payment and adjustment audits to evaluate performance?

- Which adjustment types require management approval? What dollar threshold are the staff permitted to adjust off the accounts receivable? What dollar threshold is the billing manager permitted to adjust?

- What is the adjusted or net collection rate for each payer?

Denials

Your medical practice could be experiencing higher denials from a particular payer. Unless your staff systematically work the denials and conduct an appropriate appeal process, revenue may drop precipitously. Issues to investigate include:

- What is the percentage of claims that are denied by the payer on first submission?

- What are the major reasons for claim denials by category, for example, coding, incorrect/incomplete registration, patient not eligible on date of service, no referral or authorization, medical necessity, and so forth?

- Are the denials due to payer error, medical practice error, or a combination thereof?

- Where are these denials originating?

- What action can you take to reduce these denials?

Account follow-up

Once you have investigated patient volume, payer mix, your fee schedule, and other factors that could contribute to low collections, it's time to look into account follow-up. As we previously discussed, we recommend that staff follow accounts by payer guidelines, but at least every 30 to 45 days. This ensures that you identify inadequate coding, potential denials, and e-claims submission failure before they become a larger problem for the medical practice. Issues to investigate:

- What is your policy regarding insurance follow-up after the claim is submitted but before it has been paid — that is, if there is no response from the payer?

- What is your policy regarding appeals?

- What is your policy regarding patient follow-up, including statements, telephone calls, letters, payment plans, and collection agency accounts?

Patient financial clearance

The saying "garbage in, garbage out" applies to physician billing. If the demographic and insurance data are not accurate, a denial is assured. A medical practice's ability to "bill it right the first time" ensures a revenue stream that minimizes wide fluctuations. Issues to investigate include:

- What percentage of denials is due to mistakes made during the registration process (demographics or insurance)?

- Are you reviewing your procedure and diagnosis codes to ensure accuracy based on payer guidelines and documentation?

- Are you verifying insurance coverage and benefits eligibility?

- Are you collecting the patient's portion of the bill — copayment, co-insurance, amounts applied to the deductible, and any balance due on a patient's account — at the time of service?

- Are you accepting credit and debit cards?

Payment posting

When a medical practice delays the payment posting process, it does not record revenue during the appropriate period. The medical practice also may not be taking advantage of interest earnings on bank deposits. If the medical practice makes inaccurate payment postings, there are problems in revenue and daily reconciliation falls short, requiring rework. Medical practices need to move to electronic payment remittance where possible to reduce staff expense and minimize manual errors. Issues to investigate include:

- What is the lag time from receipt of the payment to posting of the payment?

- When are payments deposited at the bank?

- Are payment posters flagging $0.00 or low payments for appeal — by line item?

- Do you have the appropriate number and level of staff to enter the payments?

- Are payment posters categorizing adjustments correctly?

- Have you maximized the use of electronic payment remittance and funds transfer?

- Do you routinely compare actual payments versus contracted or expected payments to identify incorrect payment amounts?

Claims process

The claims process may be encumbered. If a medical practice transmits less than 95 percent of its claims electronically, the claims process has not been optimized. (This assumes that 95 percent of your payers accept claims electronically.) Medical practices that move to electronic claims for the majority of their claims submissions realize substantial savings and faster turnaround time for remittance. If staff are not working the edit reports sent back to the medical practice on claims that have not passed through the clearinghouse because of a problem, this negatively impacts revenue performance. Issues to investigate include:

- What percentage of your claims do you submit electronically?

- How quickly do you prepare and mail paper claims?

- Do you work edit reports (paper and electronic) and examine them to eliminate the cause of problem edits on a daily basis?

- If you are using a claims clearinghouse, what process are you using to monitor claims reaching the payer?

Contract management

After you sign contracts with payers, you need to manage them. It is possible that the payer is not reimbursing at the contract level. It is also possible that there is a delay related to payment or that the payer is requiring pre-authorization when the contract states otherwise. Issues to investigate include:

- Are you getting the volume and type of patients you expected?

- Are you competitive in the scope, delivery, and quality of services provided?

- Do you comply with contract provisions such as access, timely filing, and pre-authorization?

- Is the payer in compliance with contract provisions such as pre-authorization and timeliness of payment?

- Is the payer responsive to claim/payment inquiries? Does the payer allow inquiries to be performed on its Website? Do its staff answer the telephone and respond to e-mails?

- How much of your resources do you spend on collecting? That is, does the payer deny every claim, hold payment in a pending status, or otherwise encumber the follow-up process? In an earlier chapter, we ask you to evaluate payer difficulty compared to Medicare. For those payers with a higher difficulty than Medicare, are you ready to prove that to the payer?

- Are you positioning your medical practice for contract renegotiation and renewal?

When you review your contracts and payer performance, you may want to use a liquidation table. This type of payer analysis compares payer mix with accounts receivable. For example, if a payer represents 45 percent of your gross charges, but only 30 percent of your net collections, that tells you that this payer pays you faster (liquidates cash at a faster rate) than other payers.

This is only one measure of payer performance and should not be used alone. Use Figure 19.3 to format your own liquidation table.

Credentialing

Another reason for low collection levels could be a delay in credentialing or enrolling new providers in the medical practice. Many medical practices experience six-to nine-month delays from some payers to credential new providers. Each medical practice must identify someone who is accountable for enrolling new providers with the payers, local hospitals, and other accrediting bodies. Initiate this activity as far in advance of the provider's arrival as possible to ensure that he/she is paid for services. Otherwise, you can expect cash flow disruptions related to referrals, authorizations, and, of course, payments.

FIGURE 19.3 ■ Sample Liquidation Table

Payer	Percentage of Payer Mix	Percentage of Accounts Receivable	Liquidation Rate
Blue Cross	14	10	Faster
Commercial	12	6	Faster
HMO	11	13	Slower
Medicaid	6	9	Slower
Medicare	40	15	Faster
Workers' Comp	5	15	Slower
Self Pay	10	30	Slower
Other	2	2	Even
Total	100	100	

© 2009 Walker, Woodcock, Larch. Reprinted with permission.

If the physician sees patients but is not successfully enrolled as a participating provider, you need to determine if these services should be written off, submitted as non-participating claims, or held until credentialing is completed and paid as participating. It is important to review each payer contract regarding how to bill for non-credentialed providers. It may be that the payer allows you to bill if another physician in your practice supervises the services that are performed, or the payer may offer retroactive coverage or allow another mechanism so the medical practice is assured of payment. You should not routinely write off these charges without checking to determine the contract provisions with the particular payer related to credentialing. If your contracts do not include language regarding the treatment of non-credentialed physicians, consider adding it.

Each medical practice needs to actively manage the credentialing process for its physicians. You should be able to ask and answer the following types of questions regarding the credentialing process:

- Are you actively managing the credentialing process to maintain data related to timeliness of response by payers?
- Do you know how each payer handles claims for non-credentialed providers?
- What process is in place to ensure that new physicians have accurately completed their credentialing paperwork prior to arrival?

Each payer has different rules related to credentialing and enrollment. Develop checklists to help you ensure the forms are completed correctly. Figure 19.4 is a sample of a Medicare enrollment checklist, identifying the more frequent errors and omissions.

FIGURE 19.4 ■ Sample Errors and Omissions in Medicare Enrollment

- Signatures and dates are missing.
- Wrong person signs the forms. A billing agency cannot sign.
- The date the applicant started working at a location is missing.
- Attachments are missing.
- Non-physician practitioners fail to complete information about their training.

- Legal business name does not match the name on the tax documentation.
- Correspondence address cannot be the billing agency's address.
- "Adverse Legal Actions and Overpayments" is not answered.
- Income reporting method not completed or incorrect.
- Physician's signature is missing.

Source: CMS. See www.cms.hhs.gov/providers/enrollment/forms/checklist.pdf (link active as of August 1, 2008) for more specific information.

Medical practices should recognize fluctuations in revenue performance before they affect the practice's bottom line. Figure 19.5 summarizes the issues to investigate on a regular basis by a medical practice related to its revenue and collections activities.

ADMINISTRATIVE DASHBOARD

Many medical practices find it useful to develop an administrative dashboard of key financial and productivity indicators. The dashboard serves as an "early warning signal" to your medical practice that key billing areas are not performing at expected levels. This permits the medical practice executive and billing manager to observe the problematic performance and proactively take action to communicate and/or resolve the process variation to leaders and physicians.

Follow these 10 steps to create an administrative dashboard for your medical practice:

1. Identify the key measurement categories for your practice. For example, revenue cycle, productivity, financial, patient access, and quality.

2. Brainstorm the key measures that are to be tracked and monitored.

3. Develop operational definitions for these key measures.

4. Identify targets and goals for each of the key measures.

5. Design the dashboard to include the data and the graphs that will be reported.

6. Delegate responsible party(ies) for the dashboard construction.

7. Ensure systematic review of the dashboard with key practice leaders.

FIGURE 19.5 ■ Key Revenue Indices: Issues to Investigate

Low Collections → **Low Charges** → **Low Volumes**	How many billable services do you provide? What is the mix of billable services?	

Low Collections

Low Charges

Low Volumes
- How many billable services do you provide?
- What is the mix of billable services?

Change Entry Backlog
- When are outpatient and inpatient charges entered with respect to date of service ("lag time")?
- Do you have the appropriate staff to enter the charges?

Low Fees
- When did you last review your fee shcedule?
- Identify your top 25 codes, extract an EOB for each code from a sample of payers. Do the allowances match your fees? If so, they are too low.

Coding Practices
- Have the codes and/or levels of code that you bill for shifted towards codes with lower or no reimbursement?

Low Reimbursement

Credentialing
- Have the providers for whom you are billing been credentialed by all payers? If not, what is the status of their applications?

Payer Mix
- What is your payer mix (based on charges) for your top five payers during the past 12 months and the prior 12 months?
- Calculate the average gross collection for each payer, and utilize a weighted average based on your payer mix to determine expected gross collection rate.
- Has your payer mix shifted toward payers with lower allowance schedules?
- Are there services for which your payers have discontinued payment and/or are considered non-covered services?

Excessive Adjustments
- What is the amount of contractual adjustments your practice made during the past 12 months?
- Can your billing system verify that payments from insurance companies received on every claim are appropriate?

Excessive Denials
- What is the percentage of claims that are denied during the first submission?
- Identify your five major denials by category (for example, coding, incorrect/incomplete registration, patient not eligible on date of service, no referral/pre-authorization).

Inefficient Follow-up
- What is your policy regarding insurance follow-up after the claim is received (that is, the "appeal" process)?
- What is your policy regarding insurance follow-up after the claim is submitted but has not been paid (that is, no response from the payer)?
- What is your policy regarding patient follow-up, to include statements, telephone calls, and payment plans?

Insufficient Patient Financial Clearance
- What is the percentage of claims that are denied due to mistakes made during the registration process (demographics or insurance)?
- Are you editing your procedure and diagnosis codes and modifiers to ensure accuracy (based on payer guidelines)? [assumes you document appropriately]
- Are you verifying insurance and benefits eligibility, if applicable?
- Are you collecting the patient's portion of the bill at the time of service (copayment, co-insurance, balance)? Can you accept a credit or debit card?
- Are you collecting on past-due balances at the time of service?

Payment Posting Backlog
- When are payments entered with respect to their receipt by the office? When are they deposited at the bank?
- Do you have the appropriate staff to enter the payments? Are they categorizing adjustments correctly?

8. Share the dashboard with practice staff so that they understand the role they play in each measure and can know their performance outcomes.

9. Take "deep dives" based on the measurement outcomes.

10. Continuously revisit the key measures reported on the dashboard to determine if measures should be added or replaced.

An alternative to a formal dashboard is a snapshot of leading financial indicators to regularly review and monitor. These represent performance expectations for each step in the revenue cycle. Comparing your medical practice's performance with your expectations lets you intervene at an early stage so you can take action to enhance revenue performance. Evaluate your medical practice's performance with expectations at least monthly so you know ahead of time if a key element of your revenue cycle is broken or performing at suboptimal levels. We provide a snapshot of leading financial indicators and targets for each for the revenue cycle in Figure 19.6. These indicators serve as early warning signs for your medical practice. If they are systematically monitored, you should have no surprises related to fluctuating revenue for your medical practice.

Now that we have benchmarked performance and investigated leading indicators to ensure an optimal revenue cycle, let's calculate the cost of your billing operation.

BENCHMARKING THE COST OF YOUR BILLING OFFICE

Evaluate four measures when analyzing the cost of your physician billing operation. These include:

1. Cost of front-end billing as a percentage of net collections;

2. Cost of back-end billing as a percentage of net collections;

3. Cost of back-end billing per claim; and

4. Cost of back-end billing per FTE physician.

When analyzing the cost of your billing operation — particularly when comparing costs with other medical practices — it is important to recognize the billing and collection functions included in the cost analysis. For example, one medical practice may include the front-end billing functions in its reporting of billing costs while another may only report back-end billing functions. Additionally, some medical practices may include related functions such as contracting, credentialing, accounting, payroll, bookkeeping, training, and information systems in the cost of billing. Because there are so many functions related to billing, it is critical to ensure that you measure "apples to apples."

Cost of Front-end Billing

Front-end billing functions, which are registration (including insurance verification and benefits eligibility verification), time-of-service collections, referrals and pre-authorizations, coding, charge capture, and charge entry, typically are at a cost

FIGURE 19.6 ■ Snapshot of Leading Financial Indicators and Targets

Billing Function	Expectation	Target
Registration	Demographic and insurance information obtained	98 percent accuracy
Prior authorization	Determine prior authorization for services	98 percent accuracy
Time-of-service collections	Collect copayments, patient accounts balances, deductibles, co-insurance	Copayment: 98 percent Others: 75 percent
Coding	Physician coding	Chart audits for coding accuracy Rejections for incorrect coding at 0–1 percent of visits
	Certified coders for surgical procedures	All certified by (date)
Claims/statements	Support documentation for claims Edits completed Claim denial/rejection rate	100 percent 100 percent same day < 7 percent
Charge entry	Days lag (date-of-service to date-of-entry)	24 hours outpatient 48 hours inpatient
Account follow-up	Every 30–45 days Percentage accounts receivable > 90 days Net collection rate	100 percent accuracy 15 to 20 percent 97 percent or greater
Payment posting	Cash posted and balanced Credit balance report	100 percent Fully researched and resolved within 60 days
Collections	Patient account sent to collections	Within 90 days
Denials	Percentage denials due to referrals (specialists) Percentage denials due to past filing limits	< 2 percent 0 percent
Management reporting	Reports available within 10 days after month-end	100 percent

© 2009 Walker, Woodcock, Larch. Reprinted with permission.

equal to 2.5 percent of net collections. (See Figure 19.7.) Many medical practices, however, elect to spend more on the front-end billing functions, resulting in less cost on the back end because this additional focus on front-end billing results in error-free claims submitted to payers and collection of out-of-pocket payments at the time of service (if permitted by payer contracts). Therefore, the current trend is to see this percentage of investment in front-end billing functions increase with a corresponding decrease in investment in back-end functions.

FIGURE 19.7 ■ Front-end Billing Costs

Billing Function	Cost as a Percentage of Net Collections*
Registration	1.00%
Chart abstraction/coding	1.00%
Charge entry	.50%
Total	2.50%

*Note: Costs will be higher than these levels if your staff are highly multitasked or work processes are encumbered.

© 2009 Walker, Woodcock, Larch. Reprinted with permission.

Medical practices typically overlook the cost of front-end billing functions. This is due to the fact that the staff involved in front-end billing typically reside outside of the billing office and their costs are not considered to be part of the billing operation for financial reporting purposes. You should assess the cost of the staff involved in front-end billing. Estimate the time they spend in the performance of registration, time-of-service collections, referrals and pre-authorizations, coding, charge capture, and charge entry — six of the key functions of a front-end billing operation. Compare your charges with the average costs for front-end billing operations reported in Figure 19.7.

FIGURE 19.8 ■ Back-end Billing: Cost as a Percentage of Net Collections

Specialty	Cost as a Percentage of Net Collections*
Surgery and anesthesiology	4–6
Medical specialties	6–8
Primary care	7–9
Radiology and pathology	8–12
Emergency medicine	11–13

*Note: This cost is for back-end billing functions only (once a charge becomes a claim and all the steps that follow). It does not include coding, charge capture, or charge entry. Actual cost depends on the level of service and communication, range of activities provided, specialty, market, and payer mix (for example, a high percentage of self-pay patients will increase costs, perhaps even above these ranges). If you have extraordinary reimbursement management, analysis, and/or reporting, these activities may also result in a higher cost.

© 2009 Walker, Woodcock, Larch. Reprinted with permission.

Cost of Back-end Billing

The cost of back-end billing can be computed as a percentage of net collections and on a cost-per-claim basis. The average billing cost as a percentage of net collections is 8 percent (see Figure 19.8) and the typical cost per claim ranges from $5.00 to $7.00 (see Figure 19.9).

Cost as a Percentage of Net Collections

Typically, the cost of back-end billing as a percentage of net collections varies based on (1) the specialty and (2) the services performed. When you compare your cost of billing with other medical practices, it is important to understand the services included in the cost calculation supplied by other medical practices. The ranges for back-end billing costs as a percentage of net collections that we typically find are reported in Figure 19.8. Note, however, that the actual cost for your back-end billing operation depends on a number of factors including the range of services, payer mix, resources devoted to front-end billing to ensure optimal time-of-service collections and submission of clean claims, and other medical practice-specific factors.

Cost Per Claim

Isolate the cost of the billing office from the general operating expense of the medical practice to determine whether your medical practice has allocated sufficient resources to back-end billing functions. You can then calculate the cost per claim, so you can identify whether you have allocated appropriate resources to your revenue cycle. We provide an example of determining the cost of a billing office in Figure 19.9. In this example, the cost per claim is $5.93. Medical practices typically incur a cost per claim ranging from $5.00 to $7.00, so the overall cost in this particular example falls within this threshold and is acceptable.

FIGURE 19.9 ■ Back-end Billing: Cost per Claim

COST PER CLAIM
1. Determine billing office costs
2. Compute cost per claim (billing office costs divided by claims)

Example:	Billing Office Cost	Practice Anywhere
	Hardware/software	$75,000
	Claims/statement processing	$72,000
	Staff compensation	$220,000
	Staff benefits	$50,000
	Office supplies	$15,000
	Space	$30,000
	Telephone/communications	$9,500
	Miscellaneous	$2,500
	Total	**$474,000**

Assuming 80,000 claims: Cost per claim = $5.93

Benchmark = $5.00 to $7.00 per claim

The Efficient Frontier — Balancing Performance and Cost

When analyzing the cost of your billing operation, don't forget to include your performance expectations. If the cost of your billing operation is at 8 percent and you'd like it to drop to 6 percent, how much performance are you also willing to forfeit? Are you able to cut the right costs out so that performance (net collection rate, for example) will not be hampered? Perhaps one of the questions you need to answer is, "How much billing expense are you willing to spend to obtain what level of revenue performance?"

There is no absolute answer, but the key is to strive for the optimal balance of costs and performance. This balance is reaching the point at which you cannot spend any more money to yield a positive return. In other words, each additional dollar invested in your revenue cycle would return less than $1.00 in net collections. The "efficient frontier" describes the ideal ratio of performance to cost — along the spectrum of costs. Reaching the "top" of the efficient frontier is achieved when you maximize your performance at the minimum cost. This concept is depicted in Figure 19.10.

FIGURE 19.10 ■ The Efficient Frontier

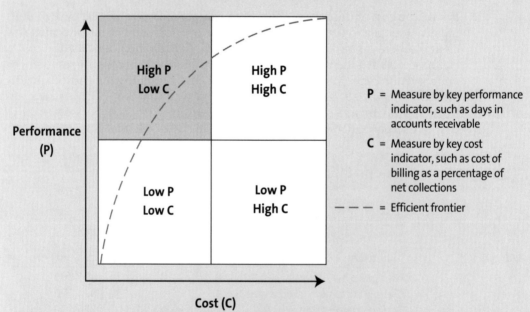

Cost (C)

High P/Low C: The "efficient frontier"; ideal scenario. Practice maintains high performance at a low cost. It is likely that front-end revenue cycle processes and payer strategies have been maximized, thus putting a lower cost burden on the "billing staff." Cash flow, accounts receivable, and costs are optimized.

High P/High C: Next-to-ideal scenario, UNLESS costs are significantly over benchmarks. It is of note that every practice could get to this quadrant with enough spending. Thus, performance may be "high" but at a significant cost.

Low P/Low C: If performance is low AND costs are low, there may be an opportunity to improve performance BY INVESTING in the revenue cycle.

Low P/High C: ALERT: There is a problem. The practice is spending over the benchmarks, and the performance is lower than industry averages. A full review of the revenue cycle is recommended.

© 2009 Woodcock. Reprinted with permission.

Maintaining this balance requires constant vigilance. Only those medical practices that monitor their revenue cycle process, the individual performance of each resource in that process, and the impact of technology will achieve the balance on a long-term basis.

We now turn to techniques for reimbursement management, then discuss key management reports, policies, and procedures.

TECHNIQUES FOR REIMBURSEMENT MANAGEMENT

We recommend the following techniques to ensure optimal reimbursement. These techniques do not take the place of the work needed to capture a charge, generate a claim, and follow up on that claim. Rather, they represent additional steps that you can take to ensure that your medical practice receives appropriate compensation for the services it performs.

Keep Current on Payer News

If your medical practice's physicians contract with payers, you must stay current on changes dictated by the payers. Payers communicate key information regarding reimbursement matters, such as which services are covered and changes in requirements for claims submission. Payers communicate in many ways — such as via newsletters, faxes, e-mails — and increasingly via their own Websites. For some payers, you need to subscribe to the e-newsletters or e-mail services to stay current. For other payers, a frequent review of the Website is the only way to know if you have all the information. Someone on your staff must regularly read this information, communicate the information and the projected impact, if applicable, and promptly implement medical practice changes consistent with payer instructions. The medical practice executive or billing manager is often responsible for reading payer communications and transferring the relevant information to the physicians and staff. The billing manager can delegate this responsibility to a staff member, but it's important to ensure that someone is formally assigned the responsibility for this duty. Rotating this assignment is an excellent way to educate and provide a development opportunity for staff. Some medical practices assign the individual to read the payer news, highlight what is important for the practice, and post it in the staff lunchroom. Others have the staff member present the information at the weekly staff meeting. Rotating the assignment to other staff members over time keeps a fresh perspective on the material.

Institute Formal Reimbursement Management Practices

We recommend the following reimbursement management practices for your revenue cycle:

- Review the top 25 procedure codes (by frequency and by dollar) for your medical practice and the actual-versus-expected payer reimbursement for your top 10 payers;
- Develop tools for payment posters to ensure flagging of low or incorrect reimbursement;

- Audit your payment posters. At least quarterly, pull 10 payments and review the accuracy and timeliness of payment posting, including the use of contractual and non-contractual adjustments;

- Ensure that the maximum number of payer reimbursement schedules are loaded into your practice management system or contract management software to permit comparison with expected reimbursement levels;

- Analyze non-contractual adjustments by reason and correct the cause of the problem;

- Develop an appeal process for $0.00 payments. There are different filing deadlines for appeals; usually they involve shorter deadlines than claims submission;

- Develop payer-specific plans to manage billing for non-credentialed physicians;

- Monitor the percentage of payments collected at the time of service; for example, track how much money was collected and compare it to what could have been collected at the time of service;

- Calculate the net collection rate by payer;

- Ensure follow-up of payment plan accounts;

- Ensure follow-up of "do not bill" accounts or claims that are in suspense or "on hold;"

- Prioritize the management of inbound mail. Staff should manage patient correspondence when it is received, as patients may be providing new information to ensure payment;

- Develop a patient collections policy to ensure equitable treatment for those with financial hardship; and

- Track collections and appeals for timeliness, appropriateness, and trends.

As discussed in Chapter 18: Leveraging Technology to Enhance the Revenue Cycle, we advocate the use of an automated contract management solution to carry out the recommendations presented above regarding insurance collections. As discussed in Chapter 13: The Patient Collections Process, we advocate the use of credit worthiness software; many products perform the recommendations presented above regarding patient collections. In sum, formal reimbursement management initiatives can be automated.

Track Revenue That Is Still Outstanding

It is also important to manage and monitor the level of revenue that is still outstanding and due your medical practice. This extends beyond simply knowing the level of the medical practice's outstanding accounts receivable. You must understand the detailed reason for and dollar amount of the revenue owed to your medical practice.

Below are a number of categories to investigate:

- Payments in process;

- Contractual adjustments not yet adjusted;

- Bad debt not yet adjusted;

- Claim edit lists not worked;

- Accounts receivable to be pursued;

- Charge tickets not entered;

- Claims in suspense;

- Claims not mailed; and

- Denied claims pending appeal.

Tracking the reasons for denied and open claims allows your medical practice to allocate resources to ensure claims are paid, as well as to fix the root cause of the problem to avoid payment delays in the future.

KEYS TO MANAGEMENT REPORTING

We strongly encourage the use of data to determine opportunities to enhance revenue cycle performance. Share the data with physicians and staff and provide the appropriate education tools and resources for individuals involved in the physician billing process.

Share unblinded data: Share unblinded data when possible by including names and/or practice locations on reports. The use of data to influence behavior and change cannot be underestimated, as physicians and medical practice executives become actively engaged in identifying areas of opportunity and improvement. Remember, peer pressure is a powerful influencer of change.

Produce timely reports: Issue monthly billing and collection data by the fifth working day of the month; otherwise they lose their relevance and prolong the opportunity to implement changes. If you are unable to produce reports this quickly, consider distributing all data electronically, eliminating nonessential reports, or reducing the number of reports. You can produce non-essential or supplemental reports later and use them as historical documents, or allow users to query their own reports.

Use graphs: Billing is such a complex process that the data needed to monitor performance can be overwhelming. Formulate graphs for key data, displaying historical performance and the industry benchmark. Record text adjacent to the graph to indicate the nature of an unexpected change or variation. A pictorial description of the revenue cycle may seem elementary, but graphs can convey important information to physicians and managers who may not have the time to carefully study the reports.

Include benchmarks on reports: Include internal and external benchmarks on the graphs and reports so physicians, staff, and managers have a measurement tool to determine the appropriateness of current performance outcomes.

Conduct full benchmarking at least quarterly: Full benchmarking should include a financial and performance review of the revenue cycle.

Ensure that all reports reconcile to a system report: Do not generate financial reports in the accounting office that do not reconcile with billing reports from your practice management system. If there are variances between reports, explain these variances.

Use exception reporting: Use exception reporting to analyze reimbursement, timeliness, cost, and other parameters as appropriate. On a quarterly basis, select new measures to examine.

Exercise caution when using rolling averages: Rolling averages are an excellent way to identify trends, smooth monthly variations, and perform revenue projections for budgetary purposes, but they can mask recent variations in billing and collection performance, preventing you from recognizing early warning signs of problematic performance.

Match reports to your audience: Identify the medical practice's decision makers and clarify what they require in their management reports. If these individuals are detail-oriented, provide them with detailed reports. If they are not, present a brief oral summary. Do not provide more reports than necessary. The data provided to the audience should be exactly what the audience wants to see and how it wants to see it so you can facilitate active discussion of the current state and plan for future action.

Tell your story: Use your management reports to tell your story. Do not simply provide a graph or a report without reflecting your analysis or conclusions. For example, if February is your lowest collection month every year, note that in a footnote in the report. Physicians and others who read the report may not remember this annual trend, but the footnote will avert unnecessary stress about revenue performance that month.

Role play: Picture yourself in the monthly physician board meeting while you present an analysis of last month's revenue performance. Ask yourself if your physicians really understand what you are presenting. What if days in accounts receivable are up, yet percentage of accounts receivable over 120 days is down and bad debt write-offs are up — how are you doing? Some medical practices translate the traditional performance measures into a scorecard or report card with a letter grade, such as A, B, C, D, or F. This can help your physicians interpret performance more easily.

You should regularly analyze a number of month-end reports, as well as ad hoc reports specific to a particular billing function. We provide a list of recommended routine and ad hoc reports below. If you are unable to obtain these reports from your practice management system, contact your vendor. The vendor may have had some new software updates or releases that are critical to robust reporting or there may be new options.

Month-end, routine reports include:

- Gross charges billed and net revenue collected;
- Report of services billed for each provider;

- Total accounts receivable;
- Aged trial balance by payer, specialty, and provider;
- Adjustment report showing all contractual and non-contractual adjustments;
- Payment report showing all payment types;
- Time-of-service collections by location;
- Credit report; and
- Transaction summary report.

Ad hoc reports include:

- Lag time from payment receipt to date posted;
- Lag time from date of service to date of entry;
- Claim edit report and categories, determined by percentage of claims;
- Non-contractual adjustments, by category;
- Top 25 procedure codes (by frequency and by dollar) linked to reimbursement by top 10 payers; and
- Percentage of claims fully paid by 30, 60, 90, and 120 days.

Tools 42–47: Sample Management Reports (see pages 386–390)

With these six tools, we provide examples of management reports to demonstrate the relevance of including trend data in your reports. In this fashion, the medical practice executive and billing manager can provide a relevant comparison of the current state over time and tell the story regarding conclusions drawn from the data. You can also add benchmarks to determine if your medical practice is competitive with its peers.

By actively managing and analyzing your revenue cycle, you can avoid surprises associated with fluctuations in revenue performance. By carefully understanding the key impacts to your revenue cycle, benchmarking your billing operation, investigating reasons for low collections, monitoring leading indicators, examining the cost of your billing operation, and creating accurate and timely management reports and policies and procedures, you can be proactive in managing reimbursement for your medical practice.

TOOL 42	Sample Accounts Receivable Aging Report

This format makes it easy to see which aging buckets are increasing and decreasing.

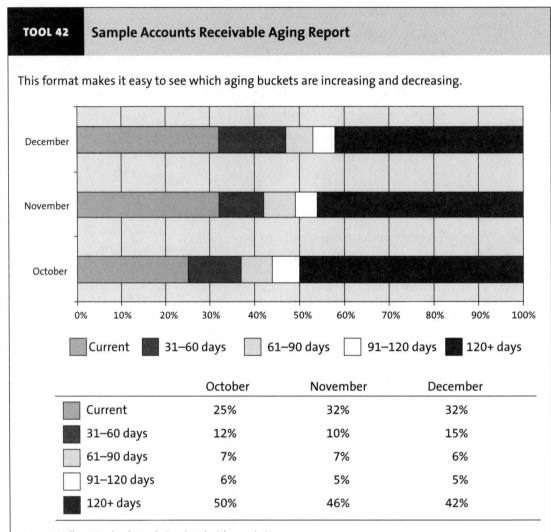

		October	November	December
	Current	25%	32%	32%
	31–60 days	12%	10%	15%
	61–90 days	7%	7%	6%
	91–120 days	6%	5%	5%
	120+ days	50%	46%	42%

TOOL 43	Sample Billing Financial Report

One-page reports force you to focus on only the most important indicators for your practice.

FINANCIAL ACTIVITY

For the period ending month, year

Data is provided as sample only

(in millions)	Month Actual	Month Budget	Month Variance	Fiscal YTD Actual	Fiscal YTD Budget	Fiscal YTD Variance
Gross charges	$26.00	$25.00	$1.00	$161.00	$153.00	$8.00
Contractual adjustments	$11.70	$11.25	$0.45	$72.45	$68.85	$3.60
Net charges	$14.30	$13.75	$0.55	$88.55	$84.15	$4.40
Gross collections	13.70	12.50	1.20	81.00	78.00	3.00
Refunds	(0.50)	n/a	n/a	(2.00)	n/a	n/a
Net collections	$13.20	$12.50	$0.70	$79.00	$78.00	$1.00
Net collection rate	92.3%	90.9%	1.4%	89.2%	92.7%	(3.5%)
Days in accounts receivable	68	73	(5)			
Days in accounts receivable >90 days	23.9%	30.0%	(6.1%)			

Payer Mix

	Percentage to total accounts receivable	Accounts receivable >90 days
Blue Shield	21.3%	22.5%
Commercial	12.8%	28.0%
HMO	17.4%	16.1%
Medicaid	9.1%	37.6%
Medicare	18.9%	11.1%
Miscellaneous	5.8%	36.9%
Patient responsibility	14.7%	25.0%
Total	**100.0%**	

Notes

- Gross charges are above budget by 4 percent month-to-date and by 5.2 percent year-to-date.
- Net collections are favorable to budget month-to-date and year-to-date.
- Days in accounts receivable are favorable to budget by five days.
- Blue Shield is the payer with the largest portion of total accounts receivable (21.3 percent).
- 38 percent of Medicaid receivables are greater than 90 days.

© 2009 Walker, Woodcock, Larch. Reprinted with permission.

TOOL 44	Sample Charge Lag Report

This report shows several types of charge lag measures and trending over time.

		March	June	September
Average Charge Entry Lag Days				
Definition: Number of days between date of service and date charge was entered	Inpatient	27	22	19
	Outpatient	12	9	5
Average Claim Lag Days				
Definition: Number of days between date charge was entered and date claim was produced		6	6	5
Average Payment Lag Days				
Definition: Number of days between date the claim was produced and date of first payment		47	38	31

© 2009 Walker, Woodcock, Larch. Reprinted with permission.

TOOL 45   Sample Denial Graph

This one-page report shows denial detail and trends over several time periods.

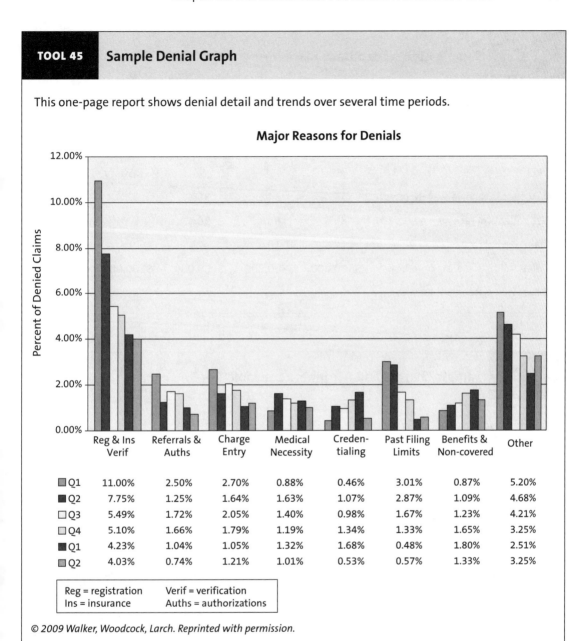

Major Reasons for Denials

	Reg & Ins Verif	Referrals & Auths	Charge Entry	Medical Necessity	Creden-tialing	Past Filing Limits	Benefits & Non-covered	Other
Q1	11.00%	2.50%	2.70%	0.88%	0.46%	3.01%	0.87%	5.20%
Q2	7.75%	1.25%	1.64%	1.63%	1.07%	2.87%	1.09%	4.68%
Q3	5.49%	1.72%	2.05%	1.40%	0.98%	1.67%	1.23%	4.21%
Q4	5.10%	1.66%	1.79%	1.19%	1.34%	1.33%	1.65%	3.25%
Q1	4.23%	1.04%	1.05%	1.32%	1.68%	0.48%	1.80%	2.51%
Q2	4.03%	0.74%	1.21%	1.01%	0.53%	0.57%	1.33%	3.25%

Reg = registration   Verif = verification
Ins = insurance   Auths = authorizations

© 2009 Walker, Woodcock, Larch. Reprinted with permission.

TOOL 46 **Sample Abbreviated Dashboard**

Create a dashboard report for your top three to five performance measures. Track monthly and trend over time. Compare your performance to targets.

	Jan-10	Feb-10	Mar-10	Apr-10	Target
DRO	60	58	55	50	40
% Accounts receivable >90 days	35%	34%	36%	32%	20%
Net collection rate	86%	88%	90%	92%	97%
Claim denial rate	12%	10%	8%	9%	7%
Dollar value of claims on edit list	$500,000	$300,000	$200,000	$100,000	$75,000

© 2009 Walker, Woodcock, Larch. Reprinted with permission.

TOOL 47 **Sample Charges and Accounts Receivable Trends**

Tracking two variables on a report permits a more advanced examination of trends and relationships between variables.

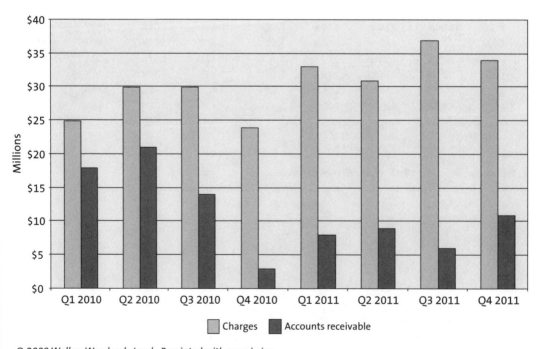

© 2009 Walker, Woodcock, Larch. Reprinted with permission.

POLICIES AND PROCEDURES FOR THE REVENUE CYCLE

Well-documented policies and procedures are considered primary tools to ensure an appropriate compliance environment and to measure, evaluate, and systematically improve business processes. As part of the overall compliance environment, we strongly recommend that you create formal policies and procedures relating to all aspects of the revenue cycle. Key components of such billing and collection policies and procedures should be consistent throughout the entire medical practice. Even if you have several specialties sharing a practice site, it is important to have just one set of policies and procedures. Staff and patients perceive the medical practice as one entity and can become frustrated by different rules and processes. Variable policies and procedures can also increase business risk to the medical practice.

We provide samples of policies and procedures for key billing and collection functions throughout this book that you can customize for your medical practice. A list of policies and procedures that should be addressed in a formal policy and procedure manual for a medical practice include the following:

THE PATIENT FINANCIAL CLEARANCE PROCESS:

- Medical practice brochure
- Patient registration
- Financial policy
- Insurance verification
- Benefits eligibility
- Authorization for services

THE PATIENT CHECK-IN AND CHECK-OUT PROCESSES:

- Time-of-service payments
- Medicare non-covered services (Advance Beneficiary Notice)
- Waiver of patient financial responsibility
- Financial agreement for surgery/procedures

THE CHARGE CAPTURE PROCESS:

- Manual charge ticket
- Charge ticket accuracy and completeness
- Charge and office visit reconciliation
- Charge and service reconciliation (non-office services)

THE CODING PROCESS:

- Coding policies and procedures

THE CHARGE ENTRY PROCESS:

- Fee schedules
- Outpatient charge entry

- Timeliness and accuracy of data entry
- Lag time: Date-of-service to date-of-claim release
- Charge correction

THE CLAIMS MANAGEMENT PROCESS:

- Timely claims submission
- Billing primary and secondary payers
- Billing capitated plans
- Billing workers' compensation
- Claim edits

THE PATIENT STATEMENT PROCESS:

- Timeliness and accuracy of patient statements
- Returned mail

THE PAYMENT AND DENIAL POSTING PROCESS:

- Payment posting
- Bank deposit/lockbox
- Interest payments
- Credit balances and refunds
- Account write-offs and adjustments
- Settlements
- Bankruptcy
- Estates
- Insufficient funds

THE INSURANCE FOLLOW-UP PROCESS:

- Insurance follow-up procedures
- Capitation follow-up procedures
- Small balance adjustment

THE DENIAL MANAGEMENT PROCESS:

- Claim denials

THE PATIENT COLLECTIONS PROCESS:

- Patient collections cycle and procedures
- Collection agency
- Collection disputes
- Financial hardship
- Payment plans

INTERNAL CONTROLS:

- Employee background checks
- Time-of-service payment controls
- Deposit of patient receipts
- Bank statement reconciliation

Conduct regular audits of compliance with policies and procedures using a systematic audit plan. You can routinely consider updates to policies and procedures by reviewing one policy and procedure at each monthly staff meeting and discussing any policy updates that may be required.

CHAPTER 20

Regulations Impacting the Revenue Cycle

In previous potholes chapters, we discuss pertinent laws and regulations related to specific aspects of the revenue cycle. It is important that your medical practice devise a plan to ensure that it is current regarding all laws and regulations related to the revenue cycle.

In this chapter, we highlight two areas of regulatory impact with overarching relevance and importance for the revenue cycle: (1) the need for a corporate compliance plan and (2) the need to ensure that your medical practice is compliant with the Health Insurance Portability and Accountability Act (HIPAA).

In this chapter, we discuss:

- Compliance plans
  - Key elements
  - Fraud and abuse
  - Federal audits
  - Compliance resources

- HIPAA
  - HIPAA transaction and code sets
  - HIPAA translations
  - HIPAA privacy
  - Business associates agreement

DEFINING YOUR COMPLIANCE PLAN

Developing, implementing, and operating an effective corporate compliance program is simply good business. An effective compliance program ensures that clinical services are documented, coded, and billed appropriately — steps that effectively contribute to optimal revenue performance.

Key Elements of a Compliance Plan

CMS recommends that corporate compliance plans include the following seven key elements:[1]

1. A commitment to compliance;
2. Designation of a compliance officer;
3. Effective training and education programs;
4. Auditing and monitoring of your plan;
5. Effective lines of communication;
6. Internal investigation and enforcement; and
7. A process to respond to offenses.

In today's enforcement environment, an effective corporate compliance program should consider, at minimum, the following potential business risk areas as part of its overall compliance initiative:

- Billing for items or services not sufficiently documented;
- Creation of employment and contractual relationships with sanctioned individuals and/or organizations;
- Anti-kickback laws, Stark law, HIPAA, and other regulations;
- Compliance with applicable requirements associated with tax status, including those related to fair market value;
- Risk associated with billing vendors as it relates to coding compliance and liability, supervision, and other areas;
- Proper collection and submission of copayments and other amounts received at the time of service;
- Compliance with patient, medical record, and other health data confidentiality provisions and information practices; and
- Appropriate security hierarchy related to user account management in the practice management system.

Fraud and Abuse

A compliance plan is meant to ensure that a medical practice's physicians and staff avoid pursuing activities that might be considered fraudulent or abusive. The definitions of fraud and abuse provided below may appear somewhat similar; however, the real difference between fraud and abuse is the person's intent.

Fraud: An intentional action that someone makes, knowing it is false, that could result in unauthorized payment.

Abuse: Action that is inconsistent with accepted, sound medical, business, or fiscal practices. Abuse directly or indirectly results in unnecessary costs to the payer through improper payments.

---

[1] "Compliance Program for Medicare Fee for Service Contractors," http://www.cms.hhs.gov/MedicareContractingReform/Downloads/compliance.pdf (accessed May 24, 2008).

Figure 20.1 depicts the most frequent types of fraud and abuse, according to the United States Department of Health and Human Services (HHS).[2]

FIGURE 20.1 ■ Common Types of Fraud and Abuse

Common Types of Fraud	Common Types of Abuse
▪ Billing for "phantom patients" who did not really receive services ▪ Billing for medical services or goods that were not rendered ▪ Billing for more hours than there are in a day ▪ Paying a "kickback" in exchange for a referral for services or goods ▪ Misrepresenting as medically necessary non-covered services ▪ Using false credentials	▪ Unintentionally filing duplicate claims to the Medicare program, even if it does not result in a duplicate payment ▪ Collecting more than 20 percent co-insurance or the deductible on claims filed to Medicare ▪ Billing for services grossly in excess of those needed by the patient

Source: The Center for Medicare and Medicaid Services

State and federal regulatory authorities consider most fraud and abuse in the health care industry to be illegal. Payers also have assumed strong positions on fraud and abuse, given the impact these have on health care costs. Patients, too, have a vested interest, due to concerns regarding security and confidentiality of patient records, in particular.

Federal Audit Plans

The Office of Inspector General (OIG) is an independent organization within the HHS that has the simultaneous responsibilities of reporting directly to the HHS Secretary and communicating with Congress on issues related to fraud, waste, and abuse.

The OIG conducts audits of health care organizations, including medical practices. Each year the OIG outlines its audit priorities in a work plan document.[3] Your coding and billing compliance training, as well as your auditing and monitoring efforts, should take the OIG's annual work plan into consideration.

The following list highlights recent areas that the OIG has identified for scrutiny.[4] Your medical practice should address these areas in its compliance planning:

- Ensuring that you are not billing for undocumented items or services;
- Complying with appropriate bundling of services/procedure codes;

---

[2] http://www.cms.hhs.gov/FraudAbuseforConsumers/04_Rip_Offs_Schemes.asp (accessed June 3, 2008).

[3] The OIG's annual work plans are issued at http://www.archives.gov/oig/pdf/audit-plan-2009.pdf (accessed February 2, 2009).

[4] Ibid.

- Ensuring you are not engaging in upcoding;

- Ensuring proper resolution of overpayments;

- Appropriately using provider identification numbers;

- Using proper modifiers;

- Ensuring that you are not billing for services provided by unqualified or unlicensed clinical personnel (state laws vary);

- Ensuring that compensation for coders and consultants does not provide any financial incentive to improperly code claims;

- Establishing a process for reporting potential and known violations; and

- Encouraging communication for reporting incidents of potential fraud through an anonymous voice-mail box that supports non-retaliation for reporting concerns.

In addition to its annual audit work plan, the OIG maintains a list of persons found guilty of fraudulent activity. When hiring a new provider or employee or contracting with a billing-related vendor, first consult the OIG Website to determine if the candidate is on the List of Excluded Individuals/Entities (LEIE).[5]

If you have not already developed a compliance plan for your medical practice, use the seven key elements, the potential business risk areas, and the OIG's audit priorities outlined above as a guide to development. Additional resources regarding compliance plans are found in the Additional Resources section of this book.

A medical practice should not develop a compliance plan if it does not intend to actively monitor the plan's effectiveness. The mere existence of a plan, if not actively followed, may do more harm than good. The medical practice may inadvertently migrate from an *unintentional* violation to an *intentional* violation by not adhering to its formalized plan.

Resourcing Your Compliance Effort

Most medical practices have already determined the staffing resources to ensure a dynamic compliance program. If you haven't reviewed your compliance resources lately, it would be appropriate to evaluate this area, as the program should be subject to periodic, systematic review. Medical office compliance certification can also be pursued to ensure that your compliance officer is qualified in this area. The size and complexity of your medical practice impact the need for a dedicated compliance officer and the number of staff assigned to these functions.

Federal and state agencies' tolerance levels are narrow, and there continues to be heightened scrutiny regarding billing and other areas related to the delivery of health care services. High-profile enforcement actions demonstrate the harsh reality that an effective, well-coordinated compliance program must be a critical, high-priority component of any medical practice.

---

[5] OIG's List of Excluded Individuals/Entities is found at http://oig.hhs.gov/fraud/exclusions/exclusions_list.asp. (accessed February 2, 2009).

THE HEALTH INSURANCE PORTABILITY AND ACCOUNTABILITY ACT (HIPAA)[6]

When Congress passed the HIPAA in 1996, it changed the way the health care industry does business in the United States. HIPAA Title I protects health insurance coverage for workers and their families when they change or lose their jobs. Title II covers HIPAA administrative simplification. These provisions require HHS to establish national standards for electronic health care transactions and national identifiers for providers, health plans, and employers. It also addresses the security and privacy of health data. Adopting these standards improves the efficiency and effectiveness of the nation's health care system by encouraging the widespread use of electronic data interchange (EDI). The many areas of the HIPAA have caused medical practices to make operational and policy changes.

The goals of HIPAA are to:

- Allow people to keep their health insurance coverage when they change or lose their jobs;
- Reduce health care fraud and abuse;
- Establish administrative standards to promote electronic health care transactions;
- Streamline medical claims processing; and
- Protect and safeguard patient information.

Standardizing electronic transactions should, over time, reduce the cost of billing and the cost of communicating with payers, though the greater emphasis on patient privacy and security standards has caused increased costs for many medical practices.

HIPAA Transaction and Code Sets

The HIPAA transaction and code sets standards are rules that standardize the electronic exchange of health-related administrative information, such as claim forms. They apply to electronic transactions only. The rules are based on EDI standards, which allow for the exchange of information from computer to computer without human involvement. With few exceptions, the standards apply to each and every provider, payer, and clearinghouse that transmit any health information in electronic form.

A "transaction" is an electronic business document. Under HIPAA, a handful of standardized transactions replaces hundreds of proprietary, non-standard transactions currently in use by payers operating in the United States. For example, the paper CMS-1500 claim form is replaced by an electronic claim, which is transaction number 837. Each of the HIPAA standard transactions has a name, a number, and a business or administrative use. Payers, claims clearinghouses, and practice management systems are adopting these formats.

---

[6] This section is based on regulations promulgated by HHS. The regulations can be found at http://www.cms.hhs.gov/EducationMaterials/.

The transactions were created to achieve the following standards:

- Unique identifiers for each individual, employer, health plan, and health care provider;
- Code sets for selected data elements;
- Assurances of security and confidentiality for health information; and
- Electronic signatures for health information transactions.

HIPAA Transactions

The HIPAA transactions of particular importance in a medical practice are reported in Figure 20.2. The purpose and benefit of each of these transactions are also described.

FIGURE 20.2 ■ HIPAA Transaction and Code Sets

Name of Transaction	Number	Business Use
Eligibility inquiry and response	270 and 271	*Purpose:* For inquiring about the status of a patient's eligibility for benefits and details regarding the types of services covered from a payer, and for receiving information in response from the payer. *Benefit:* Medical practices will not realize any real expense reductions related to this process until they perform electronic, batch eligibility. Implementing the 270/271 eligibility transaction allows medical practices to electronically verify eligibility for all payers.
Referrals and prior authorizations	278	*Purpose:* For obtaining referrals and authorizations accurately and quickly, and for receiving prior authorization responses from the payer or utilization management organization (UMO) used by a payer. *Benefit:* Obtaining referrals and authorizations is time-consuming and expensive. The HIPAA standard 278 automates the referral and authorization transactions between medical practices. Medical practices that have utilized this electronic transaction have eliminated all paper referrals and authorizations and no longer chase missing referrals.
Claim/encounter	837	*Purpose:* For submitting claims to payers. *Benefit:* The 837 claim form is the electronic equivalent of a CMS-1500 claim form. A standard claim form eliminates the need to maintain payer-specific requirements for claim specifications. It reduces the cost of claims processing and results in an increased percentage of clean claims submitted to the payer.

(continued on next page)

FIGURE 20.2 ■ HIPAA Transaction and Code Sets *(continued)*

Name of Transaction	Number	Business Use
Claim/encounter *(continued)*	837	Part of the 837 transaction is a coordination of benefit transaction. No longer do billing staff have to print secondary claims and attach them to primary EOBs for billing of secondary payers. Instead, the transactions are processed automatically in electronic format.
Claim status inquiry and response	276 and 277	*Purpose:* For inquiring about and monitoring outstanding claims and for receiving information in response from the payer. Claims status codes are now standardized for all payers.

Benefit: Billing staff spend considerable time following up on open or non-response claims. The usual follow-up method is by telephone or via the Website, which are both labor-intensive processes. Once payers implement the claim status inquiry transaction, medical practices can send a batch file inquiring about the status of claims, and they receive an electronic file from payers with the results of these inquiries. This greatly improves the efficiency of the insurance follow-up process. |
| Health care payment and remittance advice | 835 | *Purpose:* For replacing paper EOBs and explaining all adjustment data from payers. The 835 also permits auto-posting of payments to the accounts receivable system.

Benefit: The electronic remittance advice improves the efficiency and accuracy of the payment posting process. Staff can devote time to reimbursement management functions, rather than manually post the payments to patient accounts. |
| Health claims attachments | 275 | *Purpose:* For sending detailed clinical information in support of claims, in response to payment denials, and other similar uses.

Benefit: This transaction enhances efficiency and timeliness with which additional information and documentation is provided to the payer. The current manual process is supplanted by a streamlined, electronic process. |

Based on HIPAA materials reported at http://www.cms.hhs.gov/EducationMaterials/Downloads/Whatelectronictransactionsandcodesets-4.pdf (accessed January 8, 2009).

Now that you have a familiarity with the key HIPAA transactions, look at Figure 20.3: Using HIPAA Transactions as Part of Your Workflow, to learn where each of these transactions can be used in your medical practice. Taking advantage of these electronic transactions shorten the time to payment and reduce the cost of your revenue cycle.

FIGURE 20.3 ■ **Using HIPAA Transactions as Part of Your Workflow**

Medical Practice   **Payer**

Scheduling and Registration

Send eligibility inquiry (270) to payer | Payer checks patient index and responds (271)

Pre-visit (3–7 days before appointment)

Resend eligibility (270) to confirm and send referral and authorization request (278) | Payer responds to eligibility (271) and verifies doctor and medical necessity and responds to the 278

Billing

Send claims (837) | Receives 837 and sends acknowledgement; runs through pre-adjudication edits and sends reply (277) indicating claim status

Payments and Collections

Receives remittance advice (835) from payer in response to 837; for no-response claims at 15–35 days send claims status request (276); may need to resend 837 with attachment (275) based on 277 reply | Payer sends 835 remittance advice and sends 837 on to secondary payer; replies to 276 claim status request with 277 reply

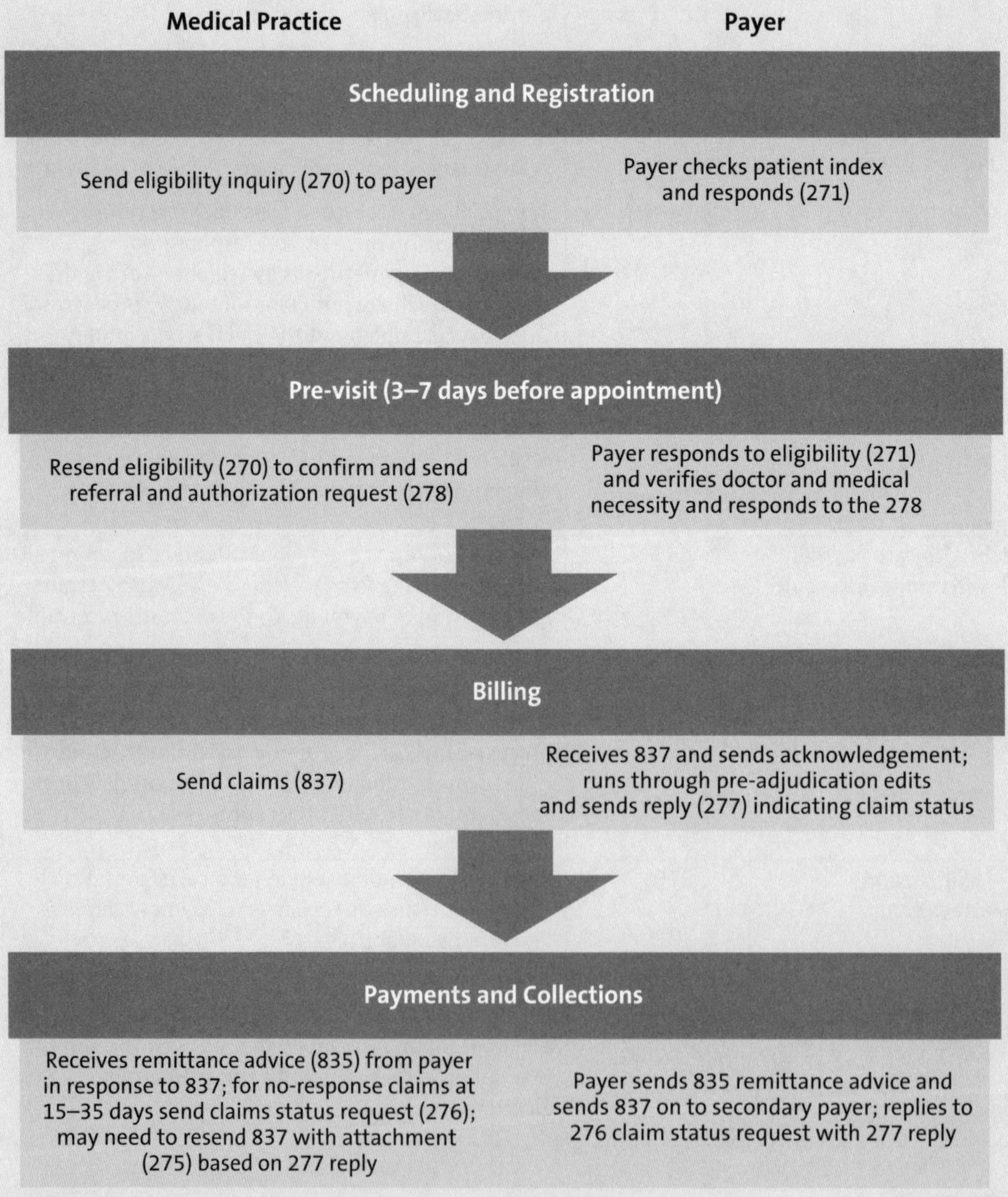

© 2009 Walker, Woodcock, Larch. Reprinted with permission.

At the present time, not all payers have implemented the HIPAA transactions. If all payers implemented these standards as they were designed, medical practices would realize significant, positive benefits. The HIPAA transactions permit medical practices to reduce transaction and staff costs, improve claims management, decrease payment lag times, and increase patient satisfaction.

In the early years of HIPAA, payers were slow to adopt these transaction standards and code sets. This caused some medical practices to delay modifying their billing workflow and data collection processes, implementing changes to their practice management systems, and/or purchasing HIPAA-ready e-commerce services until they were sure that payers were moving in this direction in a timely fashion. We can only hope this will continue so that all medical practices can benefit from this part of the regulation.

HIPAA Privacy[7]

The HIPAA privacy regulations took effect in April 2003. The privacy portion of HIPAA sets a national standard for accessing and handling medical information. Before HIPAA, privacy of health information varied by state. Now, health care providers, payers, and other health care organizations are required to follow the minimum standards set by HIPAA.

The privacy regulations have three major elements:

- They define who may see or use patient health information (PHI) and what they can do with it;
- They place limits on the uses and disclosures of health information to the "minimum necessary" amount needed for the task; and
- They establish new patient rights concerning patient health information.

Via the privacy regulations, patients now have the right to:

- receive the Notice of Privacy Practices from each medical practice;
- access and copy medical and billing records;
- request an amendment of a medical or billing record;
- understand the accounting of some disclosures of PHI;
- request restrictions on the uses and disclosures of PHI;
- request alternative channels of communication of PHI; and
- issue a complaint to the medical practice or to the HHS.

The HIPAA privacy regulations impact many aspects of your medical practice, including the revenue cycle. It is important that you create and maintain written policies and procedures to ensure that your medical practice is compliant with these regulations. It is also recommended that you annually audit your medical practice to ensure that it is compliant with HIPAA privacy regulations. Tool 48 helps you begin this assessment.

---

[7] See www.hhs.gov/ocr/hipaa/consumer_rights.pdf (accessed January 8, 2009).

TOOL 48 **Sample Privacy Audit**

SCENARIO 1: Someone calls about the patient's account balance.

Expected action: Yes   No

a. Staff exercise professional judgment.   ____   ____

b. Staff determine if this access is permissible.   ____   ____

c. Staff determine if there is documentation that the patient   ____   ____
    has granted this access.

d. Staff determine if this is an emergency situation.   ____   ____

e. Staff determine if the patient is incapacitated.   ____   ____

f. Staff determine the minimally necessary information   ____   ____
    that can be provided to the caller.

SCENARIO 2: Charges are transmitted between the practice sites and the billing office.

Expected action:

a. Charges are placed in a sealed envelope or locked container.   ____   ____

b. Access to the charges is limited to those with a specific function   ____   ____
    related to charges; for example, charge entry or changes to charges.

c. Charges are stored in a secure area.   ____   ____

SCENARIO 3: The billing office receives a request for patient data.

Expected action:

a. A written policy and procedure exists for data requests.   ____   ____

b. Policies and procedures are in place for attorney requests.   ____   ____

c. The staff member's actions are consistent with policy.   ____   ____

d. The only data released is that which is documented in the   ____   ____
    release signed by the patient.

e. No data are released for unauthorized purposes.   ____   ____

f. A log is maintained regarding data that are released.   ____   ____

SCENARIO 4: Staff access patient medical records (electronic or manual).

Expected action:

a. A written policy and procedure exists for staff access to   ____   ____
    medical records.

b. The only billing staff that access medical records are those who   ____   ____
    need to research the record for pertinent billing and collection data.

c. Disciplinary action is taken against staff who have   ____   ____
    unauthorized access.

(continued on next page)

TOOL 48 (continued)	Sample Privacy Audit

SCENARIO 5: Staff maintain and dispose of billing records.

Expected action: Yes   No

a. Secure, back-up systems exist for all billing and collection records.   ____   ____
b. All records that contain PHI are maintained in a secure area.   ____   ____
c. All records that contain PHI are shredded when no longer needed.   ____   ____

SCENARIO 6: Equipment is physically situated and accessed in a method that promotes privacy of patient information.

Expected action:

a. Equipment is situated in a fashion to promote confidentiality and   ____   ____
   security, including computer screens, facsimile machines, and printers.

b. Computers:
   i.   Computer passwords are issued to staff.   ____   ____
   ii. Staff do not share their computer password with others.   ____   ____
   iii. There is a time-sensitive log-out to the computer screens.   ____   ____
   iv. Staff log out when they are not utilizing their computers.   ____   ____
   v.   No PHI data are stored on the local computer drive (for example, ____   ____
        the "C" drive of the computer).

c. Mobile devices:
   i.   Passwords are used for smart phones, PDAs, laptops,   ____   ____
        and other devices if PHI is stored.
   ii. Data encryption (if necessary) is utilized.   ____   ____
   iii. Data that reside on the mobile devices are limited.   ____   ____
   iv. Staff who have access to mobile devices with PHI data is limited.____   ____
   v.   Any loss or theft of mobile devices is reported immediately.   ____   ____

© 2009 Walker, Woodcock, Larch. Reprinted with permission.

HIPAA Business Associate Agreement

A medical practice is required to determine with some assurance that anyone or any entity with which it does business will safeguard PHI information that it creates or receives. For example, if your medical practice contracts with a technology vendor that will have access to or manage your practice management system, PHI will be shared with that company. As part of your vendor contracting, require all vendors to sign a Business Associates Agreement (BAA). This BAA details your requirements for safeguarding patient information. Sample Business Associates contract provisions are provided by the Office for Civil Rights, United States Department of Health and Human Services.[8]

Attention to regulations and compliance-related activities is simply good business. Prioritizing knowledge of and compliance with federal, state, and payer regulations focuses both physician and staff attention to critical elements of the billing and collection process. Ultimately, these efforts optimize the efficiency and performance of the revenue cycle.

------

[8] Sample BAA can be found at www.hhs.gov/ocr/hipaa/contractprov.html (accessed January 8, 2009).

Conclusion and Future Implications

In this book, we share our recommendations to improve the revenue cycle of your medical practice (or other ambulatory care setting). Your medical practice's ability to align its revenue cycle with the changing reimbursement environment consistent with payer consolidation, payer complexity, changing reimbursement methods, the age of consumerism, and regulatory changes is vital to ensuring superior performance. Successful billing and collection performance depends on avoiding the potholes in the road to getting paid and establishing expected performance outcomes at each step of the process.

We deem the following elements critical to successful revenue generation in the medical practice:

- Alignment of your revenue cycle with the changing reimbursement environment;
- Articulated accountability and responsibility for the entire revenue cycle;
- Appropriate resourcing of front-end billing by leveraging technology and performing patient financial clearance prior to the patient visit;
- Effective staffing organization, infrastructure and expertise;
- Appropriate leverage of information technology and management reporting;
- Proactive monitoring of leading indicators to assess billing and collection performance;
- Streamlined and systematic billing and collection processes (avoiding the potholes);
- Compliance-driven policies, procedures and practices; and
- Leaders at all levels of the organization involved in leading change.

Clients often ask us to assist in prioritizing the actions they should take to enhance their revenue cycle. Each medical practice must determine those priorities based upon its current performance compared with expected levels of performance and other indicators. However, we offer the following top-three priorities to assist medical practices that embark on the journey to enhance their revenue cycle.

Priority 1: Invest in Front-end Billing

The current reimbursement environment requires medical practices to appropriately resource their front-end billing functions. This is critical if a medical practice seeks to reduce costly rework, improve patient collections by collecting at the time of service and staff the revenue cycle at appropriate levels.

Immediate tasks to invest in front-end billing:

- Increase focus and attention on patient financial clearance functions;
- Increase collections at point of care including copayments, co-insurance, deductibles and patient-responsibility balances; and
- Decrease claim denial rates by mastering the steps needed to ensure a "clean" claim.

Priority 2: Leverage Technology

Technology can greatly assist in enhancing the efficiency and effectiveness of the revenue cycle.

Immediate tasks to increase automation:

- Increase electronic charge capture and charge entry;
- Increase electronic funds transfer and electronic payment remittance;
- Increase online eligibility and claims status; and
- Pursue real-time claims adjudication.

Priority 3: Increase Productivity

The key to ensuring superior performance is to hold staff accountable for specific billing and collection functions.

Immediate tasks to increase productivity:

- Define staff performance expectations;
- Measure and report performance outcomes and results, and share data with physicians and staff;
- Avoid batching and delaying work;
- Reside as much of the work as possible at the point of care.

It is important that medical practices avoid simply adding more staff to perform work "the way we've always done it." As we describe in this book, the work itself — the processes, tools and methods by which your staff perform the work — may need to change before your medical practice can optimize its revenue cycle.

We sincerely hope that this book has given you a broader understanding of the specific functions and processes required to achieve a successful revenue cycle and to optimize revenue for your medical practice. Most importantly, we hope that it serves as a useful tool in helping you, the leaders of your medical practices, avoid the potholes in the road to getting paid so that you can continue to do the important work you have chosen — meeting the health care needs of your community.

As we conclude, let's remember the recurring themes we mentioned early in the book:

- Putting patients first and developing a patient-focused billing and collection process;
- Doing it right the first time, thereby minimizing rework and lost revenue opportunities and reducing billing costs;
- Performing work in real time, rather than batching work to be performed at a later date, thus enhancing efficiency;
- Emphasizing front-end billing, given the changes in the reimbursement environment and the increasing out-of-pocket payments by patients for their health care services;
- Leveraging technology to improve revenue cycle performance and resource utilization;
- Aligning your medical practice's policies and practices with the changing reimbursement environment;
- Measuring performance outcomes — both quantity and quality — to recognize early warning signs through leading performance indicators;
- Diagnosing each pothole in your revenue cycle to identify opportunities for improvement;
- Taking action to lead change in the medical practice involving billing and collection so that advanced billing practices can be adopted and implemented; and
- Using data to communicate the need for change and to measure and analyze change efforts.

We wish you success on your journey to getting paid. Reduce your errors, leverage your technology and increase your productivity — don't leave any money that is due your practice uncollected!

Additional Billing and Collection Resources

This list of resources has been compiled for your reference, and does not represent our commercial endorsement of any particular product or association. You may want to investigate these and other resources as you continue to refine your journey on the road to getting paid.

Note: Specific URLs are cited in this section, which were active at the time of this book's publication. Unfortunately, these Websites are subject to change. If the URL is not active, please access the home page of the organization for information.

WEBSITES

Centers for Medicare & Medicaid Services (CMS). CMS has designated a provider area on its Website for information and questions and answers pertaining to physician practice and billing. It can be found at www.cms.hhs.gov/center/provider.asp.

Compliance Program Guidance for Third-party Billing Companies. Compliance program information and guidance can be found at http://oig.hhs.gov/fraud/docs/complianceguidance/thirdparty.pdf.

Coordination of Benefits. Basic information regarding coordination of benefits and reporting can be found at www.cms.hhs.gov/COBGeneralInformation/.

Federal Register. The Federal Register is the official publication for rules, proposed rules, and notices of Federal agencies and organizations. It can be found at www.gpoaccess.gov/fr.

Medicare Coverage Database (MCD). This database outlines National Coverage Determinations (NCD) and Local Coverage Determinations (LCD). It can be found at www.cms.gov/mcd.

Office of the Inspector General (OIG). The OIG is the federal agent typically involved in CMS audits. It publishes an annual list of focus areas for audit which can be found at http://oig.hhs.gov/publications/workplan.asp.

Patient Friendly Billing®. Patient Friendly Billing® is a collaborative effort between HFMA, AMA, MGMA, and other interested parties to promote clear, concise, and correct patient-friendly financial communications. Free information, white papers, sample patient statements, brochures, and other tools to facilitate patient-friendly billing can be found at www.patientfriendlybilling.org.

Prompt Payment Laws by State. Each state has adopted a prompt payment law which designates the timeline required for payers to pay on a "clean claim." Each state's prompt payment law can be found at www.elizabethwoodcock.com.

The Fair Debt Collection Practices Act. The Fair Debt Collection Practices Act outlines specific rules and procedures related to account collection. It can be found at www.ftc.gov/bcp/edu/pubs/consumer/credit/cre27.pdf.

CDS AND DVDS

Auditing E&M Coding to Enhance Practice Revenue and Compliance (CD). Author/Presenter: Jeannie Cagle. Available at www.mgma.com. Item 7023.

Best Practices: Denial Management (DVD). Author/Presenter: Elizabeth Woodcock. Available at www.mgma.com. Item 7077.

Get Paid the First Time: Analyze your EOBs to Increase Cash Collections (CD). Author/Presenter: Betsy Nicoletti. Available at www.mgma.com. Item 7090.

Increase Your Revenue with Appropriate Reimbursement for Non-Physician Services (CD). Author/Presenter: John F. Bishop. Available at www.mgma.com. Item 7025.

Increasing Leverage in Payer Negotiations (CD). Author/Presenter: Randy W. Cook. Available at www.mgma.com. Item 7027.

Mastering Patient Flow: The Efficient Physician (DVD). Author/Presenter: Elizabeth W. Woodcock. Available at www.mgma.com. Item 7078.

Patient Collections in an Era of Consumer-Directed Health Care (DVD). Author/Presenter: Elizabeth W. Woodcock. Available at www.mgma.com. Item 7080.

Patient Inducement and Discounts. What you Can and Can't Do (CD). Author/Presenter: Robert A. Wade. Available at www.mgma.com. Item 8018.

Ways to Maximize Effective Collections. Author/Presenter: Tracy L. Spears. Available at www.mgma.com. Item 7017.

BOOKS

Grider, Deborah J. *Medical Record Auditor, Second Edition.* Chicago: AMA, 2007. Available at www.ama-assn.org/.

Hajny, Thomas J. *Looking for the Cashcow: Action Steps to Improve Cash Flow in Medical Group Practices*. Dubuque: Kendall Hunt Publishers, 2002. Available at www.mgma.com.

Johnson, Bruce A. and Deborah Walker Keegan. *Physician Compensation Plans: State-of-the-Art Strategies*. Englewood: MGMA, 2006. Available at www.mgma.com.

Levinson, Stephen R. *Practical E/M: Documentation and Coding Solutions for Quality Patient Care, Second Edition*. Chicago: AMA, 2008.

MGMA Cost Survey Report and MGMA Performance and Practices of Successful Medical Groups. Published annually. Available at www.mgma.com.

Nicoletti, Betsy. *The Field Guide to Physician Coding*. Greenbranch Publishing, 2007. Available at http://shopmpm.com/field_guide_to_physician_coding.asp.

Physician's Guide to Implementing Medicare's Physician Quality Reporting Initiative: An Insider's View 2009. Chicago: AMA, 2009.

Satiani, Bhagwan. *The Smarter Physician: Conquering Your Practice's Billing and Reimbursement*. Englewood: MGMA, 2007. Available at www.mgma.com.

Schraffenberger, Lou Ann and Lynn Kuehn. *Effective Management of Coding Services, Third Edition*. Chicago: American Health Information Management Association (AHIMA), 2007. Available at www.ahima.com.

Stanley, Kay. *Maximizing Billing and Collections in the Medical Practice*. Chicago: AMA, 2006. Available at www.ama-assn.org.

Tennant, Robert M. and Aaron N. Krupp. *HIPAA Toolbox: Information Critical to Your Practice, 2nd Edition*. Englewood: Medical Group Management Association (MGMA), 2003. Available at www.mgma.com.

Trites, Patricia A. *Compliance Guide for the Medical Practice: How to Attain and Maintain a Compliant Medical Practice*. Chicago: American Medical Association (AMA), 2007.

Waters, Joanne M. and L. Lamar Blount. *Mastering the Reimbursement Process, Fourth Edition*. Chicago: AMA, 2001.

Wenzel, Frederick J., and Jane M. Wenzel. *Fundamentals of Physician Practice Management*. Health Administration Press (HPA), 2005.

Wolper, Lawrence. *Physician Practice Management: Essential Operational and Financial Knowledge*. Jones and Bartlett, 2005. Available at www.mgma.com.

Woodcock, Elizabeth W. *Mastering Patient Flow to Increase Efficiency and Earnings, Third Edition*. MGMA and Woodcock and Associates, 2009. Available at www.mgma.com. Audio Recording Abridged Version of this book is also available at www.mgma.com. Item 7076.

Woodcock, Elizabeth W. and Bette A. Warn. *Operating Policies and Procedures Manual for Medical Practices, Third Edition.* Englewood: MGMA, 2006. Available at www.mgma.com.

ARTICLES

Armandi, Lara M. and James J. Field. "A Method for Evaluating Payer Performance." *MGMA Connexion* (April 2007).

Ealey, Tom. "Out of Sight and Out of Control?" *MGMA Connexion* (January 2007).

Gans, David N. "Riding the Tiger: Medicare Payments Inadequate, but Leaving the Program Not Always an Option." *MGMA Connexion* (January 2008).

Keegan, Deborah Walker. "Are You Ready for the Perfect Storm? Align Your Practice with the Changing Health Care Environment." *MGMA Connexion* (January 2008). 2008 Edward B. Stevens "Article of the Year."

Milburn, Jeffrey B. "Mining for Gold: Extract Revenue from Unprocessed Claim Denials." *MGMA Connexion* (January 2007). 2007 Edward B. Stevens "Article of the Year."

Trites, Patricia A. "Want to Reduce Denials and Reductions? Start with Diagnosis-Coding Documentation Guidelines." *MGMA e-Connexion* (March 2007).

Woodcock, Elizabeth W. "Total Account Ownership." *MGMA Connexion* (January 2007). Finalist, 2007 Edward B. Stevens "Article of the Year."

Woodcock, Elizabeth W., Bob Browne, and Jennifer Jenkins. "A Physicians Due." *Journal of the Healthcare Financial Management Association* (July 2008).

ASSOCIATIONS RELATED TO BILLING AND REIMBURSEMENT

American Academy of Professional Coders (AAPC), www.aapc.com

AAPC is a certifying body for coders, awarding the Certified Professional Coder (CPC) designation upon successful demonstration of coding expertise.

American Association of Healthcare Administrative Management (AAHAM), www.aaham.org

AAHAM is a professional organization in health care administrative management.

American College of Medical Practice Executives (ACMPE), www.mgma.com

ACMPE is the standard-setting and certification body of the Medical Group Management Association (MGMA).

American Health Information Management Association (AHIMA), www.ahima.org

AHIMA is a certifying body for health information management, coding, and health care privacy and security.

American Medical Billing Association (AMBA), www.ambanet.net/AMBA.htm

AMBA targets small, independent, and third party medical billers.

American Medical Group Association (AMGA), www.amga.org

AMGA is a professional trade association for medical groups and organized systems of care, with members representing 87,000 physicians providing health care to 80 million Americans.

America's Health Insurance Plans (AHIP), www.ahip.org

AHIP is a national trade organization representing member companies that provide health insurance benefits.

Association of Certified Fraud Examiners (ACFE), www.acfe.com

ACFE certifies fraud examiners and provides a forum for certified fraud examiners to maintain currency in their field.

Healthcare Billing and Management Association (HBMA),www.hbma.com

HBMA is a trade association representing third-party medical billers. HBMA members process physician and other provider claims.

Healthcare Financial Management Association (HFMA), www.hfma.org

HFMA is a membership organization for health care financial management professionals comprised of members employed by hospitals, integrated delivery systems, long-term and ambulatory care facilities, managed care organizations, medical group practices, public accounting and consulting firms, payers, and government agencies.

Medical Association of Billers (MAB), www.physicianswebsites.com

MAB is a medical billing association for persons involved in billing, coding, electronic claims, and compliance education and training.

Medical Group Management Association (MGMA), www.mgma.com

MGMA is a professional trade organization for medical practice executives and physician executives that assists its membership through information, education, networking, and advocacy.

Professional Association of Health Care Office Management (PAHCOM), www.pahcom.com

PAHCOM is a national organization providing professional development opportunities, continuing education in health care office management principles and practice, and certification for health care office managers.

COMMON ACRONYMS IN THE PHYSICIAN BILLING PROCESS

ABN	Advance Beneficiary Notice
ACR	Adjusted Collection Rate
AMA	American Medical Association
A/R	Accounts Receivable
ASP	Application Service Provider
BAA	Business Associates Agreement
CBO	Central Billing (or Business) Office
CCI	Correct Coding Initiative
CDHP	Consumer-directed (or driven) Health Plan
CMS	Centers for Medicare and Medicaid Services
COB	Coordination of Benefits
CPT®	Current Procedural Terminology®
DOB	Date of Birth
DOE	Date of Entry
DOS	Date of Service
DRO	Days in Receivables Outstanding
E/M	Evaluation and Management
EDI	Electronic Data Interchange
EHR	Electronic Health Records
EOB	Explanation of Benefits
EPR	Electronic Payment Remittance
ERISA	Employee Retirement Income Security Act
FDCPA	Fair Debt Collection Practices Act
FFS	Fee for Service
FIFO	First in First out
GCR	Gross Collection Rate
HCPCS	Healthcare Common Procedure Coding System
HDHP	High Deductible Health Plan
HHS	Department of Health and Human Services
HIPAA	Health Insurance Portability and Accountability Act
HMO	Health Maintenance Organization
HSA	Health Savings Account
ICD	International Classification of Diseases
ICD-CM	International Classification of Diseases-Clinical Modification

IDS	Integrated Delivery System
IVR	Interactive Voice Recognition
LCD	Local Coverage Determination
NCCI	National Correct Coding Initiative
NCR	Net Collection Rate
NCD	National Coverage Determination
NEC	Not Elsewhere Classified
NOS	Not Otherwise Classified
NPI	National Provider Identifier
OCR	Optical Character Recognition
OIG	Office of the Inspector General
P4P	Pay-for-Performance
PHI	Protected Health Information
PHR	Personal Health Records
POC	Point of Care
PMS	Practice Management System
PPO	Preferred Provider Organization
PQRI	Physician Quality Reporting Initiative
RBRVS	Resource-based Relative Value System
RTCA	Real-time Claims Adjudication
TAO	Total Account Ownership
TOS	Time of Service
WRVU	Work Relative Value Unit

Index

In this index "*f*" refers to figures and "*t*" refers to tools.

A

ABN. *See* Advanced Beneficiary Notification (ABN)
Abuse, 396–397, 397*f*. *See also* Fraud, investigating
Address database (USPS), 24–26
Address service requested (USPS), 146
Adjustment (denial) codes, 154–156, 369–370
Administrative dashboard, 374–376
Advanced Beneficiary Notification (ABN), 57, 63, 89
Aged trial balance (ATB), 359–360
AHIP. *See* America's Health Insurance Plans (AHIP)
"All products" clause, 265
America's Health Insurance Plans (AHIP), 123
Analysis. *See* Benchmarking
Application service provider (ASP), 336–337
Appointment reminders, 22
ASP. *See* Application service provider (ASP)
ATB. *See* Aged trial balance (ATB)
Audits, internal, 308–311, 309*f*, 310*f*
Authorizations. *See* Referrals and authorizations

B

BAA. *See* Business Associate Agreement (BAA)
Back-end billing
  benchmarking, 279–286, 279*t*, 280*f*, 281*f*, 282*f*, 283*f*

collection process, 12–13, 13*f*
  costs, 378*f*, 379, 379*f*
  staff responsibilities, 276–277
Bad debt adjustments, 154, 235, 237–238, 361
Benchmarking, 353–393, 377*f*
  accounts receivable, aging of, 359–360
  additional measures, 361–362
  administrative dashboard, 374–376, 390*t*
  billing office costs, 376–381, 378*f*, 379*f*
  case study, 362–364, 362*f*
  days in accounts receivable, 358–359
  fluctuating charges, 366–368
  fluctuating reimbursement levels, 368–374, 373*f*, 374*f*, 375*f*
  gap analysis, 364
  key areas of, 353–356
  net collection rate, 357
  performance vs. cost, 380–381, 380*f*
  policies for, 391–393
  reimbursement management, 381–382
  reports, 383–390, 386–390*t*
  revenue tracking, 382–383
BI systems. *See* Business intelligence (BI) systems
Bill review companies, 269–270
Billing and collection. *See also* Back-end billing; Charge capture process; Contract and reimbursement management; Reimbursement environment; Revenue cycle
  "about your bill," 47*t*
  Advanced Beneficiary Notification (ABN), 57, 63

Billing and collection *(continued)*
 centralizing, 321–323
 code of commitments for, 325f
 in contract negotiations plan, 265
 decentralizing, 320–321
 discount policy, 55–56
 fees, 30, 54–55
 fluctuations in, 366–368
 front-end billing, 12–13, 13t, 274, 276,
  286–288, 408
 hybrid billing models, 323–324
 internal billing office, 330
 outsourcing, 324–329
 oversight of, xviii
 patient financial clearance, 19–20
 patient statements, 139–148
 payment methods, 56
 prior balances, 52
 receipts, 57
 rescheduling protocols, 52
 resources for, 411–412
 for surgeries and procedures, 53, 54t,
  64–65, 69
 technology for, 340–341
 time-of-service collection, 46–48,
  50–53, 51t, 314–317
 waiver of patient financial
  responsibility, 235–236
Blending, 268–269
Bundled services, 92–93
Business Associate Agreement
  (BAA), 405
Business intelligence (BI) systems, 338

C

Capitation funds, 160
Cash management, 305–308, 307t
CBO. *See* Centralized billing
Centers for Medicare & Medicaid Service
  (CMS), 180, 259–260
 enrollment errors, 374f
 financial hardship, 234
 Medicare Physician Fee Schedule
  (MPFS), 93
 payment formula, 93
 Physician Quality Reporting Initiative
  (PQRI), 270
 professional courtesy, 237
Centralized billing, 321–323
 vs. hybrid models, 323–324
 transitioning from or to, 330–331
Change, in reimbursement, 1–7, 2f
 consumer-directed health plans, 3–4
 delivery system, 2f, 4–6

 payers and, 2–3
 regulations, 4
Charge capture process, 67–83
 auditing, 74–75
 charges received, 75
 closed-loop process, 73f
 coding and, 346
 diagnostic tool for, 77–83
 lag time tracking, 74, 74f
 leading performance indicators, 77
 overview of, 67–68
 responsibility of, 68–69
 service variance analysis, 75–76
 tools for, standardizing, 69–71
 updating, 76
 verification process, 71–72, 72f
 workload ranges for, 76, 288
Charge entry process, 101–118
 auditing, 112
 batch charges, 109
 benchmarking, 367
 "clean" charges, 110
 completeness of, 102–103
 deductibles, 112
 diagnostic tool for, 114–118
 documentation, 106–107
 electronic charge entry, 108–109
 fee schedule, 103–105, 104f
 fee schedule review, 106, 107t
 leading performance indicators, 113
 link coding, 112
 modifiers, 105
 "netting the charge," 105–106
 overview of, 101–102
 point-of-care charge entry, 109
 pre-adjudication edits, 107–108, 108f,
  121, 122f, 342
 quality assurance review,
  110–111, 111t
 separation of duties, 111–112
 technology and, 109–110
 timelines for, 109
 workload ranges for, 113, 288
Charge tickets, 303
Check-in process
 diagnostic tool for, 61–65
 error-rate reporting, 48–50, 49t, 50t
 insurance cards, 58
 leading performance indicators, 60
 overview of, 44–45
 patient identification and
  verification, 59
 patient obligations, 52–53
 performance expectations, 59
 real-time patient data updates, 57–58

receipts, 57
rescheduling protocols, 52
staff responsibilities, 48
time-of-service collection, 46–48,
   50–53, 51*t*
workload ranges for, 60
Check-out process
"about your bill," 47*t*
diagnostic tool for, 61–65
error-rate reporting, 48–50, 49*t*, 50*t*
financial agreements, 46*t*
leading performance indicators, 60
overview of, 45–46
receipts, 57
staff responsibilities, 48
time-of-service collection, 46–48,
   50–53, 51*t*
workload ranges for, 60
Checks, managing, 248–249, 301,
   302, 305
Claims management, 119–138
benchmarking, 371–372
"clean" claims, 128*t*, 355
clearinghouse role, 125–126, 126*f*
cost to rework, 17–18, 17*f*
deadlines, filing, 122–123
definition of, 119
diagnostic tool for, 136–138
edit function, manual, 127
edits (adjudication), 121, 122*f*
edits, tracking, 129–130, 129*f*
electronic claims, 123–124, 123*f*
leading performance indicators, 135
overview of, 119–120
payer Websites, 134
quality assurance review, 126–127
real-time claims adjudication (RTCA),
   132–134, 133*f*
rebills, 120
regulation compliance, 125
scrubbing software, 127–128, 129
secondary claims, 120–121, 132
submission formats, 124
suspended claims, 131–132
workload ranges for, 134
"Clean" claims, 101, 110, 125, 128*t*,
   196, 323–324, 355
Clearance, financial. *See* Patient
   financial clearance
Clearinghouses, 125–126, 126*f*
Closed-loop charge capture process, 73*f*
CMS-1500 Field 19, 95
CO. *See* Contractual obligation (CO)
COB. *See* Coordination of benefits (COB)

Coding process, 85–99
benchmarking, 367–368
claim edits, 130
CMS-1500 Field 19, 95
denial codes, 154–156
diagnosis codes, 87–89, 95
diagnostic tool for, 99
education and competency, 90–91
leading performance indicators, 98
modifiers, 87, 105
ordering codes, 94–95
overview of, 85–86
payment code hierarchy,
   160–163, 161*f*
place-of-service codes, 94*f*
procedure codes, 86, 95
regulation compliance, 96–97
reimbursement and, 92–94
responsibility of, 89–90
terms, common, 86*t*
tools and technology for, 91
workload ranges for, 97
Collection. *See* Billing and collection
Collection agencies, 238–240, 239*t*,
   253–254
Collection rates, xxvi
Communication
centralized billing, 322
decentralized billing, 321
outsourced billing, 326
patient billing, 243–244, 244*t*
patient statements, 142, 143*t*,
   145, 225
with payer, 187–188, 381
Compensation plans, 295–297
Compliance program, 395–398
Consumer Price Index for Medical
   Care, 263
Consumer-directed health plans, 3–4,
   7, 266
Contract and reimbursement
   management, 257–271
benchmarking, 372, 373*f*
contract negotiations plan, 262–267
credentialing process, 261–262, 261*f*
diagnostic tool for, 271
internal review of, 267–268
negotiation, 368
overview of, 257–258
payer reimbursement tactics, 268–270
pay-for-performance plans, 270
practice-payer relationship, 258–261
Contractual obligation (CO), 164
Coordination of benefits (COB), 121
Copayments, 52–53

Correction and reversals (CR), 165
Cost
  of billing office, 376–381, 378f
  fees, 30
  of outsourced billing, 326–329
  to patients, 19
  vs. performance, 380–381, 380f
  of reworking a claim, 17–18, 17f,
      218–221, 220f
  transparency in, 28
CPT. See Current Procedural
      Terminology (CPT)
CR. See Correction and reversals (CR)
Credentialing, payers, 210–211, 261–
      262, 261f, 372–374, 374f
Credit and debit cards, 56, 165
Credit worthiness, 26–27, 246–247, 351
Current Procedural Terminology (CPT),
      85, 86, 87, 96

D

Days in accounts receivable, 358–359
Decentralized billing, 320–321
  vs. hybrid models, 323–324
  transitioning from or to, 330–331
Deductible, 9–10
Delivery system changes, 2f, 4–6
Denial codes, 154–156, 201–202,
      202t, 203t, 206t. See also Denial
      management process
Denial management process, 195–223.
      See also Payment and denial
      posting
  appealing, 215–216t, 216–218
  benchmarking, 370, 389t
  common errors, 196–197, 196f,
      197–198f
  contract negotiations plan, 266
  cost of reworking claims,
      218–221, 220f
  data collection, 199, 200t, 201t, 212,
      212t
  deconstruction and resolution,
      203–211, 206t
  denial codes, 201–202, 202t, 203t
  diagnostic tool for, 222–223
  leading performance indicators, 221
  medical necessity, 207f
  overview of, 195
  payer report card, 219t
  preventing, 199–200
  staff follow-up, 213, 214–216,
      215–216t
  tools for, 211–212, 213–214
  workload ranges for, 189–190, 221

Deposit, 55
Diagnosis codes, 87–89, 95
Discount policy, 55–56
Document management, 348–349
Documentation. See Coding process
Downcoding, 269
DRO. See Days in accounts receivable
Dunning cycle, 141

E

EDI. See Electronic data interchange
      (EDI)
EFT. See Electronic funds transfer (EFT)
EHR. See Electronic health record (EHR)
Electronic admittance advice (ERA),
      151–152, 300
Electronic charge entry, 108–109
Electronic data interchange (EDI),
      349–350
Electronic funds transfer (EFT), 150, 345
Electronic health record (EHR), 303
Electronic payment remittance (EPR),
      149, 345–346
Email, 347
Employee Retirement Income Security
      Act (ERISA), 166–167
Employees. See Front-office staff;
      Revenue cycle staff; Staff
EOB. See Explanation of benefits (EOB)
EPR. See Electronic payment remittance
      (EPR)
ERA. See Electronic admittance advice
      (ERA)
ERISA. See Employee Retirement Income
      Security Act (ERISA)
Explanation of benefits (EOB), 55,
      120–121
  denial codes, 201–202, 202t
  HIPAA code sets, 164–165
  payment and denial posting, 149–150,
      151f, 153, 155

F

Fair Debt Collections Practices Act
      (FDCPA), 228
Fair Isaac Corporation (FICO), 246
Fees, 30, 54–55
  application service provider, 337
  billing, 240–241
  in contract negotiations plan, 264
  modifiers, 87
  of outsourced billing, 328–329
  policy for, 115–116

schedule determination, 104–105, 104*f*
schedule review, 106, 107*t*, 367
Field 19, CMS-1500, 95
Financial clearance. *See* Patient financial clearance
Financial hardship policy, 234–235, 254–255
Financial lenders. *See* Medical lending companies
Financial policy
 example of, 40–41
 importance of, 28–30, 31*t*
 for surgeries and procedures, 46*t*, 53, 54*t*, 64–65
Fluctuating charges, 366–368
Fraud, investigating, 311–312, 396–397, 397*f*
Front-end billing
 benchmarking, 376–378
 collection process, 12–13, 13*f*
 costs, 378*f*
 as priority, 408
 staff responsibilities, 274, 276
 staffing levels for, 286–288
Front-office staff
 auditing tool, 49*t*
 cash management, 305–308, 307*t*
 cash-at-time-of-service scripts, 51*t*
 error-rate reporting, 48–50
 "if not, why not" program, 55
 insurance cards, 58
 monthly denial report, 50*t*
 patient identification and verification, 59
 real-time patient data updates, 57–58
Functional outsourcing, 329

G

Gap analysis, 364
Geographic practice cost index (GPCI), 93
Global periods, 88
Global services, 92–93
GPCI. *See* Geographic practice cost index (GPCI)
Guarantor, 20, 226. *See also* Patient collections

H

HCPCS. *See* Healthcare Common Procedure Coding System (HCPCS)
Health Insurance Portability and Accountability Act (HIPAA), 120, 150, 182, 399–405

Business Associate Agreement, 405
 code sets, 164–165
 credentialing process, 262
 privacy, 403, 404–405*t*
 transactions and code sets, 399–403, 400–401*f*, 402*f*
Healthcare Common Procedure Coding System (HCPCS), 87
HIPAA. *See* Health Insurance Portability and Accountability Act (HIPAA)
Hybrid billing models, 323–324

I

ICD-CM. *See* International Classification of Diseases, Clinical Modification (ICD-CM)
Incentive plans, 295–297
Instant messaging, 347
Insurance
 benefits eligibility, 24, 25*t*, 59
 card scanning, 58
 coverage verification, 23, 25*t*, 40
 patient identification and verification, 59
 payment posting, 150
 secondary coverage, 26, 120, 132, 169–171
 take-backs, 160
 waiver of patient financial responsibility, 235–236
Insurance follow-up, 177–194
 accounts receivable, 183
 diagnostic tool for, 191–194
 electronic work files, 185–186
 leading performance indicators, 190
 "non-par" claims, 187, 258–261
 open claims follow-up, 181–182, 182*f*
 outstanding accounts, 178
 overview of, 177–178
 patient information request, 187–188
 payer adjudication cycle, 179
 payer communication, 187–188
 prioritizing work, 178–179, 179*t*
 prompt payment laws, 189
 rebilling, 182–183
 records, 179
 small balance adjustment level, 183–184
 staff education, 186, 186*t*
 staff organization, 184–185
 strategies by payer, 179–181
 workload ranges for, 189–190
Internal billing office, 330
Internal controls, 299–318
 for adjustments, 303–304

Internal controls *(continued)*
  bad checks, 302
  cash management, 305–308, 307*t*
  charge tickets, reconciling, 303
  definition of, 299
  duty segregation, 304–305
  internal audits, 308–311, 309*f*, 310*f*
  lockboxes, 300
  new employees, 302–303, 313–314
  overview of, 299–300
  payment reconciliation, 300
  physician responsibility, 304
  policies for, 313–318
  security measures, physical, 311
  signature stamps, 302
International Classification of Diseases,
    Clinical Modification
    (ICD-CM), 87

K

Kiosks, 45, 341

L

Lagging performance indicators,
    365–366, xxvii
Laws. *See* Regulations and legal
    considerations
LCD. *See* Local Coverage Determinations
    (LCD)
Leading performance indicators, 17,
    365–366
  benchmarking, 377*f*
  charge capture process, 77
  charge entry process, 113
  claims management, 135
  coding process, 98
  denial management process, 221
  insurance follow-up, 190
  vs. lagging, xxvii
  patient check-in/check-out, 60
  patient collections, 250
  patient financial clearance, 36
  patient statements, 147
  payment and denial posting, 171
Legal considerations. *See* Regulations
    and legal considerations
Lending companies. *See* Medical
    lending companies
Linking, 269
List of Excluded Individuals/Entities
    (LEIE), 398
Local Coverage Determinations (LCD),
    88–89
Lockbox, 152–153, 300

M

Manual charge ticket policy, 79–81
Measurements. *See* Benchmarking
Medicaid, 180
Medical credit scores, 351
Medical lending companies, 27–28,
    56–57
Medical necessity, 92, 207*f*, 266
Medical practices
  organizational structure, 289–291,
    290*f*, 291*f*, 292*f*
  priorities in, 407–409
Medical services
  payment process, xxvi*f*
  self-audit, xxvii–xviii*f*
Medical tourism, 4
Medicare. *See* Centers for Medicare &
    Medicaid Service (CMS)
Medicare payment formula, 93
Medicare Physician Fee Schedule
    (MPFS), 93
*Medicare RBRVS 2007: The Physician's
    Guide* (Smith & Fischoff, Eds), 264
Modifiers, 87, 105
MPFS. *See* Medicare Physician Fee
    Schedule (MPFS)

N

National Correct Coding Initiative
    (NCCI), 88
National Coverage Determinations
    (NCD), 88–89, 206
National Provider Identifier (NPI), 262
NCCI. *See* National Correct Coding
    Initiative (NCCI)
NCD. *See* National Coverage
    Determinations (NCD)
NCR. *See* Net collection rate (NCR)
Net collection rate (NCR), 104, 357
"Netting the charge," 105–106
Non-contractual allowances, 153–154
Non-covered services, 92
Non-participating providers, 187,
    258–261
NPI. *See* National Provider Identifier
    (NPI)

O

Office of the Inspector General (OIG),
    96, 397
Organizational structure, 289–291, 290*f*,
    291*f*, 292*f*
Outbound collection calls, 243
Outsourcing billing, 324–329

vs. centralized billing, 321–323
code of commitments for, 325f
cost of, 326–329
vs. decentralized billing, 320–321
functional, 329
vs. hybrid models, 323–324

P

P4P plans. See Pay-for-performance (P4P) plans
Paperwork management, 348–349
Patient billing advocates, 233
Patient collections, 225–256
  bad checks, 248–249
  bad debt, credit reporting, 237–238
  billing advocates, patient, 233
  billing fees, 240–241
  code of ethics, 228, 229f
  collection agencies, 238–240, 239t, 253–254
  collection cycle, 226, 227t
  credit worthiness, 246–247, 247t, 248t
  diagnostic tool for, 251–256
  financial hardship policy, 234–235, 254–255
  leading performance indicators, 250
  letter and phone scripts, 228, 228t
  overview of, 225–226
  patient dismissal, 241
  patient financial obligation, 245, 245t
  patient satisfaction and feedback, 249
  payment plans, 229–231, 230t, 231t, 255–256
  professional courtesy, 236–237
  protocols for, 226
  records for, 243–244, 244t
  small claims court, 241–242
  staff responsibilities, 232
  telephone calls, 243
  waiver of patient financial responsibility, 235–236
  workload ranges for, 249
Patient financial clearance, 19–41
  address authentication, 24–26
  benchmarking, 370–371
  benefits eligibility, 24, 25t, 59
  checklist for, 32t
  credit worthiness, 26–27, 246–247, 247t, 248t
  diagnostic tool for, 37–41
  financial policy, 28–30, 31t
  insurance coverage verification, 23, 25t, 40
  leading performance indicators, 36

medical lending companies, 27–28
overview of, 19–20
patient registration data, 21–23, 232–233, 342
patient responsibility, expectations for, 27
payer guide, 33, 33–35t
pre-visit process, 21, 21f, 43–44
real-time, 22–23
referrals and authorizations, 30
secondary insurance coverage, 26
workload ranges for, 36
Patient responsibility (PR), 27, 164
Patient statements, 139–148
  billing email, 145
  diagnostic tool for, 148
  final notice letters, 144
  follow-up, 143
  information-only, 142
  leading performance indicators, 147
  notes, communication, 142, 143t, 145, 225
  online payments, 144–145
  overview of, 139–140
  Patient-Friendly Billing®, 141–142
  quality assurance, 140–141
  returned mail, 145–146
Patient-focused billing, 340–341
Patient-Friendly Billing®, 141–142
Payer initiated (PI), 165
Payer interfaces, 350
Payers. See also Contract and reimbursement management; Denial management process
  adjudication process, 121, 122f
  appealing, 216–218
  claim perspective, 198–199
  coding and, 92–94
  complexity, administrative, 3
  consolidation of, 2
  contract negotiations plan with, 262–267
  correspondence, 187
  credentialing, 210–211
  guide sheet for, 33, 33–35t
  insurance follow-up, 179–181
  knowledge of, 273–274, 294t
  organizing staff by, 184–185
  patient financial obligation, 245, 245t
  payment categories for, 161–163, 161f
  performance and, 354
  practice information and, 166
  practice relationship, 258–261
  reimbursement methods, 3
  reimbursement tactics, 268–270

Payers *(continued)*
secondary claims, 120–121
Websites of, 134
Pay-for-performance (P4P) plans, 3, 270
Payment and denial posting, 149–176.
See also Denial management
process
account adjustments, 153–154
accuracy in, 156–158, 157–158*f*
benchmarking, 371
capitation funds, 160
credit/debit card safechecks, 165
denial codes, 154–156
diagnostic tool for, 172–176
electronic payments, 150–152,
151*f*, 301
ERISA regulation, 166–167, 174
HIPAA code sets, 164–165
insurance payments, 150
leading performance indicators, 171
outstanding balances, 167–168
overview of, 149
patient payments, 152
payer reimbursement levels,
168–169, 168*t*
payment code hierarchy,
160–163, 161*f*
payment elements, 149–150
payment exception reports, 167
pre-paid monies, 159
receipt logs, 159
refund process, 169, 170*t*, 174–175
reimbursement levels, 168–169, 168*t*
remote deposit and lockbox services,
152–153
secondary claims, 169–171
staff performance, 163, 164*t*, 165*t*
take-backs, 160
unidentified payments, 159–160
workload ranges for, 171
Payment plans, 229–231, 230*t*, 231*t*,
255–256
Payment variance, 158
Payments. *See also* Patient collections
cash, 305–308, 307*t*
checks, 248–249, 301, 302, 305
credit and debit cards, 56, 165
electronic payments, 144–145,
150–152, 151*t*, 243, 301
plans for, 229–231, 230*t*, 231*t*
Performance indicators. *See*
Benchmarking; Lagging
performance indicators; Leading
performance indicators

Physician productivity, 354–355
Physician Quality Reporting Initiative
(PQRI), 89, 270
PI. *See* Payer initiated (PI)
Place-of-service codes, 94*f*
Point-of-care charge entry, 109
Policies
Advanced Beneficiary Notification
(ABN), 63
charge and office visit
reconciliation, 82
charge and service
reconciliation, 82–83
charge entry correction, 118
charge ticket accuracy, 81
claim denials, 223
claim submission timelines, 137
claims management, 137–138
data entry timeliness, 116–117
discount policy, 55–56
fee schedule, 115–116
financial hardship, 234–235
financial policy, 28–30, 31*t*,
40–41, 46*t*
insurance coverage verification, 40
insurance follow-up, 192–194
internal controls, 313–318
lag times, 117
manual charge ticket, 79–81
new employees, 302–303
outpatient charge entry, 116
patient collections, 227*t*, 252–256
patient financial clearance, 38–41
patient information brochure, 39
patient registration, 38–39
payment and denial posting,
173–176
revenue cycle, 391–393
for surgeries and procedures, 64–65
time-of-service collection, 62–63
waiver of patient financial
responsibility, 64, 235–236
Potholes, overview, flowchart, 13–16,
14–15*f*
Poverty levels, 248*t*
PQRI. *See* Physician Quality Reporting
Initiative (PQRI)
Pre-adjudication edits, 107–108, 108*f*,
121, 122*f*, 342
Predictive dialers, 243, 350
Pre-visit process, 21, 21*t*, 43–44
Privacy regulations, 403, 404–405*t*. *See
also* Health Insurance Portability
and Accountability Act (HIPAA)

Procedure codes, 86, 95
Professional courtesy, 236–237

R

RBRVS. *See* Resource-based relative value scale (RBRVS)
Real-time claims adjudication (RTCA), 132–134, 133*f*, 346–347
Rebills, 120
Receipts, 57
Referrals and authorizations, 30
 check-out process and, 45
 in contract negotiations plan, 266
 denial management process, 209–210
 technology for, 342–343
Refund process, 169, 170*t*, 174–175, 310
Regulations and legal considerations, 395–405. *See also* Health Insurance Portability and Accountability Act (HIPAA)
 compliance program, 395–398
 Federal audit plans, 397–398
 privacy, 403, 404–405*t*
 prompt payment laws, 189
 Stark II laws, 236–237
Reimbursement environment, 1–7
 beliefs underlying, 6–7
 delivery system change, 2*f*, 4–6
 finance change, 2–4, 2*f*
Reimbursement management, 381–382
Rejections, EOBs, 153
Relative value unit (RVU), 93, 94–95, 361
Remote deposit and lockbox services, 152–153, 301
Resource-based relative value scale (RBRVS), 103, 264
Retail-based clinics, 4–5
Revenue cycle, 9–18, xxv, xxvi*f*. *See also* Benchmarking; Centralized billing; Decentralized billing; Outsourcing billing; Regulations and legal considerations; Revenue cycle staff; Technology
 back-end billing, 12–13, 13*f*
 billing and collection potholes, 13–16, 14–15*f*
 billing and collection tasks, 12*f*
 cost to rework a claim, 17–18, 17*f*
 definition of, 10–11
 front-end billing, 12–13, 13*f*
 organizational structure, 289–291, 290*f*, 291*f*, 292*f*
 parties, 9–10, 9*f*
 responsibility, 11*f*

staff workload ranges, 17
 tracking, of outstanding balances, 382–383
Revenue cycle staff, 273–298
 back-end billing, 276–277, 279–286, 279*t*, 280*f*, 281*f*, 282*f*, 283*f*
 compensation plans, 295–297
 competency and accountability, 293–294, 294*t*
 front-end billing, 274, 276, 286–288
 by function, 275–289
 involvement, in performance, 297–298
 organizational structure, 289–291, 290*f*, 291*f*, 292*f*
 overview of, 273
 payer-specific knowledge, 273–274, 294*t*
 process dependency, 275
 work linkages, 274–275
 workload ranges for, 287*f*, 288–289
RTCA. *See* Real-time claims adjudication (RTCA)
RVU. *See* Relative value unit (RVU)

S

Scrubbing software, 127–128, 129
Secondary claims, 120–121, 132, 169–171
Security measures
 cash management, 305–308, 307*t*
 fraud, investigating, 311–312
 physical, 311
Service variance analysis, 75–76
Signature stamps, 302
Silent PPOs, 269
Skip-tracing tools, 146
Small claims court, 241–242
Staff. *See also* Front-office staff; Revenue cycle staff
 accountability, internal controls, 301
 coding education, 90–91
 compensation plans, 295–297
 compliance program, 398
 contract review, internal, 267–268
 denial management process, 213–214, 215–216*t*
 deployment models, 278–279
 duty segregation, 304–305
 employee hiring policies, 302–303, 313–314
 error-rate reporting, 48–50, 50*t*
 front-office auditing, 49*t*
 by function, 275–289

Staff *(continued)*
  "if not, why not" program, 55
  insurance follow-up, 186
  involvement, in performance, 297–298
  job titles for, 54
  organizing by payer, 184–185
  patient collections, 232, 245
  payment posting performance, 163,
    164*t*, 165*t*
  performance expectations, 43, 59, 339
Staff workload ranges. *See* Workload
    ranges
Stark II laws, 236–237
Statements, online, 341

T

Take-backs, 160
TAO. *See* Total account ownership (TAO)
TDI. *See* Total difficulty index (TDI)
Technology, 333–351
  application service provider, 336–337
  coding process, 91
  decision-making regarding, 337–338
  electronic charge entry, 108–109
  electronic claims, 123–124, 123*f*
  electronic payment remittance,
    150–152, 151*t*, 301
  electronic work files, insurance follow-
    up, 185–186
  email and instant messaging, 347
  evaluation of, 334–338, 335*f*
  information requests, tracking,
    343–344, 344*f*
  kiosks, 45, 341
  for leading indicators, 338–340
  online patient payments, 144–145,
    243, 340–341
  overview of, 333–334
  patient email, 145
  patient-focused billing, 340–341
  Patient-Friendly Billing®, 141–142
  performance expectations, 355–356
  pre-adjudication edits, 342
  predictive dialers, 243, 350

  for real-time work, 345–347
  resource utilization, 347–351
  scrubbing software, 127–128, 129
  support for, 351
Timely filing (contracts), 265
Time-of-service collection
  check-in/check-out process, 46–48,
    50–53, 51*t*
  policy, 62–63, 314–317
  staff responsibility, 288
Total account ownership (TAO), 275
Total difficulty index (TDI), 282*f*, 283*f*
Transactions, 399–403, 400–401*f*, 402*f*
Trends
  in delivery systems, 2*f*, 4–6
  in finances, 2–4, 2*f*

U

Unidentified payments, 159–160
Uninsured patients, 233
"Usual, customary, and reasonable"
    reimbursement, 104

W

Waiver forms, 57, 235–236
Workload ranges
  by activity, 287*f*, 288–289
  back-end billing, 280*f*, 281*f*
  charge capture process, 76
  charge entry process, 113
  claims management, 134
  coding process, 97
  denial management process,
    189–190, 221
  insurance follow-up, 189–190
  overview of, 17
  patient check-in/check-out, 60
  patient collections, 249
  patient financial clearance, 36
  payment and denial posting, 171

Z

Zero-pay EOBs, 153